Stairway to the Breeds

by
Ian Kay

Published by Scribblers Publishing Limited

First published in 1997

Printed by Trio Graphics, Gloucester, GL2 5EL. ENGLAND.

ISBN 1-871644-04-6

Contents

Breed index

Acknowledgements

The compilation of a book such as this, could not be possible without the knowledge and dedication of other writers, artists and photographers, many of them from past decades, who unfortunately are no longer with us.

I offer my thanks for their contributions, and list their names in alphabetical order to unsure that I do not, in any way, appear to be grading their skills. I also offer my apologies to anyone who may have been inadvertently omitted.

I have photographs of some of these people which I would like to include. Firstly, one of Arthur Rice, who left us such a vast number of excellent photographs. The picture shows him on a visit to his friend and fellow Ancona breeder, Mr. W. W. Driver in 1929. They used the horse and trap to visit another friend in the neighbourhood. On their return, Arthur was 'snapped' sitting alongside Mr Driver's daughter Betty, who later became a keen breeder of Anconas.

The second picture of Arthur, shows him judging Anconas at the Crystal Palace. The expert in FIG 3 is W. Powell -Owen, judging a Croad Langshan pullet in 1924. It was quite customary for 'P O' to place birds on a table or basket when assessing their qualities.

4

Mr. Lewis Wright.   Mr. Harrison Weir.   Mr. W. B. Tegetmeier.
"FATHERS OF THE POULTRY INDUSTRY"—THE GREAT TRIUMVIRATE.

FIG 4. Shows the three wise masters, Lewis Wright, Harrison Weir, and T. B. Tegetmeier.

Continental Breeds and Customs

By C. S. TH. VAN GINK.

These notes are contributed with the eventual object of standardising Breed Type in Europe, and in the meantime of encouraging international opinions on poultry subjects of common interest to readers of " The Feathered World."

C. S. Th. Van Gink.

FIG 5. Was taken from the Feathered World, when Cornelis Van Gink wrote his own weekly column for the magazine.

FIG 7. My great friend Ken Atterby ready for action. Ken and his wife Ruby have been the photographic advisers for all my books on Poultry, and their knowledge has been of great assistance.

FIG 6. Edward Brown returning from 'The Palace' after receiving his knighthood.

5

FIG 8. The Bleazard family, who with their patience and dedication collected and preserved the collection of over a thousand books and magazines, which were then handed to me. This collection began during the First World War, and without them much of the information and photography in this book would not have been possible.

FIG 9. My father and mother who from an early age encouraged me to acquire information and knowledge from many of the old expert breeders of exhibition poultry.

Scribblers Publishing Limited wish to acknowledge our guest writers:
Sue Bower   Silkie
Will Burdett   Orpington
Harold Critchlow   Hamburgh
Eric Parker   Poland
and Lana Gazder, Sue Bruton and Doreen Smillie for their contributions to the breeds of
Fayoumi, Sulmtaler and Appenzeller respectively. Also to the following, to whom we are
very thankful for their help, support, advice and knowledge.

Kenneth Atterby.	Van Leer.
Aldrovandi.	Ludlow.
Herbert Atkinson.	Lydon.
The Bleazard Family.	Chris Parker
Edward Brown.	Arthur Rice.
Fancy Fowl	Hans Schippers
Feathered World	Simpson.
Finterbusch.	Stead.
Cornelis Van-Gink.	John Tarren.
Glynda Green	Ayscough Thompson.
Stephen Hicks.	Harrison Weir.
Horsegood.	Whippel.
Bruff Jackson.	Josef Wolters.
Kramer.	Lewis Wright.

FOREWORD

From Local Club Shows to Classics, from Lancashire to Lincolnshire, via poultry shows at virtually every point in the United Kingdom, knowledge and experience spanning two generations have been gained to enable this unique book to be written.

Over the past 50 years I have often referred to the author as a 'great friend, great competitor, judge, but no relation'. However, the one relationship we do have is 'simply poultry' and this book is a 'STAIRWAY', built step by step, on generations of breeding and exhibiting poultry.

Covering 101 breeds, on which much research has been undertaken, the book deals with their strengths and weaknesses, origins and comparison, breeding procedures and beauty.

The book is not only full of sound advice, but humorous where necessary, and recalls many of the beliefs of famous old names of the past, which have not previously been published.

The book states 'No two shows are the same.' Having read it, there is no book to compare with this one and the fancy is fortunate that for only the second time this century such a book has been published.

'STAIRWAY TO THE BREEDS' is full of sound content, written in a free flowing style ..... fascinating, rewarding and interesting reading!

DAVID KAY

Introduction

To write a book there has to be a reason, and the reason for this book is that there are many people wanting to acquire more knowledge and facts about all the various breeds of poultry and miniature fowl.

'Stairway to the Breeds' leads you step by step through over 100 of the soft feathered varieties, outlining their standard requirements and breed characteristics, including behaviour and either showing or utility potential. Where possible, tracing a breed's family tree, gives you the facts in a precise and easy to read manner.

The breeds are fully illustrated by top class photography in both colour and monochrome, which includes some prints from bygone eras.

We have invited several guest writers to contribute detailed descriptions, and observations, on their own specialist breeds. These include Will Burdett, Eric Parker, Sue Bowser, Harold Critchlow.

At this period in history, many of the large poultry breeds are scarce and in the hands of only a few specialist breeders. The Rare Poultry Society organises their future conservation. The book explains the origin and operations of this organisation.

Advice is given on the breeding procedures which will produce the best results to maintain a high standard of stock, including the use of double mating where this is considered beneficial.

For those people wishing to exhibit their stock, the general procedure of showing is outlined including advice on show preparation.

Not for 50 years has such work been compiled, and it was felt that many of these facts should be recorded in one volume before they are lost forever.

Our gratitude extends to past authors and historians who have recorded their findings since the world of exhibition poultry started to develop in the second half of the nineteenth century. Without their writings, we would be much less informed and we reproduce many of their major conclusions and observations, ensuring that they continue to be available for future generations to benefit from.

We have added to their views our own conclusions as to the origins of the various breeds of poultry, using the advantage of a further 100 years forward in time.

Ian Kay, Poplars Farm, Cumberworth, Alford, Lincolnshire.England

The progress from crossbreed to show champion

Throughout the history of Exhibition Poultry, there have been many instances of successful breeders commencing their association with fowls by keeping a few crossbred bantams, the intention being to supply the household with a regular supply of freshly laid eggs. Quite often, these birds were passed on by a friend who no longer required them.

If the sole object of keeping poultry is simply to supply the household requirements, then crossbreeds, or the commercial hybrid, are excellent. These hybrids are scientifically bred for that purpose; unfortunately they do not look very attractive.

If maximum output is not the main criterion then there is more pleasure to be obtained by keeping a pen of pure bred birds, especially when the breed has been carefully selected to suit your own individual taste.

Crossbreds can be very attractive birds. In certain cases they can be shown. Many of the Lancashire and Yorkshire shows have classes for 'The likeliest crossbred laying bird'. To win, you have to exhibit a very attractive looking bird, which also has the body formation of a correct utility fowl.

FIG. 1 Kenneth Hawkey's Indian Game cockerel which had the distinction of winning the magnificent Gold Trophy for supreme champion at the Dairy show in 1928. This was the first time the trophy was offered for competition, being in memory of the late Chris Isherwood. Fanciers from all over Britain subscribed towards the cost, which was over £100. The trophy is now offered for competition at the Poultry Club's National show, with an estimated value of £30,000.

The next step forward

The original scheme for keeping poultry can be very innocently altered, by an afternoon's outing to the local agricultural show or garden fete.

At these events many very attractive breeds of poultry are displayed, with some of them offered for sale.

A quick 'directors' meeting' by the family makes the decision to purchase some pure bred stock. They may not realise it at the time, but this expansion into breeding pure bred stock may change their whole lifestyle.

Within a short period of time their interest in poultry keeping could expand into conserving one or more of the endangered breeds. This appears to be a progressive and rewarding step forward.

However, the poultry keeping activities of the family are just one step away from being fully involved with the breeding of show quality birds.

This is usually accelerated by visits to friends and relatives who also keep pure bred birds and comparisons are commenced.

FIG. 2 The accompanying photo shows the winning entry in a parade at the Leslie show in 1935.

A return visit to the show

In the late twentieth century, it is not uncommon for most members of the household to become increasingly interested in poultry keeping, each one with his or her own particular choice of favourite breed.

Consequently, an outing is arranged to visit their local Small Livestock show, this time with a definite intention of inspecting all the breeds on display, before arriving at a conclusion as to the ones which will suit their desires.

On a second visit to an exhibition, your attitude can be entirely different from the first one.

To merely have a quick look at the various breeds would be sufficient to satisfy your curiosity. However, the accumulation of a little more knowledge and a deeper look into the various breeds create a lot of unanswered questions.

The information to obtain these answers is often very limited, and, as with many other aspects of life, the more knowledge you obtain, the deeper becomes your desire to obtain more.

To enable newcomers to breeding and exhibiting poultry, the next portion of the book will answer many of the questions which were in the mind of the hypothetical family I have just been describing.

The advice given will hopefully assist them to become breeders of Champion Birds.

Why are some breeds more popular than others?

There is an old saying, 'One man's meat is another man's poison,' and it is proved correct with people's opinions of breeds in poultry.

A White Crested Black Polish hen can be one person's pride and joy, whilst to another exhibitor it is 'Ornamental'.

Consequently, we have this large selection of breeds to choose from, every one of which is someone's 'pride and joy'.

One pointer to a breed's popularity is in the Old English Game Bantams. The club hold their annual show at Stafford in conjunction with the National Federation of Poultry Clubs' event. They have the largest entry of all the clubs with over 700 birds. The interesting point is, the birds are spread over a wide range of colours and all conform to the same shape and style, but in the standard of perfection, points allocated for colour are only 9 out of the total 100.

The basic principle of the breed is that whatever colour you hatch there are classes for, and also a name for the colour. These names can include 'miller's breasted', 'almond breasted', or even a 'fig pudding'. One delicately shaded Cinnamon and Blue female has acquired the delightful name of a 'honey dun' which describes the ground colour, as being representative of a newly removed honey comb.

In Waterfowl the fastest developing part of the major show scene has been the Call Duck. These birds increase in number and popularity every year. Again the general principle of their standard is shape, type and general conformation being of paramount importance. Markings play only a small part in most of the colours.

The appeal of the breeds appears to be that many different colours can be hatched from one breeding pen, and, especially with O.E. Game, you never know which variation Mother Nature is going to send you. Actually the same situation exists in fancy pigeons, where the extremely popular breed of Modena exists in a whole range of colours, all applicable to the same body structure, with again the colour of the 'new arrival' not known until the first body feathers begin to appear.

These points can be relevant to a breed's popularity and will be mentioned several times before the end of the book.

If you attempt to analyse the major breeds of soft feathered poultry, the ones which are classified as 'Heavy Breeds' prove to be dominant in numbers and probably in show quality at the present time.

Their potential to win supreme honours is also a proven fact, and my observations are that a large percentage of new breeders initially prefer birds which are massive looking,

11

and probably more docile in their nature. They certainly require much lower fencing to keep them within their boundary limits. Mother Nature, being what she is, has arranged that the ones listed as Light Breeds eat less food, have a longer active life and, when you carry out a visual inspection, you find that she has reserved a lot of the highly attractive and strikingly coloured birds for this category. She knew full well that with their long wings and lighter bodies they could quickly fly out of harm's way - a crafty old lady is that one!

Do some breeds require extra attention?

In this day and age of instant requirements and automatic gadgets for everything, there is a decline in the breeds which require extra attention to keep them in perfect show condition. Leghorn cocks, with their large combs, require to be protected from the frost. Buff Rocks need to be shaded from direct sunrays to prevent colour fading. The long tails on Yokohamas need to be kept in full feather; lobes on the Minorcas can require regular attention to prevent them becoming blistered. The foregoing are all reasons for their decline in popularity.

Breeds which require double mating, i.e. cock breeders or pullet breeders (more on this subject later), are also out of favour. To many new fanciers it is simply too much trouble when separate breeding pens are involved for the same breed. Hence the popularity of the OEG when one pen can produce a whole variety of colours.

Another reason for a breed's decline is that modern poultry breeders usually keep the breeds for pleasure, unlike those of the past who kept them as a commercial farming enterprise which formed part of their livelihood.

Are there too many breeds?

During the last few months, whilst writing about all the breeds of poultry, I have often asked myself the question whether we have too many breeds for them to exist in a healthy condition.

Having completed the breed summary, I realise that every breed has its own appeal and charm. Therefore, to suggest elimination of a certain breed would be wrong, for some of them may eventually fade away through lack of support. This has always been the case, that a newly created breed fails to capture the fancier's imagination, and fairly quickly declines.

There are some breeds which are now in very few breeders' careful hands, and it is hoped that some new fanciers will appreciate their virtues, and continue with their preservation.

At the present time the attraction seems to be introducing breeds from other countries. It is hoped that this is not to the detriment of our own native breeds.

What is the best way to obtain the correct breeding stock?

FIG. 3 Was taken by the Feathered World columnist 'Quill', who captured H.S. (Bert) Anthony in Ayr station. Uncle Bert was about to unload his team of birds after exhibiting them at the town's Agricultural Show. The caption to the Photo was 'Homeward Bound'? Quill then explained that Bert spent half the summer travelling by rail from one agricultural show to the next, often feeding and even washing birds in the Gents' Toilet!.

In this chapter, I have enlisted the assistance of Uncle Bert. He is based on a true character who was probably the greatest poultry showman ever. H. S. Anthony came from Euston, and he, along with my father John Kay, passed on to me a large percentage of my early knowledge of exhibition poultry.

Like myself, Bert was the son of a successful exhibitor - Robert Anthony - who vacated his job in the cotton mills to create for himself a full time living from breeding and showing exhibition poultry and waterfowl.

Again the similarity is that both of us, from the age of 14, toured the country showing a team of birds consisting of anything from 20-100 birds, providing we could get a driver for the vehicle, though in Bert's case it was a lot earlier in history, and much of this travelling was done by steam train He had been known to wash some of his birds in the 'Gents', particularly if they had become stained in-between the closely held agricultural shows. This procedure would, I have no doubts, raise a few eyebrows or tempers if attempted nowadays in a Piccadilly Circus loo!

Brr,Brr,Brr,Brr-HELLO

Ian-Now uncle Bert, I am ringing to ask if you could part with a few words of your wisdom on the subject of breeding good showbirds.

Bert-I'll do anything Ian to oblige you. What have you in mind?

I-What's the main advice you would give to any newcomer to poultry breeding which would enable him to reach the top of a particular breed?

B-Firstly be very careful to obtain the correct breeding stock right from the start.

I-In what way?

B-Well for a start, I do not recommend that you buy a bird from here, a bird from there, put them to breed together, and hope for the best. This method should result in healthy chicks, owing to their hybrid vigour and could produce some good show stock. Much would depend on the parentage and back breeding of the birds in question. The next problem would be getting the correctly balanced breeding pens to continue breeding future generations. Obviously some of these problems vary within the different breeds.

I-The hybrid vigour which you mention, surely this would be more beneficial in large fowl, where size is of utmost importance, whilst in the miniatures, keeping them from being over large can be a problem.

B-Absolutely, and especially so in a Bantam Breed, such as Pekins where the outcross almost always results in them growing like storks and completely losing their low to the ground characteristic.

I-Does the availability of initial stock vary in different breeds, and, if so, does it mean that there could be different advice offered depending on the breed?

B-Very much, and if you were to contemplate a minority breed, you would probably be very grateful to be able to obtain any sound birds which were well representative of the breed in question. They may HAVE to be purchased from different breeders and then by selective breeding and possibly purchasing, you will eventually establish top class stock and will be entitled to call them your own strain of that particular breed. It could be a long procedure, involving the disposal of many inferior quality birds.

Where possible, when getting your original birds, try to establish their ancestry. In most breeds, if you carefully trace back through a bird's pedigree, you will find that the best ones have a common relationship to a particular line of breeding, often so far back in history that the originator of that blood line is no longer with us.

I-Really? I thought that without a Ringing scheme it was more or less impossible to trace origins of blood lines.

B-To a point yes, but, word of mouth can be a wonderful conveyor of well preserved information. There are still breeders living who have memories and connections with birds during the boom years of the late 1940s, or even pre-war days. During these periods there were one or two breeders who dominated each particular breed. This blood is still around today and, if found, can produce excellent results.

I-Do you mean men like Harold Walkey, with his White Wyandottes, who was one of the top breeders for several decades?

B-Quite correct, but did you realise that the bulk of Harold's best birds, were descended from Hugh Gunn's stock. For many years he made a comfortable living from breeding and showing nothing but White Wyandottes. When he retired and sold up he retained the best old cock and sent it via British Rail to Harold as a present. That bird bred some of the best birds out in the following year, and his progeny continue to do so to this day.

I-How do you know that?

B-Because of two special features. One was that many of them had a smooth surface to their comb, not as heavily spiked as the ones shown by Walter Bradley, the show manager for Lord Dewar. The other feature was the peculiarity of the cock's spurs, which faced downwards, and very often were not fixed firmly to the bird's leg. Therefore they waddled about a bit.

I-Do you know where Hugh Gunn obtained his original stock?

B-No. That's something which I have never heard mentioned. I would suggest that here is a typical case of the statement, which I made earlier, of a man buying stock from different places and creating for himself, and others who followed him, an entirely new strain.

I-You mention that Hugh's birds had a smooth textured comb; surely this is a fault!

B-Yes to a small degree, and should lose the bird a few points, but the rest of the birds were so good, that this small fault could be out pointed, and it was not nearly so noticeable on the females which were usually the strongest part of both Harold's and Hugh's birds.

I-So there are special features running through most breeds which can highlight a particular strain. What about bad points? Are there any of these which trace back in history?

B-Let's answer the second part of your question first. If there was a bad fault, consistently occurring, then the breeder killed the whole lot with that fault, to eliminate it from the strain. Don't forget that in years gone by there were no large combines of 'broiler birds' that were bred solely for eating, and in those days roast chicken was considered a delicacy and a luxury reserved for Christmas, Easter and special events like the mother in law coming for tea. Consequently, exhibition poultry breeders were confident enough to rear larger batches of birds, knowing full well that there was a ready made and profitable market for the surplus, either as stock birds or as 'dressed poultry'. One example of this can be vouched for by your father. It was in Rhode Island Reds, where especially the Muzzlewhite strain regularly bred a percentage of Frizzle feathered birds, and even though his daughter Mrs Mitchell carried on with the strain after his death, you do not see any of them being bred nowadays. Presumably Frizzle had been introduced to the strain, probably during the development of the Red Frizzle Fowl, which the standard describes as being the colour of the Rhode Island Red. Here the fault has been eliminated by the exclusion from the breeding pen of both sexes with the unwanted peculiarity. There was no point in its inclusion because the birds bred from this line, even though not fully turned back in their feathers, were certainly soft feathered, and lacked feather quality, lacking the brilliant lustre, red colouring which is required in the R.I.R standard.

In answer to the first part of your question, what you might experience is a 'trait' which occurs and can be most annoying because it is usually on good quality specimens, which is the reason why the point has not been eliminated 100 years since. An example of this is in Black Orpingtons, where an excellent bird can show traces of white in the ear lobes. This was thought to trace back to the 1880s when William Cook was making the breed and, in doing so, supposedly used Black Minorca blood. I sometimes doubt this as I cannot see what use a long backed, big combed, tight feathered bird with white ear lobes would be to him in developing a square bodied, loose and fluffy feathered heavy breed, with the emphasis on a small comb. But white in the ear lobe is still evident in some present day Black Orpingtons, and it is nearly always on good birds.

This same white touch in the lobes is also quite common amongst the English type Buff Cochins which were descended from the Shanghais.

There is definitely a relationship between Black Cochins and the original imported Langshans, and probably one between Buff and Black Cochins, so I would suggest that it is some combination of these breeds which was largely responsible for the eventual development of the Black Orpingtons, and it was from here that the traces of white appeared in the lobes.

15

I do not wish to doubt Wm. Cook's claims as to the original breeds he used in the creation of Orpingtons, but I suggest that the birds which contained Black Minorca were eliminated in favour of birds with a stature more in keeping with the present day Orpington.

Another interesting point is that we have just been talking about Rhode Island Reds, which were developed by using some type of Cochin (Shanghai) blood, and the standard for R. I. Reds allows the ear lobes to contain white on their surface, providing that it does not cover more than half the area. There could be food for thought, if you were attempting to trace the early origin of white in the ear lobes.

I-So these traits are allowed to continue because the birds carrying them excel in other features, and the fault is only evident in a small percentage of the birds bred.
B-That's about it. The good point is that if they keep reappearing, then it means that you are still continuing with the same bloodline. I would always breed off one of these birds. Even though it carries this small fault, it guarantees the 'family's' continued existence and its ability to produce excellent results. Once you have managed to get hold of a bit of the right blood, then you don't need to breed dozens of chicks to get a few winners, you'll get them from an odd sitting or two!

I-Yes we have the situation with our Pekins, and from talking with Tom Corner and many years before that with Harry Snowden, we can trace it back to Fred Bancroft which must be over 60 years. I often wish that we knew the origin.
B-It probably started from one hen as with the Heath Bros. and their Spangled Old English Game Bantams. You still see that peculiar dent in the middle of the comb and it's nearly always on a good one.

I-I suppose that the enlarged gullet or 'dewlap' on Captain Duckworth's Light Sussex hens was the same thing and that was always on birds with well marked hackles.
B-Yes that's right, and have you noticed how many Light Sussex Miniature cockerels which have good hackles, also have a bad comb end. It is short of spikes and finishes in a funny lump which could do with eliminating, because I've also seen it on females and it spoils them.

I-In this day and age there always seems to be a desire for some thing instant. What steps can be taken to establish some good birds quickly within one of the popular and highly competitive breeds?
B- Yes, it used to be instant mashed potatoes. Now it's scratch cards! In many ways we have just covered this point. Spend a little time investigating the exhibitors who continually win with the particular breed you fancy. I do not mean over one season's showing, but for several years. This should prove that he or she is consistently breeding the correct birds. Don't be put off by the fact that a person wins more with one sex than the other. It is a good sign!

In nearly all breeds the best strains are dominant in one sex. This point can show itself very much in one year of breeding. If you carry the point to the ultimate, you would do as Eddie Edmunds did with his White Wyandotte Bantams, have two completely separate strains of them, one for cocks and one for females. And it worked. He could consistently show four or five birds in every class at the Club Show, and have nearly all of them in the top cards. The interesting thing was that if you mated the two strains together they produced rubbish!

Having located your choice of supplier, you should find that most genuine breeders are most helpful in assisting keen newcomers in the hope that they will continue with their life's work, and will be only too pleased to explain their own birds' history, either how long they have bred them, or that they are continuing the work of 'Joe Bloggs' in the year 'dot'.

These people should offer you a correctly mated breeding pen of stock, which, with the experience of their own stock, should produce the goods.

A quick illustration of this would be if you went to a show and saw a good bird winning a class, your first reaction might be that it would be a good piece of business to try and buy it, but a far better idea would be to buy the two parent birds, then next year you would have the opportunity to breed many winners for yourself.

Another point to bear in mind is that in many of the breeds the birds only remain show birds for a single season. Once moulted they can lose some of the vital features which made them winners. Buff rocks, Rhode Island Reds and especially Leghorns are examples. There is of course the converse where Belgians, Orpingtons and Pekins can fill out and improve, sometimes lasting for years. In many of the Black Red coloured birds, the breast colour of the males moults speckled with brown flecks, whilst Anconas and Speckled Sussex tend to moult with large white tips to the feathers which is called going 'gay' and, can render them as only fit for breeders. Again this can vary within strains of the breed, and attempts should be made to obtain one which can be relied upon to retain its colour for several moults.

If a R.I. Red pullet moults and lays at the same time it will usually come with uneven colouring, the pigmentation going into the egg rather than the feather colour, but a future moult, when she is not laying, will again revert to a correct colour level.

The point to stress here, is that it is not always the best showbirds which make the most successful breeders, so if a person wants instant success it must be decided if that means immediate showing, or purchasing the correct birds hopefully to breed instant success. Bearing in mind that, as stated, the showing span in some of the breeds can be short lived, and they will require replacing with another equally good and fit bird.

I- You have just mentioned Double Mating. Could you explain a little more about it.
B-Well this is where you require two separate breeding strains of the same breed to produce show birds. It is a point which very often deters new starters from taking up a breed. I have just said that double mating can be beneficial in many breeds, but in some it is absolutely essential. These are mainly the ones with pencilling or lacing involved, and the ones where the males have solid black coloured breasts and the wings on the females are even shaded colouring. Probably the most evident is the Partridge Wyandotte, where the two sets of birds involved are so far apart in looks that you might as well refer to them as separate breeds. There isn't a list produced which shows the breeds where double mating is required. The point is more passed by word of mouth. What has happened in most breeds is that the female line is the one mainly bred, because it makes economic sense to have a good quantity of potential show quality females, and just an odd one or two breeding males. This occurs regularly in the self black coloured breeds which have yellow pigmentation - e.g. Leghorns and Wyandottes. It is not required in the black breeds possessing dark legs and feet, such as Orpingtons, Australorps, Minorcas, etc.

I-All this is very interesting but as yet you have not given me a direct answer to the question, can a newcomer make a short cut to instant success. I am worried that with your wealth of knowledge, you have outlined the correct way forward but some of it may deter people from starting in poultry, and believe that breeding white mice might be easier!
B-Well if I were to commence breeding mice I would adopt much the same principles as I have just been stating. However instant success can really depend on luck. You can have an example where one person goes to the local market or poultry show and buys a trio (one male and two females), which prove to be closely enough related to breed successfully, without being brother and sister which can often produce weak stock. Again, with the right luck, the birds in question descend from one of the top strains, as

17

aforementioned, and the new owner records the progeny from the two females separately, then mates them together and they breed even better birds the next year. He could be made for life. Especially if he spent £1 with Camelot on his way to the market, because with his luck that day he would be sure to have won the jackpot!.

FIG. 4 A beautiful silver Rosebowl. It is the 'Quill' challenge trophy which was presented annually at the Dairy Show for the Champion Breeding pen of birds. As with the 'Isherwood Gold Cup', it is now offered for competition at the 'Poultry Club National'.

FIG. 5 Shows the Champion trio at Crystal Palace in 1922, once again with White Wyandottes, this time shown by John Wharton.

FIG. 6 Shows Lord Dewar's winning trio in 1929, at Crystal Palace .

FIG. 7 Shows the Trio of White Wyandottes which won the trophy for Sir Duncan Watson in 1936.

Selecting the best birds from your youngsters.

Having obtained a good breeding pen of birds which have then produced a batch of youngsters, the next step will be to grade them. They will fall into four categories. Firstly, the ones with serious faults which are better disposed of during the early stages of rearing. You will then be attempting to select the birds which are going to be of showing potential. To do this you will be carrying in your mind a photocopy of the breeds standard.

In the section feature of this book there is a summary of all the soft feathered breeds of poultry, and, in most cases, the vital and outstanding points of that breed are highlighted. Consequently, whilst feeding your stock, you should find yourself criticising some of them for deficiencies, whilst admiring others for their excellence and looking forward to presenting them to the show world. The big unanswered question will be, 'Are they as good as you think they are ?'

There is no such thing as the perfect specimen, and only experience will teach you that even the most respected judges vary in their assessment of a bird's qualities.

In the main part of the book, I have been very careful to highlight the parts of a bird which carry the most influence on a judge's decision. These parts of a bird which carry so great an influence are not always awarded the corresponding amount of points in the breed's standard.

Many of these standards have been in existence for a long time, and the points allocated do not always illustrate the modern day representation of the breed. Light Sussex are a perfect example of this. Some of the standards have recently been updated and breeds do alter over a period of time. However, I believe that the main features of the breed should always be retained.

Preparing the birds for showing.

To discuss fully the art of exhibiting your birds is really a book in itself. I will therefore briefly outline the main points of procedure. The amount and type of preparation varies within the different breeds.

The first procedure is carefully to quieten your proposed show bird, to insure that when the judge attempts to take him or her out of the pen for closer examination it is not a battle of wills. It has been known for untrained birds to be seen flying around the exhibition hall.

Your bird must also be used to living in the type of pen in which it will be displayed in the show. These are known as 'training pens'.

Many of the breeds require a shampoo, or bath to use the usual Poultry term. This is done several days prior to the event, which gives the birds time to dry out completely, and allows the feathers to return to their original positions.

With some breeds, especially the Hard Feathered ones, a good sponging of the plumage, plus a vigorous scrub of the legs and feet, will be sufficient.

The show society will provide the correct size of pen for you to display your bird in, but you will have to arrange for yourself the correct size of container in which to transport your birds to the show.

In the olden days these were specially manufactured using cane and wicker, but in recent years cardboard boxes are often used. It is important to arrive at the show with your bird in full plumage, and more details are outlined in my book 'Exhibition Poultry Volume 1'.

FIG. 8 Was taken in 1925, and shows the training pens which were used by Ian Gow during his very successful showing career, under the guidance of Poultry manager Michael Harrison. Ian is seated at his desk reading a poultry magazine.
The total length of this exhibition house was 100 feet. When washing a white bird prior to showing, it is essential for it to be completely immersed in the water, and soaked right through to the skin. A half measure will not produce the correct results.

The White Leghorn cockerel in FIG. 9 Is perfectly happy up to his neck in shampoo suds. He then requires a good dry with a towel, before placing in a warm room to complete the operation himself.

How to enter for a show.

A question which is frequently asked me is, 'Where can I obtain information regarding forthcoming shows in my area?' Unfortunately there is no simple answer. There are so many poultry shows held in the British Isles during the year it would be quite a task for a magazine to collect and classify all of them. However, the major shows are well advertised, and the ones near to your locality can usually be located by word of mouth with fellow fanciers. These compatriots should also be able to supply the contact point for you to obtain a schedule.

Once you receive this, there will be a whole list of terminology and abbreviations which a newcomer will find hard to understand.

The book in my series entitled 'The Mini Encyclopaedia of Exhibition Poultry' will answer all your queries.

Entries for the small shows usually close two weeks prior to the event which gives you ample time to apply the final touches to your birds' preparation.

Judging procedures.

In the world of Poultry Showing, there are two basic types of judging. In the British one, the stock are judged in comparison to the other birds in the same class. The results of these comparisons are placed in the order of First, Second, Third, etc.,

This would be described as competitive showing, and suits the British way of life. It is comparable to a 100 yard sprint race, where the winner is reported as Joe Bloggs with Enoch Shufflebottom second, without declaring whether the time was 10 or 15 seconds! The winner is jubilant, but the actual achievement may not be fully convincing.

In many other countries, especially on the European continent, all the birds entered are given an award. This indicates their correctness or perfection when compared to the Breeds Standard. Sometimes this is based on the allocation of points, in others by a written critique.

This practice is occasionally used in Britain, with some events being known as 'Assessment Shows', with the bird being awarded grading certificates, plus different categories of Diplomas. The same principle is often applied to poultry sales, which are held around the country. The first method appeals to the established exhibitor, who takes great satisfaction in 'putting one over his great friend', who is for the day a showing rival.

The alternative procedure is ideal for the beginner who is wanting to learn both the good and the bad points of his stock. There have been attempts to combine the two systems but they have not proved to be very practical to incorporate.

Returning home for an inquest on the day's results.

On returning home, always remember the old saying 'There will always be another day'. This applies whether you have had success or only gained a few minor placings.

If you have achieved Best in Show, then to use a phrase by Clive Carefoot, 'There is only one way you can go now! And that is downwards.'

It is a great feeling to have won a major award, but many of the old breeders will say the same thing. 'It is hard to continually breed the birds which will keep you at the top'.

Perhaps one of the reasons for this is a desire to breed from all your winning birds. Unless correctly mated they do not always prove to be the correct breeding birds. Actually your most important breeding pen is the combination which has just bred the winners.

If your day has not been as successful as you hoped for, you will obviously attempt to analyse the reason why.

It may be quite simply through lack of preparation of your birds. If so, this will quickly improve with practical experience. It could be that another judge will see your birds in a more favourable way.

One great point to consider is the quality of the birds which have beaten you. It is possible that you were unlucky in showing against a well established strain of stock which were capable of beating anything in the country. If this was the case, it could well give you the determination to plan your breeding programme over the next few years until you have bred their equal.

This achievement would then accomplish the heading at the commencement of this chapter.

At the end of the twentieth century your journey home will be a lot quicker than that of the birds in FIG. 10 returning from the 1923 London Dairy Show.

Origins of the breeds

If you total the number of different breeds of Poultry both in this country and on the European continent, we can certainly account for over one hundred.

There will be many people like myself who are intrigued as to where many of them came from. Conversely, there will be readers who are only interested in the present day descriptions of the breeds, and may wish to turn directly to the A-Y Breed Summary. For many of those breeds there is a brief history of their early ancestry.

In this chapter the concentration is on their possible creation. I have attempted to summarise as briefly as possible the information which I have gathered from the findings of writers during previous centuries. I believe it is a subject that you can either find boring or extremely fascinating.

The exact history of the original types of poultry will possibly never be conclusively proved, though the advancement of D.N.A testing may eventually supply more concrete evidence than has been previously possible. Many of the early recordings are, I fear, based more on personal hunches than scientific evidence. Darwin held the belief that all poultry descended from the Jungle Fowl and he has many supporters for that theory.

The assumption also created a group of doubters, who wrote many columns in the poultry books printed during the second half of the nineteenth and early part of the twentieth centuries.

Types of jungle fowl quoted include Gallus Lafayetti, (Ceylon), Gallus Sonnerati (Grey), Gallus Various (Javan) also known as Gallus Furcatus. Gallus Stanleyii, (Ceylon), Gallus Ferrugineus also known as Bankiva (The Red Jungle Fowl).

The word Gallus is taken from Latin and means poultry cock, Gallina being the female version.

Observations were made as to their type of crow, their nesting habits including egg size, colour and quantity per sitting, the number of tail feathers, with various having sixteen as opposed to the normal fourteen. These birds also have a single wattle which is still evident in breeds such as Brahmas, Malines and to some extent the original Aseel Malay type of Bird. The birds' mating habits were studied to discover if the male preferred one mate or a harem.

All of these birds are similar in style in that they are of slender build and of the light breed category.

When experiments were carried out to study their adaptation to life away from their natural habitat and weather conditions, most of them were not too successful, the main exception being the Red Jungle Fowl.

Edward Brown in his books reprints illustrations of drawings done by Ulysses Aldrovandi in 1599. These were done at the University of Bologna in Italy. They include Gallus Turcicus, Gallus Patauinus and Gallus Percicus. To me they are extremely interesting in that they depict virtually all the features seen on modern day breeds, but once again they are all of light bone structure and small in body size.

That wonderful Dutch artist Cornelis Van Gink has left us with a marvellous collection of paintings which include several of the Jungle Fowl. I have also seen a line drawing done by him where he has attempted to create the resulting cross between a Jungle Fowl and what is described as a Gallus Domesticus with the birds resembling the original imports of Shanghai Fowls.

During my research I have found this phenomenon on many occasions. A writer will go to great lengths laboriously explaining his views on the development of Jungle Fowl and just when 'the wheels start to roll off the wagon' the term 'local fowl' or 'domesticated fowl of the region', suddenly appears in the attempted solution to the equation, without any indication as to what they were or where they came from.

This is not confined to breeds of bygone centuries, but is quoted as recently as the first quarter of the twentieth century in the creation of the Barnevelder and Welsummer breeds.

My own views on the original breeds are similar to 'Doubting Thomas' mainly because the types of Jungle Fowl usually quoted are all in the small light breed category.

There is an old Lancashire saying 'you cannot breed rats from mice' and it is very applicable to this part of the debate.

If more mention and details were of Gallus Gigantic then I would be less sceptical. However an American gentlemen, Professor Jim Burnette from Ohio, has only recently completed an exploration into the Brazilian Jungle to retrieve some of the Saipan Jungle Fowl.

The professor has bred these birds for many years during which they have been bred pure and with great success. The purpose of this visit was to research the birds and acquire fresh blood to maintain strength and vigour. The vital statistics of his birds are of cocks weighing up to 20 lbs and standing 2.5-3 feet high.

Now perhaps we are getting somewhere in the search for a missing link. A photo of the Saipan Game resembles the Shamos which are in Britain at the present time. They are taller than the Asil (Aseel in old spelling) but not as rangy as the modern day Malay.

The professor believes the birds to be Gallus Geganleus I have sometimes sarcastically raised the question 'If you quote the word Gallus before a type of bird does it automatically become an old species of Jungle Fowl?'

Until this part of the chapter, no mention has been made as to where the extremely loose feathering associated with many of the modern day breeds came from. There has to be a source found before the equation can be completed.

If I were to join the list of writers who based their findings on a 'feeling they had in their water' I would plump for Gallus Langshan; this breed is known to have been in China for centuries, where it was almost worshipped. Indeed there is, in the Shanghai region of China, a mountain, and built at the summit is a virtual shrine named the 'Pagoda of Langshan'. It is one of the very few instances I can recall where poultry have been held in such high reverence by a nation.

In the quest to find the original loose feathered ancestor the name Gallus Morio appears. This bird is also referred to as the Negro Fowl.

Unfortunately, little positive information seems to be available about the birds, but the qualities mentioned are for them to have a dusky coloured skin, with comb and wattles often showing as mulberry or 'Gypsy Faced'. The bird is also credited with the ability to breed some birds with Silkie feathering.

Sue Bowser makes reference to the bird in her contribution on Silkie Fowls.

In Lewis Wright's famous book on Poultry, the point is made that some of the original importations of Langshans showed to be dark coloured in their head piece and claims were made by certain breeders to have actually had Silkie feathered stock hatched from their direct imports.

If the Langshan was the original soft feathered type and was of white pigmentation, then possibly a cross with the yellow pigmented Saipan or Malay would be sufficient to create the birds which were imported to England in the 1840s as Shanghais and eventually developed into the Cochins and Brahmas which have been extensively used to further create many of the more modern breeds.

The colour of eggs laid by different breeds can also be a good indicator of a bird's ancestry. Langshans, Brahmas and Cochins all lay brown or tinted eggs whilst most of the light breeds produce white or pale cream eggs.

The time taken for incubation is also a guiding factor, with both Brahmas and Cochins requiring much nearer to 23 days then the normal birds' 21 days.

It would probably be fair comment to say that, to many people, the exploration must go much farther back in history in an attempt to find some common ancestor, which is now extinct, but was responsible for at least some of the features which we have in present day poultry. To some this may be irrelevant, but there will be others who wish to complete the jigsaw.

The Old English Game type of fowl could quite easily be directly descended from the Red Jungle Fowl, with the modern day preference for wide shoulders being developed by man probably with the crossing of Aseel type of birds.

The very distinctive Black-Red colouring of the Red Jungle Fowl is distributed throughout many other breeds of poultry.

I have a feeling that the birds which we now refer to as Sumatra figured in some of the original developments.

Historians have reported that they were capable of flying the short stretch of water between Sumatra and Java.

Also reported is that the natives used to search in the jungles for a large type of wild bird to cross with their local fowls.

In many of the early writings, there is reference to Pheasant Malay birds being imported and used to create other breeds, especially ones where double laced markings were involved. It was thought at one time the word pheasant was associated with their habits and style of walking, but further investigation suggests that it was more associated with their markings. I have also had a report that one of the postage stamps in Sumatra illustrates a long tailed bird with pheasant type markings.

Presumably these birds resulted from a Malay type bird crossed with a coloured Sumatra.

The Sumatra is the only bird to my knowledge which has more than one spur growing from the shank. Where did this come from?

Eric Parker outlines the history of the Polish and once again we have a bird possessing a unique feature, with its high rising skull and bone structure, the top of which is only covered by a fleshy skin. Interestingly Gallus Patauinus shows quite a large crest of feathers. The Naked Neck is another breed which differs from all others. The absence of feathers along virtually all the neck and crop area is only on this breed of poultry. This phenomenon can be easily transferred to other breeds, it apparently being very dominant, but again it must have originated somewhere, I doubt if it is simply a freak of nature.

The everlasting tailed birds from Japan are again different from the normal fowl. No doubt the extreme lengths have been cultivated by selective breeding, but the fact that their main tail feathers do not moult annually is unique to this type of Japanese Fowl.

There are several breeds which have five toes as opposed to the normal four, Silkies and Faverolles being examples.

The earliest birds that I can trace with this feature are from Belgium; they are the Ardennaise Fowls which live wild in the mountains 1500 feet above sea level. The birds are Black-Red Jungle Fowl in colouring and can also be seen in a Rumpless version.

There is another group of similar type birds, some of which are often described as the Mediterranean Breeds, but there are many others with little difference in the main characteristics. The early history of many of these breeds is included in their breed summary so all that I will say at present is that the Fayoumi, Bresse and Castilian appear to be amongst the oldest recordings.

The Araucana must be unique with its ability to lay blue/green coloured eggs. We know for certain that the birds exist in the jungles of Chile and Peru, and possibly many more regions.

Cornelis Van Gink makes reference to them as Gallus Inaurus and adds proof of their existence before the sixteenth century.

The birds have very distinguished and enlarged ear muffs which grow outwards in a tuft of feathers and are not seen quite the same in any other breed.

They also exist in a Rumpless version and could have more influence on other tail-less breeds than was at one time considered possible.

The points which I have just raised are all features which you might bear in mind the next time that you study drawings of Jungle Fowl, accompanied by that particular writer's claim that all breeds of poultry are the descendants of Gallus Bankiva.

To give a brief illustration for the chapter on the original breeds, I have included, in the colour section, a beautiful painting by Cornelis Van Gink, showing a pair of Black-Red coloured Gallus Bankiva.

For the Jungle Fowl, I have chosen a unique photograph, showing a live Sonneratti cock. Normally these birds are shown in paintings rather than in the flesh. These birds are sometimes known as The Jungle Cock. They are reported to have very small combs, and little if any wattles. I wondered if this bird could have been crossed in some way.

FIG 1. Shows a drawing by 'Stead' giving his impression of the original Jungle Giants.

27

FIG 2. Grey Jungle Fowl Cock.

FIG 3. A very rare pair of Grey or Sonnebat's Jungle Fowl. Photograph by Mr. G. Tullet

28

FIG 4. Is photographed from an oil painting by Herbert Atkinson. Here the artist illustrates his thoughts on the original Asils. In the breed summary for Raiza Game, I have included a drawing by 'Finterbusch' showing his interpretation of the original giant.

FIG 5. Shows another of his drawings, with a bird he describes as being a Chilean Game Cock.

FIG 6. Also by 'Finterbusch' showing a Fighting Malay, from Brazil.

29

FIG 7. Illustrates a line drawing, depicting the imaginary development of the species. The signatures suggest that it was a dual effort between Van Gink and Finterbusch.

FIG 8 and 9. Were drawn by Aldrovandi in 1599, I have never been sure quite what he was illustrating. They are described as Gallus Percicus and Gallus Patauinus respectively.

They appear to depict a half way development from Jungle Fowl to our present day domesticated breeds by

illustrating crests, rosecomb and rumpless. Also in his drawing, which I have included in the breed of Fayoumi, is a single combed bird, with red earlobes, as opposed to the ones in these pictures, that appear to be white.

Useful information to assist when reading the standards.

Whilst writing the forthcoming breed summary, I have used several words which occur repeatedly amongst the Exhibition Poultry fraternity. Some of them are very definitely open to individual interpretation.

In many cases the use of them has altered over a period of time and drifted away from the definition quoted in the Oxford dictionary.

I therefore stress that the way in which they are used is MY personal interpretation and is the one which I have found to be most frequently used by fellow exhibitors and writers.

There are many faults and deformities which are applicable to ninety nine percent of the breeds. Therefore the items in the following list are considered serious faults unless otherwise stated.

BOWLEGS
CROOKED BEAK
CROOKED BREAST
CROOKED TOES
DUCK FEET
EYES WHERE THE PUPIL IS OTHER THAN ROUND
FEATHERED SHANKS
KNOCK KNEES
MORE THAN FOUR TOES
ODD COLOURED EYES
ROACH BACK
ROUND BACK
SPLIT WINGS
SQUARE OR FLAT SHINS
WHITE IN RED COLOURED LOBES
WRY NECK
WRY TAIL

I have also omitted to mention 101 times that a certain number of points have been allocated to the breed for fitness, my belief being that if a bird is not fit, then it should not be in a show pen waiting to be assessed.

Sketches and diagrams illustrating the different types of combs and body features have been frequently published. However, one which shows the individual sections of a bird's wing often appears slightly confusing. I therefore include a sketch showing in detail the four parts - .

THE WING

The various parts or sections of a bird's wing probably cause more confusion than any other part of the breed standards.

This is mainly caused by some breeds having a particular section named by one term, whilst another breed will have the same part described by a completely different term. Some of these points have been corrected in recent revisions of the standards.

In the adjacent diagram, I outline the various terms which I have heard used to describe the different portions of the wing.

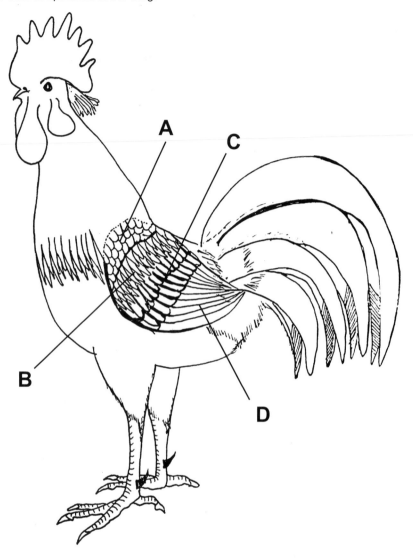

SECTION A

This is the smallest of the four parts, and is not always visible from outside the showpen, being covered by the neck hackle feathers.

This area is constructed of short flat feathers and is usually the same colouring as the breast and back of the bird.

Laced Wyandottes are a breed where the part is well featured. It is commonly called the wing butt, but is sometimes referred to as the shoulder tip.

SECTION B

This is the area which normally carries the bird's brightly coloured plumage. The feathers are of the glossy type, similar to the hackle feathers only much shorter in length. The colouring of these usually takes the same shade as the neck hackle and saddle hackle feathers, but whereas they are often striped or tipped with a different colour these wing feathers are solid colouring as in Brown Leghorns, where the colouring continues over the back of the bird, and into the corresponding area on the outer wing.

This area is commonly called the wing bow.

SECTION C

The feather shape in this section is very different from the outer parts of the wing. The area is usually known as the wing covert with these much longer and flatter feathers covering the lower part of the main wing feathers. These are the flight and secondary feathers. When the wing is closed, one lies on top of the other.

The wing coverts usually take the bird's breast colouring. A perfect example is on the Spangled Hamburgh where these coverts form two separate and parallel lines of black spangled feathers, or solid black in the Salmon Faverolle. As in many other breeds, these are termed the 'wing bars', meaning exactly the same as the wing coverts.

SECTION D

This part of the wing is the easiest to describe, and in many breeds is the most clearly defined. It is created by the outer part of the secondary wing feathers being of a contrasting colour, and when the wing is in a closed position they form the wing 'bay', the shape of which takes the form of a triangle, and is frequently referred to as the wing 'diamond'.

In this diagram, illustrating a fully opened wing, the main feathers are termed the primaries, but the much more frequently used term is the 'flight feathers'.

The parts of the wing referred to in this feature are mainly noticeable in the male birds. Usually the female's wing feathering takes the same formation as her body, though you will find in some breeds that she has a colouring highlighted in the area around her crop and upper breast. This usually corresponds with her mate's wing bow. In over marked females this colouring also extends to the wing bow as in Duckwing and Pile Game Birds, also in Brown Leghorn females where it is known as 'rusty sided' and frowned upon in the standard for showing.

In several pure white breeds, Wyandottes being a great example, there is a tendency for a small percentage of the male chickens to show a faintly red coloured wing 'bow' when fully mature. This illustrates the presence of other colouring in their genetic structure.

A more detailed study of these faults can be found in IAN KAY'S book, 'The Mini-Encyclopaedia of Exhibition Poultry', which has 80 pages including 8 of colour, covering the main principles of general poultry, husbandry, accidents, illness and good health, all listed in alphabetical order. Available from Scribblers Publishing (01636 816222) @ £4.99.

FANCY FOWL MAGAZINE also runs articles, which feature detailed descriptions of different feather patterns, and body adornments, also available from Scribblers Publishing.

A-Y LISTINGS

ALTSTEIRER

This breed is credited with being originated in Germany. I cannot find any reference to the birds in the early history books, or even a breed which is similar.

However in the breed of Styrian, which was developed in Austria, it is mentioned that the birds fell into two categories. One of them was as an egg laying utility bird, the second version was heavier built and more inclined towards meat production, whilst still retaining the ability to lay a reasonable number of eggs.

I believe that the Styrian was the version for laying, while the meat bird eventually became the Altsteirer.

At the World Poultry Congress, where the birds were first officially introduced to the public, the meat version of the breed was described by the Feathered World correspondent as being similar in markings to the Brown Sussex females. This description would be very fitting for the female in the accompanying illustration of the Altsteirer.

Whether my deduction is correct or not, the breed of Altsteirer is now very popular around the European continental shows.

The shape and balance of the birds remind me of the British Dorking, especially with their well rounded and prominent chest.

It would also be similar to the Sussex Fowl in their original type, which was at one period considered to be almost identical to the Dorking.

This point, coupled with the writer's comment on their colouring being similar to the Brown Sussex, would suggest that one of the breeds was included in their original creation.

Both sexes have a single upright comb which is red in colour. The earlobes are white, and as with the Styrian, the headgear is completed with a backward facing crest of feathers which are adequate for decoration without being cumbersome.

It has been suggested that the name of Styrian and Alsteirer are so similar that only a slight change in dialect separates them, which again suggests that the two breeds were at one period actually the same.

The Altsteirer has been Bantamised in Germany. They are listed in the American Bantam book as being of Black/red colouring. I am told a white version is now being exhibited on the continent, in both large and small fowl.

One of the earlier prints, showing a pair of Black-Red Alsteirer.

34

ANCONA

In nearly all the breeds, I can write the basic standard from memory pausing only to research the breed's history and origin. Consequently the Ancona, which forms part of the Mediterranean group of breeds, I left until late in my writings, believing with the naivety of a five year old child, that it would be straight forward. Its history is full of discussion and contradictions. Apparently the first consignment of so called Ancona Fowl came to these shores around 1850. Even the dates vary from writer to writer. Some of them were black and white, some brownish, with others showing more of a reddish pattern colouring.

Around the 1980s more importations of Ancona type fowls arrived. These were a little more uniform in type and markings, but nowhere approaching the ones seen today. The breakthrough came at about the turn of the century when fresh stock came here, both from Italy and America, which had by now started to become interested in the 'Spangled Italian Fowl', which was at one stage referred to as the Marcheghiana fowl. Harrison Weir in his writings in the early part of the twentieth century was most scathing and critical when referring to Anconas, as Lewis Wright had also been some thirty years previously. In fact, later editions of his 'Book of Poultry' had to retract his statement that they were little more than a cross between Black and White Minorcas. It was quickly pointed out to him that such a cross would at the best produce Cuckoo type markings, not spangled, and would certainly not have the pigmentation to provide the yellow legs which most of even the earliest imports of birds possessed.

The general opinion was gradually formed that the Ancona was basically the common fowl of Italy, crossed with a breed which enabled it to retain its yellow pigmentation, and at the same time supply the necessary white mottling for it to develop into the Ancona - fine, but what was it? The common fowl of Italy is accepted as the white Leghorn. This breed had been transported around the world by the Roman sailors who, in their trading, returned home with a different species of fowl. The question which I asked myself was, what breed and where from? It had to be a 'breed' which could transmit spots or spangling, not simply a mixture of black and white, as in the Exchequer Leghorn (this colour was only developed in 1904 anyhow). At this point it would be very simple to do the same as many other writers have done in the past, and state that these birds were descended from the 'Common Fowl' of the area. However this is not the style in which I have written the book. I would prefer to make a calculated assessment as to their original ancestors. From many of the previous writers' findings, it would appear that for several centuries, there has been on the European Continent a nucleus of farm yard fowls which carry the mottled plumage. These birds were breeding in many types and colours, before being eventually separated and created into breeds.

The Schlotterkamm is a prime example of spangle colouring. These birds also have single combs and white ear lobes. The Bergishe Crower is another variation of the birds. The Thuringian has beautifully spotted plumage and a single comb, but has developed a beard and muff. In France there is the Du Monte which was again single combed and bearded, or whiskered as it was once described. There was also in France a bird called the Elderfeld, but, unfortunately, I cannot trace many details, other than their great similarity to the Schlotterkamm.

The Houdan has again a spangled type of Black and White colouring, but has accumulated not only a beard, but also a full crest, presumably from the Padoue or Poland type of fowls.

I was looking for a breed which was centuries old, and the origin of the Schlotterkamm indicated the western part of Germany, adjacent to the Dutch border. In Holland, I found the Drente or Dretenche fowl. These birds had been there for centuries. They had been referred to as resembling Gallus Bankiva, which Darwin insisted was the progenitor of the Domestic Fowl.

The Drente had been in existence for a very long period of time, and can be proved by a piece of needlework, made in 1805 by a young Dutch girl, who clearly shows the birds as they are today. The Drente existed in a range of colours including Pencilled, Laced Cuckoo, and the one which I was looking for, 'Black Spangled' or 'Speckled', depending on which term the writers used.

In Holland there is also a very long established breed, which we know as the Friesian, and usually associated with being Pencilled in a similar pattern to that of our own Hamburghs. However I have located a beautiful painting by Cornelis Van Gink, for whose accuracy I have great respect. This painting shows the Friesians in a mottled colouring, which suggests a relationship with the Drente at some point back in history. (A print of this appears in the colour section of the book.)

In Germany the birds which we call Anconas were at one time listed under the heading 'Spotted Leghorn', which illustrates their early history. The original ancestors to the Ancona will probably never be traced, but whatever they were, the birds have now been developed into a highly attractive breed, which has been bred to a very high standard of perfection.

Ancona Characteristics

Every breed has certain points within its standard of perfection which, when correct, separate the top class birds from the mediocre. The Ancona is no exception.

Firstly, the tipping at the end of each feather must be pure white, not smoky grey in colour. The shape of each tip being in the form of a 'V', not in any way a splash or spangle. Secondly, the black background colouring to each feather is required to be a lustrous green sheen.

The style of the bird is for it to be fairly long in the back, with a tail carried well out, slightly spread in the female and well furnished in the males, each tail feather again to be delicately tipped with white.

The whole of the body, wing bars, hackle and saddle hackle to be evenly tipped with white, which creates an even colouring throughout.

When you open the wings, both the flights and secondaries, again, show a white tipping. The yellow coloured legs are unique in that they should have a neat line of black mottling extending down their front from the hock to the feet. The face, wattles and comb are bright red, as is the eye, but this is allowed to shade to hazel. The ear lobes should be white, but often carry a lemon shade which no one seems to object to.

The original birds all had single combs standing upright in the males and folded in the female, but in later years there was a rose comb version standardised. This comb is more of the close fitting Wyandotte shape rather than the Hamburgh one. (More details on the correct shaped single comb are in the Minorca breed.)

The Ancona is a breed which we have kept in both large and small versions, and there are one or two points which will be of interest to any newcomers to the breed, firstly, the question of 'Going Gay' which is the terminology for birds which, when they moult, become larger in their white markings. If you obtain the best strains they do not do this, and can be shown for many years, especially the females. In the males, a second year bird is allowed to have his flight feathers with rather more than a tipping of white, providing that it does not extend to more than half the feathers' length.

The tipping on a cock's hackle and saddle hackle increases slightly, and can look even more striking in an older bird; this colouring can be referred to as 'snow'.

There have been miniature Anconas for a long time and many of the birds possibly achieve a standard nearer to perfection than that obtained by their large counterpart. Their standard of perfection should be the same as that for the large bird. They share one breed club which was amongst the first clubs formed, the original one obviously catering for large fowl only, and was started during the ongoing saga with the breed's credibility and inconsistency of colouring.

It is all credit to the club and its members to have developed such a fantastically marked specimen from the breed's controversial beginning. Both large and small are excellent layers of white eggs, and if quietly handled can be a very friendly breed to keep.

Weights   *Large*   *Males*   *6-6.5 lbs*   *Females*   *5-5.5 lbs*

               Miniatures *Males*   *20-24 ozs*   *Females*   *18-22 ozs*

The 1927 Dairy Show winning cockerel. He was bred and exhibited by Dr G. G. Timpson from London.

A cock, which won the Crystal Palace in 1931. He was bred and exhibited by Mr H. Rance from Bucks.

This cock photographed in 1927, was bred by George Goodall from Chester, and was a consistent winner for him.

A Rosecombed Ancona cockerel bred by George Davies from Llandilo. He won both the Dairy Show and the Crystal Palace in 1930.

From a later period, again bred by George Davies. He won the Dairy Show in 1936.

A splendid cockerel which was successfully shown in 1935 for its breeder and photographer Arthur Rice, from Wellingborough.

The old Champion rosecombed hen bred by Arthur Rice. She won top awards at all the major shows, even when eight years old.

Bred by Mr W. W. Driver, and in 1931 won many shows including the Crystal Palace.

Bred by another noted Ancona breeder, Andrew Southerin from Padiham, Lancs. She won the Club Show in 1935.

From 1927, when she won a whole series of shows for her breeder, George Goodall from Chester.

A single combed pullet which won the 1930 Crystal Palace and many other shows for her breeder Mr W. W. Driver.

Again one of the great Arthur Rice birds, this time the 1928 Crystal Palace winner.

A cockerel from 1949, he was bred by Edwin Stephens, and won the Dairy Show of that year.

The 1968 Club Show Champion. She was bred and exhibited by Mr P. Pierpoint.

40

ANDALUSIAN

These are a beautiful breed originating in the province of Spain by that name.

They carry the typical shape of breeds from the Mediterranean, being long bodied with flowing tails carried at an angle of 45 degrees. The body has a basic colour of delicate blue, with each feather having a black lacing round the edge, giving the birds a very distinctive and attractive appearance.

The comb and face are bright red coloured, with a single upright comb in the male bird folded to one side in the female. They both have medium sized white lobes, brownish to red eyes, with their legs and feet slate grey coloured.

The birds themselves have a friendly nature, I have kept both large and miniatures, and found them a most useful breed to exhibit in the AOV and Rare Breed Classes.

I believe the main reason which holds back the breed's popularity is the fact that to produce true blue coloured you will also breed some blacks and splashes which are only useful as future breeders or laying birds. Also there will probably be some cockerels bred with red neck hackles. These make lovely curry but are just one more reason to make the breed a dream for the specialist breeder but a nightmare for someone wanting instant success with a minimum of effort.

There are some very true to type miniature Andalusians, with exactly the same markings as their large counterparts.

The same remark applies to both large and small. I believe they should be more popular with new breeders. They are a breed which will add a touch of glamour when walking around anyone's garden.

Weights   Large Fowls Males   7.5 lbs   Females   5.5 lbs

An Andalusian hen which is often quoted as being one of the best ever seen. She was bred by the Abbot family from Norfolk and was a consistent winner for them during the 1920s.

41

A cockerel which was again bred in Norfolk, this time by Mr W. Frost from Dereham. He is an excellent looking bird, and was a regular winner for him during the 1930s.

A. R. Woods' unbeaten Andalusian cock. 1st Dairy, 1st International 1968, 1st Devon County and South of England 1969.

An attractive pullet which was photographed by Josef Wolters at the Utrecht Show in 1986.

A miniature cockerel which was bred by Mr R. Compton from Staffordshire. The bird won Champion Rare Breed at the National Poultry Show.

ANTWERP BRAHMAS

This name is in some ways misleading, and yet in other ways it's absolutely correct. Belgium was amongst the first of the countries to attempt pure breeding and standardisation of stock, and many of their native breeds have been distributed to adjoining countries, and used to develop new breeds and variations to existing ones.

The Antwerp Brahma was originally imported at a period not recorded but certainly a long while since. The birds were sent direct to Antwerp Zoological Gardens, where they were bred from and distributed around the country.

The foundation stock was singled combed and had the traditional Light Brahma markings and feathered legs, but at this period many of the birds were being described as Shanghais.

Since then the birds have had a big influence in the development of many breeds, especially the ones where great size and laying qualities were essential.

The main and unique feature of the breed lies in white pigmentation to their legs, beak and skin colouring, as opposed to the yellow in the British Brahmas. Obviously these had been selected from the original Shanghais with this point being essential.

I have often quoted my belief that the first so called breed of Shanghais was a collection of cross breeds from which you could develop many variations. I am also of the opinion that Langshan blood was very strongly included in the Shanghai. This would immediately account for the white pigmentation. The ones to arrive in England were selected for yellow pigment now associated with Cochins and Brahmas.

I have a feeling that these Antwerp Brahmas have had more influence in other breeds than they have been given credit for, especially the ones carrying white flesh and table qualities. The Belgians record that both the Malines and the Flemish Cuckoo contain their blood, which in later years were developed into the North Holland Blue and the Marans. I wonder about the relationship with our own Light Sussex.

To my knowledge there are no current photographs available of the Antwerp Brahma. This picture illustrates a painting of the birds which highlights their great size and upright standing single combs.

APPENZELLER

The Appenzeller is a very interesting breed in several ways. It is of Swiss origin and their national breed, having been bred there for many centuries.

Their introduction into this country is slightly ambiguous. The earliest record of classes for them under the name of Appenzeller was in the 1982 National Federation Show at Stafford, by which time a club had been formed. The Judge was Fred Hams and there were 20 entries.

For a breed which has been in existence for so many centuries, it seems strange for them to have taken so long to be fully recognised in these shores. To relate the full history of the breed, we reprint from the Appenzeller Breed Club Manual the exact story, and offer our thanks to the club for supplying us the details.

The standard for the breed is split into two varieties, the Spitzhauben and the Barthuhner.

The Spitz, as it is often called, exists in several colour variations, the one which is the most popular being the Silver. In fact the popularity of this colour is so great, that there are many people who do not realise that there are other colours and versions.

Every breed has at least one outstanding feature which creates its own individuality, and is instantly recognisable. With the Spitz it is the crest of feathers on the bird's head, which are forward facing. These feathers are quite strong, and initially point upwards before gracefully curving over but well clear of the beak.

The general appearance of the birds is that of a typical egg laying light breed; a well rounded front which enables the crop to expand comfortably when full of tasty morsels which the birds have collected on their scavenging, a longish body to hold the egg factory, and a well boned pair of legs which are medium in length but active looking. The male birds have fully furnished tails carried well out, and close fitting wings tucked up under the tail. They have strong beaks to collect their food with. Their small comb is of the twin horned type, the eyes are prominent and alert looking, as is the whole character of the breed - stylish and active looking without being flighty.

In colouring the Silver is actually a spangled bird, and the type of spangling is that which appeals to the general public and many exhibitors. It is in the form of a small black tip and entirely different from the ones on our own spangled Hamburghs.

The interesting point is that, on many occasions, I have seen the judging of Hamburghs at a small show been given by a gentleman who was not a connoisseur of the breed, and nearly always the end result was for the winners to be the ones with very prominent little tips to the feathers, not the well rounded full moon markings which are the Hamburgh's great breed feature.

This tipping to the Appenzeller's feathering should extend evenly all over the bird, in both male and female, and even includes their crest feathers. The under-colour is dark grey. The Gold is identical in markings with the golden ground colour being described as golden yellow, which shades to golden red on the male bird's lustrous feathers in the hackles etc.

The black is self coloured, with the top colour carrying a green sheen to the plumage. The comb and face are rich red with the ear lobes a bluish white. The shanks and beak are also blue whilst the eyes are only required to be dark brown.

The second variety is the Barthuhner and is of similar type, but built on more powerful lines, being broader in the body and more muscular in the thighs. Its carriage is described as strong, and active as opposed to neat and very active.

To a casual observer the main difference is in the headpiece, which is rose combed, the leader of which is carried straight backwards. The comb itself is evenly covered with small rounded spikes, and is red in colour with white ear lobes. The wattles are small but should really be covered by the beard, which is full and delightfully described in the standard as being cheek and chin. I wonder if Tom Bartlett, the breed's first secretary in England, was influential in that wording!

This full beard means that the hackle is also more pronounced than in the Spitz, which again adds to its larger appearance.

The colours of the Barts are based on the game type pattern, which nearly gives a free licence. The blue version is based on the laced blue type as in the Andalusians and Orpingtons.

The breed has been Bantamised in the USA, but as yet there are only very few in this country, which seems a pity. I believe that the breed could prove to be very popular in a miniaturised form.

Appenzellers are one of the few breeds which we have never bred, not through dislike, more by circumstance. If I did, I am sure that the choice would be Silver Spangled Spitz. Perhaps we might find time to develop them in a Bantam version.

There is one other type of bird which is also a native of Switzerland. Little is heard of it, and I believe that there are none in this country at the present time. It is known by the delightful name of 'The little Swiss hen'. The birds can only be traced back to the beginning of the twentieth century. The area of its origin is the Amriswil locality, where it was believed to be the result of crossing Orpingtons and Wyandottes, obviously with the object of producing a breed more suitable to production of table poultry than the Appenzellers.

The following has been kindly donated by The Appenzeller Breed Society, for which contribution we thank them.

The Appenzeller Spitzhauben derives its name from the region of Switzerland where it has been bred for centuries, and from the similarity of the shape of its crest to the lace bonnets worn by the ladies of Appenzellerland as part of their traditional costume.

The Spitzhauben is considered to be similar in size and type to most European poultry before Roman times to the eighteenth century. Widely distributed in Northern Europe by Vikings, the breed survived in England in small flocks, chiefly in the Yorkshire area under the name of Hornet.

The A. Rice Poultry Photographs, dating back to the end of the 1800s, include a photograph of a Hornet cock exhibited at the 1910 World Poultry Congress held at the Crystal Palace. Mr. S.A. Rice, now in his eighties, recalls assisting his late father in photographing a pair of Hornets from the flock of F.C. Brainwhite of Suffolk in 1930, and has provided conclusive evidence that the Hornet and the Gold Spangled Spitzhauben are identical.

But the survival and development of this hardy breed in its most attractive form has been in the scattered farms below the Alpstein Mountains, where it has adapted to harsh weather conditions, and has proved able to lay quite well on a frugal diet. Like the Hornet, its English counterpart, it was unsuited to intensive commercial egg production and was replaced by hybrids, and by the 1950s had declined in numbers almost to the point of extinction, until revived by the Appenzeller Poultry Club of Switzerland.

The introduction of the Silver Appenzeller Spitzhauben to this country was entirely due to the endeavours of the Hon. Mrs. Pamela Jackson, who, whilst living in Switzerland in the 1960s, was attracted to the breed by a photograph in a magazine. After two years of fruitless search, she at last found one of the few breeders in Appenzell, and bought a cock and six pullets, and maintained them with the help of a neighbouring farmer's wife. On her return to England in 1972 she was eventually able to arrange for a few of the eggs, from her birds to be hatched in incubators at Chatsworth. From this foundation stock the development of the breed began.

The interest was first channelled through the Rare Breed Society, until the Appenzeller Breed Society was formed, with Tom Bartlett as its founding Secretary. Largely due to his efforts, interest and demand for the breed increased and strong classes appeared at shows.

Standard Weights	Spitz Males	4.5 lbs	Females	3.5 lbs
	Bart Males	6.5 lbs	Females	4 lbs

Reproduced from the Appenzeller Club Handbook, and outlines the ideals for both varieties.

A pair of Black Appenzellers which were displayed at the 1922 World Poultry Congress in 1921. Could these be the type of bird which were to be imported to Britain and become the Yorkshire Hornet?

This picture shows a typical Silver Spangled from the present era.

This photograph was taken by Josef Wolters at the 1983 Frankfurt Show, and illustrates a very attractive winning male bird.

47

ARAUCANA

In most instances if you mention a breed to me, I will immediately think of the large fowl version, and recall memories of some excellent specimens from my younger days. The Araucana is different in that my memories of them as a showing breed are the delightful Lavender Blue coloured Bantam females, with their quaint and well controlled backward facing small crests blending with a full beard and muffling which, even though it was pronounced, was not excessive. How they came to be in the country or where they came from I do not know but they certainly were very attractive. You often saw them when judging shows in the Essex or Norfolk areas.

Our own first involvement with the breed was during the 1960s, when my father obtained some large fowl Araucana eggs from a gentleman living near to Scunthorpe. Dad always had an interest in showing a few eggs, having won his original first prize with a plate of eggs laid by what would loosely be described as a Buff Orpington. He was only eleven years old at the time so obviously was extremely happy.

These blue eggs which he had obtained carried a unique history. The gentleman who supplied them had served in the First World War, and, on returning home from Peru, collected a sitting of eggs from the local birds which lived wild in the jungle. He managed to keep them in his kit-bag until the demob day. On arriving home he sat them and, from the resulting chicks, interbred them for the next 40 years without the addition of any other blood line.

The eggs which father brought home were sat, and as the old gent predicted, grew into strong healthy stock. When the chicks matured they were all Black-Red or Partridge coloured, and we continued to breed them for several years.

When the Rare Breeds Society was formed in 1969, Aracuna (original spelling), were one of the breeds with no standard, so at one of the council meetings anyone with Araucanas was invited to attend, and bring with them an example of their birds to help as a guide when finalising the draught standard.

The surprise to me was that ours were the only birds with five toes, none of the others had the additional back claw. Consequently the standard was approved for four toed birds only. I agreed, possibly reluctantly, but you cannot have a standard worded 'either or'. Our piece of history was allowed to dwindle away but with hindsight I wish that we had continued with them and done the conversion to a four toed model, but to do so would have broken the birds' original trait.

The Araucana has been in Britain longer than some people imagine. There is an interesting article about them in the November 29th issue of Feathered World. But before you go rummaging through the papers for it, the year was 1930. It was written by C.T. Davies and entitled, 'The blue egg laying Araucana from Chile'. A Mr Beever had imported some of the birds from South America. Again, as with us, a sitting of eggs was obtained by the writer who succeeded in hatching nine chicks, turning out to be six male and three female.

The mixture of birds reared was far different from ours. This man had a mixture of single and pea combs, and colour variations from Buff to one which resembled a Golden Pheasant cock bird but had a single comb.

He describes the bird as obviously of Jungle Fowl relationship. He does not refer to their toes so presumably they were straight forward four toed versions, and from the photographs they certainly appear so.

Mr Davies carried out some research into the birds' history, and the only results were that in the south of Chile there is a territory called Araucania, which is presumably where they obtained their name.

The blue egg factor appears to be very dominant when the birds are crossed with other breeds, which is presumably what had happened with this gentleman's original sitting of eggs, as opposed to the ones we received which bred true on a regular pattern. The egg colouring can be blended to Khaki, if the birds are crossed with a dark egg laying bird such as a Welsummer.

In later years, an eventful day in my life occurred at the Lincolnshire Agricultural Show, when a very impromptu and hastily arranged duty was given to me. It was to escort Princess Anne around the Poultry and Waterfowl sections of the show. I was in no way dressed for such an auspicious occasion but she did not mind in the least. I found her to be a charming and very knowledgeable person, who had the ability to converse in a friendly manner with a mere 'cock and hen' breeder.

During the conversations she related her involvement with Araucanas; apparently the family kept a flock of them on one of their Scottish estates. She also confirmed that the original blue egg laying birds in Scotland came from a ship which had got into difficulties in the area of sea close to the Orkneys.

The general appearance of the Araucana is of a Gamey type bird, not the Old English Game, more the Asiatic version's build, being rather deep in the body and wide at the shoulder with a horizontal and fairly long back. The tail is carried at 45 degrees, with the bird standing on well developed legs and thighs which are set wide apart.

The bird should feel firm fleshed when handled, and be alert and active in the show pen. A major feature is the head, with its strong beak and alert eyes. The birds should have a full beard which includes a rather different type of ear muffs that stand out very noticeably. These do not appear as pronounced in the Miniature versions. The head is then completed with its very distinctive crest, which, it is stressed, must not be allowed to become over developed. This crest is carried well to the back of the head and is compact in its feathering.

The breed exists in many colour variations mainly taking their colour standard from the Modern Game pattern, the exception being the one which I personally prefer; that is the Lavender. This should be a delicate blue/grey shading and is the type of blue often referred to as pigeon blue which is capable of breeding the correct colour in both sexes when mated together over many generations, as opposed to the laced blue as required in Orpingtons or Andalusians for example.

The comb and what little face and wattles the birds have showing should be bright red.

I have deliberately left the comb until last. It is described as an irregular pea type, and certainly the combs displayed on the male birds in particular, both in large and Miniature version, can vary in their shape and conformation. This feature is not confined to the Araucana breed, there are several more breeds with this problem, especially where there has been some recently imported continental blood used. Brahmas are a perfect example especially in the darks.

The wording pea type is often used. Sometimes it is more clearly defined as a triple pea, meaning that there are three lines of small spikes running from front to rear, with the central one being higher that the outer two.

Other similar types of comb are described as Walnut, Half Walnut, Malay Type, Raspberry, Strawberry, Acorn and one described as a Raspberry cut length wise. which offers quite a confusing collection and variation. I believe that judges vary considerably in their attitude to a bird's slightly differently shaped comb from the one described for that breed. As stated at the beginning of the breeds summary, there is a good selection of Miniature

Araucanas in circulation, with most of the colours available.

Weights	Large Fowl	Males	6-7 lbs	Females	5-6lbs
	Miniatures	Males	26-30 oz	Females	24-28 ozs

Taken in 1924, and the birds were described as being 'Pea combed Araucana'.

A very attractive miniature pullet. She was bred by Mrs Roxburgh, who was the club secretary and won first at the 1973 Alexandra Palace Club Show, the breed having just been officially approved by the Poultry Club.

Mr. George Hamer's Lavender Araucana Bantam Cockerel, a constant winner.

This very striking Rumpless Araucana was bred and very successfully shown by Dorian Roxburgh.

An unusual female; she is pure white and rumpless. The bird is owned by Ralph Strane from California, and was photographed by J. Gryner.

ARDENNES & SANS QUEUE

I include the Ardennes in the list of breeds covered by the 'Stairway', not because I have seen the birds and consider them to have great appeal, but because the history which I can gather on the breed suggests that they might have had a lot of influence in the formation of many of the more recently developed breeds.

Harrison Weir in his book 'Our Poultry' gives them a short coverage, stating that they were a very old breed which he believed had relationship with the Jungle Fowl, Gallus Bankiva, but he was of the belief that they had become almost extinct.

Edward Brown in the section of his books devoted to the history and standards for the breeds is a lot more explicit with his findings. Firstly, he praises the Belgians for their livestock husbandry, and their ability to cultivate every available piece of land no matter how small. He considers their ability in the art of breeding livestock to be the best in Europe. Their breeds are very much self contained, with the native breeds of livestock closely associated with food production and practical uses rather than any form of decorative appeal.

The Campine was obviously a great breed for egg production, whilst the Braekel especially has a reputation for being a quick maturing small table fowl.

Most of the other breeds in Belgium, are best known for their table bird qualities. There are several types of heavy boned Cuckoo coloured birds probably all relations to the Malines. The Huttegem is another very long established 'Breed'. It contains a lot of the Shanghai or Cochin characteristics, and is noted for its excellent brooding qualities, which, when combined with the very large framed body renders it capable of covering a good sitting of eggs. Some of the hens are reported as weighing up to nine pounds when in full bloom. Another variation on this Shanghai blood is the Antwerp Brahma. These birds were originally imported from China as single combed Brahmas which must have been a different strain from the ones imported to Britain. The birds also had white flesh and pigmentation, which again was different from the ones which we used to develop many of our breeds. I would suggest that this type of Brahma contained Langshan blood probably crossed with the Chittatong type of game fowl.

The Ardennes is quite definitely indigenous to the Ardennes, which is a part of Belgium known for having large areas of woodland where the birds and their ancestors survived for centuries.

The main colouring is the Black-Red family thought to be obtained from the Bankiva Jungle Fowl, but these birds were developed to weigh up to seven pounds in the males.

Again the breed is excellent tasting meat especially if 'well hung'. They have a fine textured skin and are white fleshed. Another feature of the breed is that they have five toes. They have a compact body and single combs with long wattles. Their necks are short and thick, their wings rather large, as is the tail which has a large pair of sickles. When you read these characteristics they are almost word for word the Dorking. That is why in my summary of the Dorkings' history I suggested that the Ardennes was probably the bird brought to the British Isles by the Phoenicians.

There is also in Belgium a variation of the Ardennes which can be rumpless and exists in a full range of colours. These birds are from the Liege district and are called 'Sans Queue'. Another name for them is the 'Poules des haies', which translates into Hedge Fowls. Again these birds are very hardy and capable of living semi-wild.

Edward Brown does not state how many toes these birds have, nor does he indicate that they are purely rumpless, I would suspect that the birds breed both types, especially when living in their outdoor freedom where they are at liberty to cross with the Ardennes.

The San Queue breeds in a whole range of colours, as apposed to the Ardennes where only the original Bankiva colouring of Black-Red is quoted.

The Ardennes strikes me as being rather longer established than a localised cross bred and much nearer to an original Jungle Fowl type of bird.

Weights   Males   7lbs   Females   5.5lbs

Illustrations of the Ardennes are scarce, but this group of birds show the two types in various colours.

AUGSBURGER

This breed is reported to have originated in Bavaria. Little is known of it in this country, and there is conflicting information about it from abroad, especially regarding its comb formation. Even its name is quoted in different spellings.

It was originally a dual purpose breed combining the laying qualities of a Leghorn type bird with the plentiful and tasty meat of the La-Fleche.

It was considered a hardy bird capable of ranging large areas in search of food. Its shape is of a medium length back, full fronted and powerful build. Yet its weight is only quoted for males as being 4.5/5.5 lbs, which does not endorse the description. The tail is well spread, carried high and is fully furnished. The legs and feet should be as dark as possible. The only colour quoted is black, which should carry an excellent green sheen to it - sounds to me like a salesman for pre-war Ford cars!

The shape of its comb seems to vary from twin horned to a double line of spikes. I would venture to suggest that it was a perfect example of being a glorified first cross wonder, which failed to capture the poultry breeders' imagination.

Weights   Males   4.5-5.5 lbs   Females   3.5-4.5 lbs

One of the few Augsbergers to be displayed in the British Isles. In many ways the cockerel has a resemblance to the Rhinelander.

54

AUSTRALORP

You do not require a B.A in English or Geography to decipher the origin of this breed.

The Orpingtons first taken to Australia originally were the type originated by William Cook from Orpington in Kent and, once on the island, they were transformed into a highly efficient laying fowl, whilst still retaining a similar outline to the birds' original concept. Their version had a much tighter feathering than the ones being further developed in the British Isles. Basically there are two main points of alteration; firstly the shape was developed to be slightly longer than square shaped, whilst, for an Orpington to be any good at all, it must be deeper than it is long; secondly the feathering became flat and single quilled rather than 'cup shaped' as in the Orpingtons. This is noticeable in the thigh feathering which is much reduced in quantity and contour. This reduction continues into the cushion area, which is vastly diminished to be almost non existent, with the tight feathering sweeping up to meet the main tail almost at the top, the main tail being carried at an angle of almost 90 degrees and finishing with a tight feathered point in the females. The male's tail is more similar to the Orpington's, but tighter feathered and, as with the female, carried well upwards without being 'squirrel tailed'

Being a self coloured breed and with no especially difficult areas of shape to be achieved, the headpiece becomes an important feature of the breed and is allocated 25 points. Great emphasis is placed on the bird's having a utility type of head, free from coarseness, and with prominent and expressive eyes. The face should be free from feathering and fine in texture. The wattles are not too large and cumbersome with a sound red ear lobe. Obviously the comb features highly in any judge's mind. It should have evenly cut and distributed spikes, up to six in total and be a rich red colour. The standard for Australorps only allocates 5 points for the actual comb part of the head, but anyone new to the breed should not pay too much attention to these marks; most judges will attach a far greater importance than one twentieth of the bird to the comb!

An equally important part of the bird is the colouring of the face, especially in the females. Any sign of 'gypsy face' is taboo to most judges, though a little tolerance is given to young pullets, knowing that the face will become a clearer red as she becomes fully matured.

In the breeds standard 35 points are allocated for type, with a further 27 covering the bird's utility qualities of feathering and freedom from coarseness, but curiously only 5 for the legs and feet. These should be black with white toe nails and must have white soles to them; any sign of green or willow which would indicate Java or Jersey Giant Blood is a serious fault and can be considered a disqualification in some judges' eyes.

The whole of the black coloured body feathering should carry a rich and lustrous green sheen to it. This again is a striking feature of the breed.

The Australorp returned to this country in the early 1920s and was successfully used by many poultry farmers as a commercial breed which was capable of laying large quantities of good sized eggs. Coupled with this the cockerels killed out into good carcasses of white skinned meat, the one drawback being that the black stubs and legs stood out like seagulls' droppings on a bald head. This problem was highlighted when some housewives found out that they had been sold Australorp cockerels as small sized American Bronze turkeys and were not impressed.

Their laying capabilities were demonstrated at the laying trials, where several breeders combined breeding show stock and commercial birds from the same stock.

Mr A. F. Arlett, A. J. Spink from Nottinghamshire and Thomas Clarkson, who was the uncle to Clive Bradbury, the club secretary at one time, all won at the major shows and gained copper ringed birds at the trials.

The Australorp is a breed which I have fond memories of. We have won champion utility bird with the breed at the Classic shows. Even more the breed will always be remembered by me at the first Club Show which I had the privilege of judging when I was but a lad from Lancashire.

We were also amongst the pioneers of miniaturising the breed during the 1940s, and I can remember showing one of the earlier 'models' in the A.O.V. classes at the National Poultry Show in London.

The first Bantam Aussies were seen in the early 1930s, with Mr Roy N. Corner claiming to be the originator. When Sid Newton was Poultry Manager for a man called Belbin, who was a Mill owner from Yorkshire, he was also involved with the miniatures but this strain seemed to die out during the hostilities. Consequently, they were restarted during the 1940s. Tom Clarkson and George Robinson were amongst the pioneers of the breed's reconstruction.

The miniatures are now a long way dominant of the two sizes, with some excellently shaped specimens in all parts of the British Isles. As with other breeds, I consider the miniatures should be an exact replica of the large fowl, and be approximately one quarter the size.

The breed also exists in self blue and self white forms, and should be identical to the blacks in type. Very few are seen in this country but I believe they are plentiful in Australia and South Africa.

The Australorp has been a popular breed for many years and should continue to be so. It is hardy, easy to prepare for showing and retains its showing potential for several years.

Weights	Large	Males	8.5-10 lb	Females	6.5-8 lbs
	Miniatures	Males	36oz	Females	28 ozs

Pair of Black Orpingtons from Australia depicting their ideal birds in 1930.

56

A grand Australorp cockerel from 1933. He was bred by Geoffrey Hazel from Suffolk, and won for him Best Cockerel at the Crystal Palace Club Show, plus many other senior awards. Interestingly his dam laid 209 eggs in 48 weeks at the Laying Trials.

Champion Australorp at the 1934 Crystal Palace and Olympia Shows. He was exhibited by Mr Vernon Phillips from Billericay.

Bred by Lady Burke and had a very successful show career for her during 1927.

A cock which was imported in 1923 by Australorp Farms Ltd from Herefordshire. He was bred from trap nested stock, which were capable of laying large quantities of top grade eggs.

The 1929 Birmingham and Dairy Show winning Australorp pullet. She was bred and exhibited by Mr J. H. Beever from Yorkshire.

A pullet bred by my old friend Tom Clarkson from Pilling. At the 1931 Dairy Show she won Champion Australorp for him, and then continued to be judged winner of the 'Quill Trophy' for the 'Best Utility Bird in the Show'.

Champion Australorp at the 1932 Dairy Show. She was bred and exhibited by Mr W. C. Crosland from Penistone.

Again bred by Tom Clarkson, and won best pullet at the 1938 Birmingham Club Show.

To my knowledge this is the first photograph of an Australorp miniature. She was bred in 1931 by Roy Corner from Hereford and was a noted winner for him.

Allows a comparison with more recent times. This pullet was bred by Alan Maskrey and won Champion Bantam Pullet for him.

A trio of White Australorps, which were imported from South Africa in 1937.

AUTOSEXING BREEDS

The above is a heading for what is not really a selection of colours within a breed, but a collection of different types of a breed, all with the same characteristics that their chicks can be sexed into males and females at a day old.

The originals of these breeds were developed at Cambridge University in 1929, being basically a cross between the Campine and Barred Rock breeds. These were aptly named as Cambars. Since then there has been development in sex linked crosses for many of the breeds, but only some of these have been standardised. Examples of those which missed are Ancobar, (Ancona X) and Hambar, (New Hampshire Red X).

The ones to reach the standards are Brussbar, Cambar, Dorbar and the Legbar, all of which exist in both Gold and Silver versions. In addition there are the Brockbar, Welbar and the Rhodebar, which has also been called the Redbar.

For a breed which has been made as recently as the late 1920s, the exact information as to the Cambar's foundation is rather sketchy and possibly contradictory. The Gold Cambar is from the Gold Campine male and Barred Rock female line of breeding. The Silver Campine Male is not sufficiently strong in his silver to be able to repeat the mating, and produce Silver Cambars. So this had to be achieved by other methods.

The original concept of the breed was that it would be of enormous benefit to the many small poultry units around the British Isles. By using these breeds they would no longer have to engage a professional chick sexer every time they hatched their chicks which were intended for the commercial egg producing customers. They could do it themselves, thus saving time and money. Unfortunately, the mass introduction of 'Hybrids' by the large commercial groups, which were expanding rapidly, proved to be their downfall, and the popularity which the breed had enjoyed during the 1940s quickly declined.

The breed failed to capture the imagination of the poultry fancier, and the Breed Club folded to become part of the Rare Poultry Society.

My own views are that there were too many variations within the group of breeds to be a successful show breed. If there had been one, in the Heavy Breed category (and I like the Rhodebar, which is not only attractive to look at but also a very useful dual purpose layer/table bird) and one in the Light Breed section (say the Legbar, especially in the Cream version with the added attraction of Blue/Green coloured eggs), then it would, and possibly still can, be a true showman's breed.

Actually the Cream Legbar is unique to breeds at present in this country, in that it has a single comb and also a crest at the back end of its head.

Until very recently there has been no attempt to miniaturise the breed, but Brian Sands has now perfected the Rhodebar 'Bantam'. If some enthusiast can now convert the Cream Legbar into a small version, then my forecast of a bright future for the breed may not be too far of the mark during the next century.

The first official photos of the Legbar as released by Cambridge University. The style of this bird reminds me very much of the Scots Grey. (Above right).

A Gold Cambar which has retained the Campine's hen feathering.

A Silver Cambar with greater wealth of tail furnishing.

The colouring of day old Gold Cambar chicks.

A delightful pair of Miniature Rhodebars recently developed by Brian Sands from Boston, Lincolnshire. A very attractive photo showing one of Brian's large fowl Rhodebars appears in the colour section.

Again bred by Brian Sands, and illustrates a Large Fowl Rhodebar pullet.

BARNEVELDER

The Barnevelder is one of the latest breeds to be created. The breeding programme was commenced in Holland at roughly the same period as the one for the Welsummer.

The breed takes its name from a small town called Barneveld, where commencement of the breed began just prior to the First World War (1914-1918) and resulted in the first imports being made into Britain after the war ended. A breed club was formed for them in 1922. The reason for the breed's creation was to produce a bird which was capable of laying a large quantity of good sized, dark brown coloured eggs. You could say that it was the forerunner to a modern brown egg producing hybrid.

The actual breeds used in the parent stock is to a point unknown, the eggs used having been selected purely on shape and the necessary deep colour. Many of the birds involved were simply cross breeds. The breeds involved in the crosses included Cochins, probably the partridge coloured, Black-Red Malays, Brahma types and most certainly the Croad Langshan, as I believe that this breed is the one from those I refer to as original breeds which carries the brown egg factor. Edward Brown recalls seeing some of the parent stock and describes them as including Blacks, White Laced, Brown and Buff coloured. Their combs varied between single, rose and walnut, with some birds being feathered legged whilst others were clean shanked.

The inclusion of Malay blood is interesting in that both the Barnevelder and the Welsummer have yellow legs and feet but with the distinctive dark brown coloured toe nail. Many of the Indian Game also have this feature and I believe that it is inherited from the Malay.

Included in the Welsummer's breed summary there is an interesting contribution from the late Powell-Owen who was also a great lover of the Barnevelder, with many of his observations relevant to both breeds.

The egg laying capabilities of the Barnevelder were illustrated at the Harper Adams laying trials, whilst, during the 1925/26 test, a pen of six Barney pullets laid a total of 1,212 eggs in the 48 week duration. This averaged at 202 a piece with 974 of them being first grades. The top pullet laid 240, which earned her a copper ring.

Once the birds had settled into a consistent breeding pattern, they passed into the showman's hands to develop the breed into one with uniform markings and shape etc. The result was for two types to be produced, one with the double lacing as in Indian Game, the other one less elaborately marked and originally termed Partridge or Stippled.

The self Black was approved by the Poultry Club Standards Committee in 1928. The birds had been shown for many years previously without full recognition, but even the seal of approval failed to increase their popularity. Apart from the colour of their shanks, they were very similar to the Australorp, which was enjoying good support, and self Black coloured birds are not the most popular of colours with the general fancier. Consequently the blacks were last seen motoring towards oblivion, and they appeared to be towing a trailer containing the Partridge or Single laced, as they were once called.

The original concept of the breed's colouring was such that double mating would have to be used to obtain the best results. Later the standard was altered, with double lacing on the females, but the males having a reddish brown mottling to their black breast. This can be either as an outer lacing or better still a full double lacing. The neck and saddle is black with the same red/brown edging and also showing a strongly marked quill shaft. The wing bow and also the bar can, on some of the best birds, be very well double laced. The tail and its side hangers should be black. There is a tendency for some birds to be light under coloured; this should be a dark slate colouring.

The female has basically the same double laced feathering all over, the more distinctive the better, and obviously the aim is to achieve a total covering of perfectly double laced feathers on the thighs and up to her tail, under the throat and across the back, also over the wings.

The ground colour on the female should be red-brown, the same as the male bird's and free from 'peppering'. The neck hackle should be black as should the main tail feathers. A very important feature of both sexes is that the black really does carry a beetle green sheen to it. Any sign of purple cast is bad news.

The markings are allocated 25 points. Coming slightly higher are type and size with 30 points. The bird's shape and carriage are nicely outlined by the fact that the breed has rather tight feathering; in many way similar to an Australorp which is consistent with other utility breeds.

Their shoulders are fairly pronounced with the breast full and deep, which when accompanied by a shortish back, gives the bird an appearance of being only just longer than deep, especially with the tail being carried in a well upright position. The male's tail has several furnishings, but is not too flowing in appearance and the hen's is only slightly fanned. The legs require good round bone as do those of all utility breeds, and their colour is stated to be yellow, but, especially in the miniatures, there is a tendency for them to carry a dusky coloured front to them. Both sexes require a smooth textured and utility looking head with bold and alert looking eyes. The single comb is to be evenly serrated, not too large in size, standing on a strong base and with the leader following the head's contours.

There are plenty of excellent miniatures around and, as in many breeds, probably nearer to perfection than the large fowl.

The breed is an excellent choice for anyone wishing to keep birds which are capable of winning at shows, providing some good meals, and capable of laying plenty of good sized eggs, though their colour in many cases is not as deep a brown as the Welsummer's, probably because of the showman, who, as usual, with his desire for perfection in markings, has lost the bird's ability to lay a dark coloured egg.

Weights

Large Fowl	*Males 7-8 lbs*	*Females 6-7 lbs*
Miniatures	*Males 32 ozs*	*Females 26 ozs*

Barnevelders are one of several breeds which do not photograph to their true colouring, especially in monochrome.

Consequently many of the breed illustrations used are either paintings or drawings.

A Study in Barnevelders, by Mr. Bruff Jackson, whose interesting article appears on this page.

BAR 1. Is a drawing not often used. It is by Bruff Jackson, who was an enthusiast of the breed and he illustrates his ideal birds.

BAR 2. Shows a double laced pullet which won Best Barnevelder at the Crystal Palace in 1923; she was then claimed at the Catalogue price of £20!

BAR 3. Again shows a classic winner, this time the Dairy Show in 1932; she was bred and exhibited by Mr H. Forbes-Brown from Sussex.

65

BAR 4. Shows a Black Barnevelder Cock which was successfully exhibited by Mr R. Fletcher-Hearnshaw from Burton Joyce, Notts.

BAR 5. Was bred in 1933 by Mrs Swales-Johnson. The bird had many good wins, including the Bath and West show.

BAR 6. Shows a big bodied hen which had a long and successful show career for Mr J. E. Frankcom from Hampshire.

BAR 7. Shows a hen from 1928 which appears to be well laced; she was bred by Mrs Pape who had numerous good wins with her.

66

BAR 8. Illustrates an unusual Silver Laced Barnevelder cock. He was shown in the new breed class at the Crystal Palace in 1936 by Mr W Pearson.

BAR 9. Shows another off-colour, this time a spangled hen which was bred in 1931 by Mr E. F. Piper from Doncaster.

BAR l0. Is rather unique; it shows a pair of miniature Double Laced Barnevelders which won at the Dairy show and the Crystal Palace in 1929. They were bred by Mrs K Manwaring from Kent and must have been amongst the first to be shown in Britain.

67

BASSETTE

This breed was mentioned in Britain during the 1920s and 1930s, but little has been heard of it since.

There is no mention of the birds in either Wright's 'Book of Poultry', or in Edward Brown's 'Volumes on Poultry Breeding'. This would suggest that the breed has been perfected by man in fairly recent times.

The breed would appear to be shrouded in a certain amount of mystery, certainly to an Englishman talking about a continental breed, of which very little has ever been recorded. I find them appealing, and, as in many other cases, wonder why they are not already introduced into this country.

The breed originated in the Liege area of Belgium, which is exactly the same location where the Sans Queue version of the Ardennes had been recorded for centuries. It would therefore seem to be logical to assume, that there is a relationship between the two breeds, especially as there is a distinct similarity between them. They are popular on the continent, being shown in a miniature version, although the original reference to the birds was a very successful farmyard type of laying fowl, capable of living semi-wild and searching for much of its own keep. At that period there was no standard for the birds, consequently in 1930 a breed club was formed, and a standard of excellence produced. In 1934, this standard was printed in Britain and attempts made to create interest for the breed in this country. Unfortunately, this did not prove successful.

The standard is well written, and includes one feature which I believe to be unique. The ear lobes have to be white in colour, in the shape of a triangle, as opposed to the normal round. There is a sketch of the birds showing this feature, but unfortunately no photograph of a bird illustrating that the phenomenon is possible to achieve.

The bird is described as having a single comb, which is quite large in size, upright in the male and folded in the female. They have a long back, with a broad and deep breast which is well rounded. Their tail is carried half open, and is fully furnished in the males.

Their legs should be in different shades of blue, depending on the bird's feather colouring. The colour of their toe nails is interesting; they are described as being horn coloured, as is their beak. This can also be blue in certain colours.

There is a whole range of colours listed. These include Silver Dun, Blue Wheaten, Gold and Silver Speckled, Millefleur and Pheasant.

Obviously the early breeders envisaged a great future for the breed, which as yet does not appear to have been achieved.

There is another breed of bantam, which is again recorded as originating in Belgium; that is the Doornik.

These birds are very similar to the Bassette in type, and I would suggest that both breeds are descendants of the Ardennes and Sans Queue. These breeds have been recorded as living semi wild in Belgium, since, as Edward Brown often quotes, 'time immemorial'.

Another interesting feature of the Bassette, is its involvement in 'crowing competitions', where the male birds are carried to the event in small cages and then placed in front of the judges. When the time has arrived for the contest to commence, the doors of the cages are opened and the crow of each bird is recorded. On the completion of an hour, the contest ends, and the bird which has crowed the highest number of times is declared the winner.

FIG 1. Illustrates a drawing done in 1934 with the earlobe showing the attempted triangular shape.

FIG 2. Shows a very attractive Bassette pullet which was shown at Utrect in 1985. She is described as being a silver. The photo was taken by Josef Wolters.

BIELEFELDER

The Bielefelder is a very popular modern day breed on the European Continent. The breed has not as yet caught the imagination of the British fanciers, but I have no doubt that it soon will, and that it will prove to be a successful addition.

The Bielefelder combines laying qualities with attractive colouring. In size, I would suggest that the birds fall into a group which is not fully recognised in this country. W Powell-Owen often quoted 'light heavy breeds' which would include the ones such as Australorps, Barnevelders, Welsummers as examples, these breeds being of different proportions to the giant Cochins, Brahmas, Dorkings, Orpingtons, etc.

In general style the Bielefelder is similar to our own version of the Marans, which is clean legged and Cuckoo marked.

In shape, the birds have a large-framed body, with a full and well rounded front which indicates their meat potential.

They have a single comb which is not too large, and of a fine texture as are their face and wattles. This quality emphasises their laying qualities. Their tail is carried at approximately 45 degrees, and is adequately furnished, without any part of it being so enlarged as to become cumbersome. These features are beautifully highlighted by the birds having rich yellow coloured legs and beak. The bone on their legs is of good substance and well rounded. Their feathering is quite tight, but sufficiently soft to allow their curves to be outlined.

The colours of Bielefelder fall into two categories, both of which are based on the Cuckoo coloured body feathering. One is a rich golden coloured creel, which is fully marked to include the wing bars, and the wing bay on the male bird. The neck and saddle hackles are a paler version of gold shading to a deep lemon.

The female has the same coloured hackle feathers as the male bird, which again illustrate their golden type of barring. Her breast is rich red chestnut colouring and extends well down the bird's breast area, and her wing bay is similarly coloured. The second colour of Bielefelder is a silver creel, similar in some ways to our own Silver Duckwing, imposed on to the Cuckoo based feathering.

I would describe the breed as having great potential, and can fully understand why shows can attract entries of several hundred birds to be shown at the Continental Classic exhibitions.

The breed also exists in an equally attractive bantamised version.

A colour photograph of a Bielefelder can be seen in the colour section.

BRABANTA, BRABANTER and BRABANCONNE

Historians claim this to be one of the oldest breeds in Belgium, having been recorded there many centuries ago.

The breed has a reputation for excellent laying qualities. It is a light boned breed with a reasonably sized body.

The big difference in character from almost any other breed in the British Isles is its feature of having a single comb plus a crest. The comb is upright in the male and folded to one side in the females. The crest is situated on the rear part of the head and tends to face backwards. (See colour section).

There have also been recordings of the breed showing muffling in addition to the crest, also birds with a double horned type of comb. The fact that the breed has been proved to exist several centuries ago would indicate that it has had considerable influence on other similar breeds on the continent, with a possible connection to Poland.

Certainly reference was made to it in the 1600s so it has had ample opportunity to develop into localised variations, both in Holland and Germany. Mention is also made of it in Russian poultry history, with a probable connection to the Ushanki and Russian Crested breeds.

The main confusion surrounding these birds lies in their names. Are they one breed existing in two different types, with the variation in the breed's spelling being attributed to dialect, or are they separate breeds? Edward Brown would apparently believe that they were one and the same family, with characteristic variations.

Van Gink, with two marvellous paintings, illustrates them as almost separate breeds. He quotes Brabanconne and the Brabant Fowl as being the same and having existed in North West Europe since at least the seventeenth century, with evidence from artists from that period.

Brabant being a Flemish word often translated into 'topman', the birds were formed in 1903.

The Brabanter was again referred to in the sixteenth century, showing birds with a full beard and side muffs plus a horned type of comb, the nostrils on the bird being placed high on the beak, as is often the case with crested breeds.

To me there appears to be a distinct relationship between the Brabanter and the Owl Bearded Dutch.

The birds have a long body with well furnished tail being carried at around 45 degrees. Their crop area is nicely rounded into the breast. Their legs are quite long, as is the bird's neck, which altogether gives them a very active and sprightly appearance.

There is a wide selection of colours throughout the different types, including Black, Cuckoo, Gold and Silver Spangled plus a version similar to the Owl Bearded, where the head and upper neck is in contrast to the body colour.

The breeds have been miniaturised on the continent, but as yet have not appeared in this country. When they do I believe that they could have great appeal.

71

Brabantines

by
C. S. Th.
VAN
GINK

FIG 1. Is a drawing by Van Gink during the 1930s. Interestingly he uses the heading of Brabantine.

In the colour section, there is a beautiful painting by him of Brabanconne fowl in the quail colouring.

FIG 2 and FIG 3. Were taken by Hans Schippers, and illustrate a pair of Brabanter, as shown at the present time.

72

BRAEKEL

This breed has a similar history to the contraversial one surrounding the Lincolnshire Buff and the Buff Orpington, in that there is uncertainty over the relationship between the Braekel and the Campine.

According to information which I have gathered, Braekel Fowl have been in existence for centuries and existed in a style which had a flowing feather formation. They were then taken to a part of Belgium known for its parched, barren and sandy soiled conditions, which were in contrast to the rich and fertile area of Flanders called Nederbraekel. The Braekel taken to this new environment continued to reproduce, but over many, many generations the birds became smaller in body size and narrower in feather and markings. It is claimed that this was due to their new and much poorer conditions. This loss of feather quality was extremely noticeable in the males, who lost their sickles and side hangers to become almost hen tailed. This new area was called Campine hence the name now associated with the breed.

Whether this theory is absolutely watertight must be open to debate, especially when you turn your mind to the British Silver Spangled and Pencilled Hamburghs. Here their history and development are very inconsistent in recordings and theories. They were almost certainly produced by crossing and inter-crossing many of the permutations of different localised strains living in Yorkshire and Lancashire, but almost certainly amongst them were pencilled birds from the continent. Dutch 'every day layers' have been mentioned, but later in this book we will suggest that these are actually a form of the Fayoumi Fowl. Almost certainly the Braekel or Campine were one of the breeds involved with the Hamburgh's creation.

The point here is that in Hamburghs there has always been the mention of 'moonies'. These are birds in which some of the males carry the trait of being 'hen tailed', i.e. - having no sickles or side hangers. These moonies still exist in most strains of Silver Spangled Hamburghs.

The silver and gold Sebrights created by Sir John Sebright Bart and his friends also used a bird carrying moonie blood, which resulted in the breed being standardised for the male to be hen feathered in its tail and carrying no side hangers.

Now turn your thoughts to Game Fowl, where for centuries we have had the Hennie Game, which again have the male bird's tail being minus side feathering.

Consequently I must question the assumption that land conditions altered the breed, and suggest that it was the inclusion of 'henny' type blood which created the difference in the tail structure between the Campine and the Braekel.

Whether they should be regarded as separate breeds is a decision which I hesitate to make, but will repeat the comment I have made before, that many 'breeds' mentioned in history are very often just localised variations of a recognised and standardised one.

What I would suggest is that the two types should be exhibited in the same class, and considered to be alternative versions as you would with Single or Rose combed Anconas for example.

Details of the colour and markings are listed in with the Campines.

FIG I shows a painting by Belin of his ideal Silver Braekel with full flowing tail furnishings.

FIG 2 This Gold Braekel pullet was photographed in Germany by Josef Wolters, and looks very attractive.

A Gold Braekel male bird is illustrated in the colour section of the book.

BRAHMA

Brahmas arrived in this country at the same period as the Cochins, i.e. around 1840-1850. They may well be of the same origin. This point is discussed in the earlier chapters of the book, relating to original 'breeds'.

The original Cochins were imported from China, but the Brahmas came from India and, consequently, assumed the name of that part of the country in which they were thought to have been created which was Brahmaputra. There was also reference to some dark coloured birds called Grey Chittagongs, which were presumably responsible for the development of today's Dark Brahmas.

It is thought that the first birds to be exported from India went to America, and, after a short period, some of their offspring were shipped to this country, a pen of them being a present to Queen Victoria, as were the Shanghais.

The question as to who was responsible for originally importing the birds into America was contested with much animosity and petty jealousy, several breeders wishing to be credited with their individual involvement. Lewis Wright allocates 13 pages of his book to the bickering between these 'gentlemen'; 150 years forwards in history I am interested in attempting to trace the breed's original creation. Who first brought them into the States seems quite irrelevant.

The massive size and strength of a Brahma suggest to me that the breed has a close relationship to the rather elusive bird from the jungle which is sometimes referred to as the Gallus Gigantic.

The early imports to America record male birds weighing 14 lbs, which probably exceed most of today's specimens even though the modern Brahma is amongst the largest of the breeds.

One great feature of that size and vigour is their strong headpiece. I have a belief that once you lose size in the bone structure of a bird's head, the body size quickly diminishes. This applies to any breed with the converse being illustrated by the original Old Dutch Bantams, where their diminutive but beautifully proportioned head was accompanied by the neatest little body you could imagine.

The description of headpiece in the Brahma standard is in danger of being mis-interpreted. I believe that when the original was drawn up, many of the birds were carrying massive beetle brows which overhung the eyes and were probably accompanied by floppy walnut combs the size of golf balls, hence the desire to describe the head as being small and of medium breadth. It probably was compared to the ones on 14 lbs plus cockerels but is by present day comparison a good strong head.

The comb should be three lines of small spikes known as a triple pea comb. The eye should be bright and alert, fairly prominent and surrounded by a smooth textured face. The wattles are small for a bird of this size and round in shape. One unique feature which the breed has maintained for 150 years is the unusual development and length of the lobes, these were originally termed as 'deaf ears' and extend to well below the wattles which, as just stated, are round in shape, not elongated as in the breeds like the Minorca and Leghorn.

The standard shape of a Brahma has much in common with the one approved for Cochins. This point may be disputed by some people, mainly, I believe because the Brahmas have received more concentration on the aspect of markings than the Cochins have. The Brahmas, in the main, are slightly tighter in their feathering than the Cochins; consequently they do not appear to be quite as 'fluffy' and well curved.

75

Another difference is that in Brahmas there is more tolerance towards the hock, having stiff quill type feathers protruding backwards, i.e. 'vulture hocks', than there is in the Cochin breed, though actually both standards state they are undesirable.

Even though there is a great similarity between the two breeds in type and characteristics, the leading colours in both breeds are entirely different. This point may add weight to my theory that when the original stock was imported in the 1840s, the segregation between the two was based on colour and markings rather than style.

This concentration on markings is reflected in the standard where the Brahma is allocated 40 points and the Cochin only 20 for this feature. Briefly, the shape of a Brahma should be that of a wide chested, shortish backed bird showing greater depth than length of body. The low carried front and breast areas should be free from a split. The short feathered and horizontally carried wings should fit well up under the saddle hackle feathers. These feathers should mould into a high rising tail carried almost upright. The tail should be well furnished with soft textured side hangers which give the bird an extra appearance of great width. In general outline the Brahma gives the impression of being slightly taller and higher off the ground than the Cochin, but, as before stated, this can be due to tighter feathering in many of the birds. For slightly more details on shape I suggest that you also refer to the section on Cochins.

Following the importations of Brahmas to this country in the mid nineteenth century the breed was recognised for the next 100 years in two colours, namely Lights and Darks.

The former is the colour which has, on more than one occasion, been the point of discussion as to whether it should really be termed a Columbian, as in the Wyandotte family.

The basic colour of the Light is that the hackle feathers, in both the males and females, are white with a black stripe down the centre. This stripe should be a solid black including the feather shaft, but should not extend through the feather tip, thus leaving a lacing around the feather's edges. This black stripe should extend as deep as possible into the base of the feather.

The main tail is black, as are the tail coverts, although a slight white lacing is allowed on the side hangers. The under parts right through to the underside of the tail are also white, the wing flights and secondaries are a mixture of black and white with no special markings as in the Rhode Island Reds, but the black should be solid in colour and not 'wishy-washy' and in the flights as much black as possible in breeding birds.

The final aspects of the colouring are the two which usually cause the discussion. One is the under-colour which the standard states as being either white, blue-white or slate, which to me is not sufficiently definite. If a standard requires a feature which may be hard to breed but is clearly stated, then it does offer breeders a challenge to attempt the breeding of a correct specimen.

The other point is similar in that it revolves around the amount of ticking allowed on the saddle hackle feathers. Many of us believe that this should quite definitely be allowed in liberal amounts as it is in the darks.

The standard states white, but that a slight striping is allowed on birds which have dark neck hackles. Certainly this tipping or even striping is required in the breeding pen if you wish to breed good hackled offspring. I cannot see any objection to the birds having slate under-colour and saddle hackles which are well tipped, with the birds being termed Columbian.

The standard for Light females only varies from the male in the areas where there is a structural difference in the feathers. Obviously in females there is no saddle hackle so the clear white top colour extends through to the tail, which is black with the covert feathers allowed to be edged with white, the under-colour to be as in the males.

The hackle is the same, with a solid black stripe down the centre but not extending through to the end. A good width of feather to the hackles is beneficial. If it is narrow it becomes what is termed 'cock feathered' and does not look as attractive and would not be considered a good pullet breeding bird.

These markings should extend as high up the neck as possible, and continue right round the front until meeting at the crop area.

As mentioned with the Darks, if the foot feathering can also be marked, it is one step nearer to perfection. In this case it would be black laced with white.

In Darks the standard is more definite. This colour is really a silver version of the black-red/partridge pattern. In males the under-body, main tail and foot feathering are black.

The wing is the usual pattern of clear silver bow. The bay or diamond as it is sometimes called, also shows silver when the wing is in the closed position.

The coverts form a distinct black bar of glossy feathers. The shoulder butt which is actually covered by the hackle also has a small area of short black feathers. The back of the bird is clear silver white.

The hackle and saddle hackle feathers are silver with the normal black stripe down the centre of each feather, this should extend as deep as possible down the feather towards the slate under-colour on the fluffy part of the feathers. This striped pattern should extend well up to the top of the neck and continue on the hackle feathering until almost meeting at the front of the bird.

These markings are exactly the same on the saddle hackles, which are long in structure and blend onto the tail coverts. The female's hackle is again of the same pattern with a black stripe on a silver white feather. The amount of hackle on a dark female is not as important as with the Light female, but in the 'cock' breeding pen it certainly would be.

The body feathers and markings on a dark female are identical to the ones of a partridge female in either Wyandottes or Cochins, the difference being the ground colour, which in the Dark's case should be a silvery grey very finely stippled with black. There has been a tendency in recent years for this ground colour to have a definite golden tinge to it, obviously brought about by crossing with partridge coloured birds, either Cochins or the recently introduced Gold Brahmas.

Imposed on this pale grey ground colour are the usual three distinct black marking or pencilling. The best birds have this type of markings on all their body feathers including the throat, under the tail and especially on their thighs and upper cushion feathers leading on to the main tail feathering. On really good specimens these markings extend to include the foot feathering.

In more recent years other colours have been added to the breed. These include several self coloured ones which really are self explanatory. Whites should be pure silver white throughout, with yellow beak, legs and feet. The Black should carry the traditional beetle green sheen to it. In the Blue, the main consideration is for it to have a uniform and even colouring throughout. In the Buff, again, the even colour is important. The Buff Columbian has identical markings to the light, but on a buff coloured background.

To me the interesting pointer is that, with this recent introduction to the colour range, the word Columbian is used. There is also mention of a blue Columbian soon to arrive.

And lastly the colour which is at present time probably the favourite. It is the 'Gold', meaning Golden Partridge or Black-Red, which is virtually identical to the Partridge colouring of the Cochins. Brahmas exist in a miniature version and are available in a full range of very attractive colours.

| Weights | Males 12 lbs | Females 9 lbs |
| Miniatures | Males 28-32 ozs | Females 24-28 ozs |

BRA 1. Shows my selection in Dark
Brahma cockerels. This particular bird
was bred by Mrs A. M. Hall, of Silkie
fame, and won the 1932 Dairy Show.
From the photograph he appears to be a
solid colour in his black. Mrs Hall said
that he was bred from a pure cock
breeding family.

BRA 2. Here is another large framed
Dark male. He was a noted winner for
Fred Tyldesley from Bolton, during the
1970s.

BRA 3. Illustrates a well marked Dark
Brahma hen. She was bred in 1922, and
was shown with great success for her
breeder Mr R. M. Thomas.

BRA 4. Is an American bred hen, which
shows more open markings and is not
as well pencilled on the thigh feathering.

BRA 5. Shows a good bodied hen from 1925. She was bred by Mrs W. Thompson from Notts, and was second at the Royal Agricultural Show.

BRA 6. Was again bred by Mrs Hall. She won both the Crystal Palace and Birmingham Shows in 1930.

BRA 8. Shows the 1929 Crystal Palace winner. The cockerel was again bred by Harry Leybourne, but appears to be weaker in his hackle markings than the 1911 bird.

BRA 7. Shows a strong hackled Light Cock, which was winning for Harry Leybourne in 1911, who considered him to be one of the best he had ever bred.

79

BRA 9. Illustrates my pick of the Light
Brahma females. She was bred by Mr S.
Howard from Brackley and won the
Dairy Show for him in 1921.

BRA 10. Shows the 1924 Dairy Show
winning pullet. She was shown by Mr H.
Martin Wright.

BRA 11. Is once again bred by Harry
Leybourne, this time in 1931 when she
won the Isherwood Trophy for Supreme
Champion of the Dairy Show.

BRA 12. Shows the top winning female
in 1929, which was once again bred and
shown by Harry Leybourne, who was the
Brahma Club Secretary for many years.

BRA 13. Shows a grand breeding pen of Dark Brahmas at the home of Mrs Thompson. The photo was taken in 1923, with most of the birds having been winners at the Major Shows in previous years.

BRA 14. Was taken at Mr Martin Wright's poultry pens and shows an attractive pen of Lights, mated ready for the 1923 breeding season. A photograph showing the Gold Brahma appears in the colour section of the book.

81

BREDA

This breed is thought to be of Dutch origin. It is a fairly recent importation to these shores and, up to now, has not caught the breeders' imagination. The general appearance of the breed is one of having an upright stance and fairly tight feathering except for a well furnished tail. The body is reasonably long, more or less horizontal to the ground and not too full a front, which gives it a slightly upright appearance.

It has lightly feathered legs with the feathering extending down the outer toes. One of its main features is the very pronounced vulture hock feathers, which coupled with the bird's high tail carriage are even more pronounced.

The other main feature lies in the headpiece, where there is a virtual absence of comb, merely thick skin at the front of the head, then a hollow followed by a small crest, (I do believe that there can also be a version which is absent of crest).

The wattles are well developed and bright red, which contrast with its white earlobe. These are also highlighted by the absence of feathering to the bird's face.

The breed is considered to be hardy and a prolific layer of large sized white eggs. One drawback in its reputation is the tendency to be a slow featherer in the early stages of life, causing problems during the colder weather, a point which may add fuel to one theory, that the breed was originally of Asiatic origin, where the warm weather and slow feathering would not be a problem.

One other interesting point is that the peculiar hollow in the middle of the bird's head is also present in the Singalese Game Bird's head. This could be food for thought as to some of its ancestry.

There could also be some connection with the Siberian Feather-Footed, which has a rose comb, but has many other similar characteristics including the extremely pronounced vulture hocks.

Blacks, Whites, Blues and Cuckoos are the breed's main colour formation.

To my knowledge there are no miniature Bredas in this country.

Weights   Males 6.5-9 lbs   Females 6-7.5 lbs

FIG 1. Shows a drawing which illustrated a pair of Blue Laced Breda, from a book called Kippen by Hans Schippers.

FIG 2 and FIG 3. These Black Breda or Kraaikop as they are called in Holland, were both photographed by Hans Schippers, whilst winning at the shows there.

BRESSE .

The Bresse is a breed which has declined in its following during recent years; in fact I am not sure if it has any following at all which is incredible when you think that in 1929 the British United Bresse Club had a membership of 148. What has happened to the following and why? At that period you would have thought that they were here to stay as a utility laying bird, which was also useful in the show pen. I can only think that the breed fell into a category between exhibition type Leghorns and the now extremely popular Leghorn Bantams.

The birds themselves are typical Mediterranean in style, without being as strong in the headpiece or as massive in body as the British Leghorn or Minorcas. Having said that, they have a distinctive character of their own. They originated from Bresse, which is situated on the northern side of the Alps, where the birds were kept for their fantastic laying qualities, which also combined with a very succulent and well meated carcass when killed.

I have a feeling that the Bresse could have been used in the development of the small white Hybrid laying bird. The original colour of the native Bresse was called grey, being white but ticked with black on the shoulders, and with grey bars to the wings.

The black tail had sickles which were laced with white. Perhaps there is just a suggestion of Fayoumi blood being present.

Other colours which followed were pure white, self black and blues. The birds have a reputation for being friendly in spite of their light breed classification, and, as previously stated, deserve to be more popular than they are at present in this country.

There are no miniatures at the present time.

Weights Males 6lbs   Females 5lbs

FIG 1. Shows a unique sketch of Grey Bresse, drawn by H. Ayscough Thompson to illustrate the birds displayed at the 1924 World Poultry Congress.

THE BRITISH
:: UNITED ::
BRESSE CLUB

Taken from "THE FEATHERED WORLD'S" Bresse Coloured Plate.

Year Book, 1929.

Price to Non-Members 1/- post free, from the Secretary.

FIG 2. The British United Bresse Club Yearbook of 1929.

FIG 3. Illustrates an excellent Bresse. She was bred by Ian Gow and won the 1928 Dairy Show.

FIG 4. Shows a good Black Bresse pullet. In 1928 she won Champion Black at the Club show, bred and exhibited by Mr J. H. Walton from Wiltshire.

FIG 5. Was again bred by Mr Walton, winning both the Dairy Show and the Club Show for him in 1928.

FIG 6. Is from 1926 when he was a consistent winner for Ian Gow, including the Birmingham Club Show.

BRUGE

The breeds summarised in this book are almost one hundred percent in the soft feathered category, but I have included the Bruge because I believe that they, or a very similar type of bird, have been used to develop many of today's soft feathered breeds.

The abundance of feathers on a particular breed is usually attributed to being inherited from either the Langshan, or Cochin type of original fowl.

In some of the breeds which have been developed in more recent times, and therefore should yield more information regarding the type of bird used in their creation, reference is often made to the Malay type of fowl. This may well have been correct with the original birds, which took the name Malay, but after the second half of the nineteenth century, the showmen had developed them into a long legged bird, with a sloping back and downward facing tail. I cannot think of any breed, excepting Modern Langshan, where their new shape would be beneficial to a breed's development.

The Bruge would offer a more suitable breed to use when extra bone structure and quantity of meat were sought after. The early descriptions of the Bruge describe a bird which is massive in every way, with an exceptionally well developed front and breast. Their tails appear to be more elaborately furnished than those of many of the heavy weight Game Birds.

Most countries have their own variation of strong boned Game Bird, presumably all descendants from the Gallus Gigantic. In most cases they only differ slightly.

Belgium could be said to have two of them, because, in addition to the Bruge, there is the heavy weight Belgium Game Bird, which always looks to be slightly different, having a more compact outline, and is usually black in colour.

In the northern part of France, the Combattant du Nord, is often quoted as being the same bird as the Bruge.

An interesting point about the Bruge, is that it is very popular in a blue type of colouring. This colour is not frequently found in the old fashioned Game Fowl and to me is again a pointer that the Bruge is bred from a different original source from the Malays, which are nearly always Black-Red, Partridge or Wheaten coloured.

There have been suggestions that the blue colouring, could have originated from a bird called the Madras Blue, which was reported to have been associated with the Hyderabad Game Fowl.

Another interesting feature is that the Bruge has a reputation for laying exceptionally large eggs, which is not usual in the Game breeds.

Weights   Males well over 11 lbs and Females 8-9 lbs

86

FIG 1. Shows a typical Spartan Blue Bruge cock. He was reputed to weigh 15 pounds.

FIG 2. Shows an interesting photo from 1925. It was taken in America, and was described as a 'Red Laced American Indian Game cock'. He looks to me very similar in style to the Spartan Blue Bruge cock.

BUCKEYE

The Buckeye hails from the state of Ohio in the United States of America. It is not what I would describe as a definite breed, rather more of a multi-cross of breeds, aimed at producing table fowl for the commercial market.

The breed's initial creation involved using one of the large framed game birds, which the Americans often refer to as Cornish Game, but in this country are called Indian Game. Probably some form of Malay was used, but a large sized Asil could also have been involved.

These males were mated with both Barred Rock and Cochin females, and the resulting stock were interbred, until a bird was created which resembled a pea combed Rhode Island Red. Attempts were made to get these birds standardised, but were rejected due to their body shape being inconsistent with a true R. I. Red.

This is an interesting point to consider, because, when attempting to trace the original breeding of the R I Red, both Cochins and Malay Games are regularly quoted in its history, as are the Java Fowl, which would be included in the Barred Rock's ancestry.

The Buckeye has a rich mahogany top colour, with a black tail and tail coverts. This black also extends into their flights.

To my knowledge the breed no longer exists in the USA and has never been introduced into this country. I cannot trace any records of the breed being bantamised in the States, and would suggest that it was a case where the birds failed to excite the showman, and, as with many other attempts to create a commercial table fowl, their popularity was very short lived.

Their breeding pattern, was actually very similar to that of the modern day broiler chicken, where large 'Game' cocks which look like Ixworths are mated with a type of White Rock female.

Weights.   Males 9 lbs   Females 6.5 lbs.

FIG 1. Is a drawing which illustrates the American Buckeye from Ohio.

88

CAMPINE

This extremely ancient breed exists in both gold and silver colouring, with the silvers probably being the most popular. They are an extremely attractive bird with their pure silver white hackle and fine barring, which is of a different type of barring from that of Rocks in that the widths of the bars are not equal in size but have the black bar three times the width of the white one. The black has a vivid green sheen to it. Both male and female have a very characteristic fine textured single comb and wattles, with the hen's having a slight fold to it. The eyes are a brownish red and the lobe pure white and kid like in texture.

They are one of the smaller breeds, being light boned, but possessing plenty of meat which is excellently flavoured. The breed has been in existence for a very long time. The originals could be the Braekels, which are quoted in history as having been taken away from Belgium by Julius Caesar, when he returned home after a spell of looting and pillaging. More specific mention of them commences about 500 years ago, but, at that period, they were merely a type of farmyard fowl, with silver saddle hackles and back with a much more flowing tail feathering, with the females a lot whiter in colour, in fact probably similar to the original Grey Bresse or Egyptian Fayoumi.

Their development, to the perfection we now expect, only commenced in England during the latter half of the nineteenth century.

During the earliest recordings of the breed, reference is made of a rose combed version in which the cock was hen feathered (please refer back to the Braekel), and I believe it was one of this type which Sir John Sebright used to put the finishing touches to the Silver Sebrights. The development of the first auto sexing breeds was directly due to Campine blood. Further information is available in Autosexing.

The gold is marked exactly the same as the silver, and both have slate coloured legs and feet. The development of the breed has produced a male bird which is not quite hen feathered but has very little flow of tail feathering.

In summarising, they are certainly a very attractive and useful breed, deserving of more popularity. But as with many more breeds, the fact that, to breed the best show birds, cockerel and pullet breeding pens should be mated has deterred many potential enthusiasts. Certainly they are what I describe as a showman's breed, having a distinctly worded standard of excellence, not one which is a waffled description littered with the terms 'either' 'or' of the birds.

This point has been seen in many of the recent additions to our standards list.

There are very few miniatures in the country, which offers a great opportunity for someone to enjoy developing them. Bert Tansey from Essex spent many years perfecting their finer points and the last birds I saw him show were very presentable.

Weights   Male 6 lbs   Females 5 lbs

A breed from the continent which has a relationship to the Campine, is the Groninger. Fig 6 shows a pair of them, as illustrated in the Intervet wall chart, 'Chickens of The World'.

The colour section includes a painting by Gwenllian Woods, which shows a pair of Silver Mowen. I believe these are the same breed under a different title.

FIG 2. Is an attractive silver cockerel which won the Campine Club Show in 1928 for Mr D. J. Jones from Ammanford.

FIG 1. Shows a silver Campine pullet which won at Crystal Palace, Birmingham and the Dairy Show in 1921. She was exhibited by Mrs M. E. Cooke from Pembury in Worcs.

FIG 4. Shows a good bodied bird which was bred by Mr S. H. Cleale from Chelmsford. He was bred in 1932, and won several major Agricultural shows during 1933.

FIG 3. Won the Campine Challenge Cup at Crystal Palace in 1923. He was shown by Mr F. C. Tomkins from Hertfordshire.

FIG 5. Was taken in 1921, and shows an unusual photograph of Rosecomb Campines. Both birds were winners at Birmingham and the Crystal Palace.

IDEAL SILVER CAMPINE MALE AND FEMALE

The above drawings were composed from the studies of the best living specimens found to date, and a careful study of the Campine Standard descriptions as adopted by the American Campine Club, in an attempt to present ideals that would record the progress of the breed, and show the ideal Silver Campine male and female. (Since the above drawing was made, it has been presented for criticism to the Standard Revision Committee of the A. P. A. and while the male was considered nearly ideal, the tail of the female was criticised as too gay and expanded. For ideal female tails see the colored frontispiece).

FIG 6 This beautiful drawing from America, shows a pair of Silver Campines, with the male bird showing a fully furnished tail, as 0pposed to the British 'hen tailed' type.

91

CANADIAN LEGHORN

I am including these birds as a separate breed. Technically, I suppose I am incorrect, but their style is so far removed from the British Leghorn, as to make them appear to be a different breed.

Initially the Leghorn was the native breed of Italy, and due to the bird's excellent ability to lay large quantities of economically produced eggs, they quickly became spread around the world. The situation then was that each country continued to breed and develop the birds on their own different lines and variations.

In Britain we had the situation where there were two distinct types, one called the Utility Leghorn which was bred purely as a laying-machine. The other type were the birds I was brought up with and still have a great attachment to. These had larger bodies and possibly over emphasised head features. The point which could quite easily confuse breeders of recent generations is that, during the period between the two Great Wars and during the 1940s and 1950s, many of the shows held classes for what was described as a utility version of the popular laying breeds. Unfortunately, these classes were won not by the true utility laying fowl but a slimline type of the full exhibition bird.

The development of Leghorns in Canada, and certain states of America, created a very attractive looking bird with smaller, and less developed head features. There was also a great difference in the bird's shape, compared to the British show bird. A look at the photos of the Canadian Leghorn outlines a bird showing a great similarity to the Sumatra. Indeed the one taken in 1923 showing a group of cockerels bred by a Mr J C Grant from Vancouver caused the Feathered World's correspondent to suggest that the tail in the bird which is third from the left would do justice to the Sumatra of that time.

In this section of the book, describing the Canadian Chantecler, the illustration again shows a bird with a massive tail development, not in length of feather as in the Yokohama, but in the excessive amount of side hangers and tail covert feathers.

One of the breeds used in the development of the Chantecler was the Leghorn and it is very easy to notice this inherent feature.

Many of the countries on the European continent also breed their Leghorns with similar features of a smaller comb and very flowing body and tail feathering. I appreciate that it is very attractive in appearance, but different from the birds with which I have spent all my life. I therefore, rightly or wrongly, prefer to regard them as a slightly different variety, just as I do the Oxford and Carlisle Old English Game birds.

With the male Canadian Leghorns carrying such a large amount of tail feathering, it is only common sense that the female would have a well developed tail, which would be carried well spread, rather than the 'whip tail' on our version. The balance of the birds is also different, in that they have a shorter back and their bodies are nearer to parallel with the ground. This point is also highlighted by their much shorter shanks and thighs.

Miniature Canadian Leghorns are best described by relating Fred Jeffrey's account of his own experience in developing the breed in America. He spent many years attempting to bantamise them from large fowl. One of the breeds used to decrease their size was a white Modern bantam cock. However, to obtain the desired length of tail feathering, Japanese and White Rosecomb bantams were also included. This point illustrated to me the importance laid on this feature in the American / Canadian Continent whilst, in this country, head features plus body shape and carriage would be of paramount importance.

Maybe the time will arrive in Britain when classes are provided for both types of Leghorn, as was the eventual solution to the debate regarding Oxford and Carlisle Old English Game.

FIG 1. This photograph of a group of Canadian Leghorn males was taken in 1923. They are all closely related and show the Sumatra like tail feathering.

FIG 2. Is a photograph taken in 1936. The pair of white Leghorn Bantams were winners in their native Canada.

FIG 3. Shows a typical English white Leghorn. The cockerel was bred by Lord Dewar in 1932, and won Champion Leghorn at the Olympia Grand International Show.

FIG 4. Illustrates a further comparison, this time from America during the 1920's

93

CASTILIAN

The Castilian is a long established Spanish breed, which has been in that country for centuries. The breed is widely spread around the farming areas and is known in some parts as the Zamorana fowl.

It has a basic colouring of black, but is also seen in blues and whites. There are also reports of other colourings but presumably these are little more than crossbreeds, unless selectively bred for a distinct colour over several generations.

The Castilian was almost certainly the breed which was developed to create both the present day Minorcas and what is termed in this country the Spanish. Both of these breeds are now larger in body size and general structure with very much enlarged comb and lobes, the Castilian remaining similar to the Bresse, which is a native breed in neighbouring France.

The Castilian's reputation is of an extremely efficient egg laying breed. It was brought to Britain in 1926, being a present from Prince el Pardo, who bred them on his La Quinta estate, near Madrid. They arrived by boat at Liverpool docks and then travelled by train to Euston station. They resembled a utility version of the Minorcas which had been in this country and bred for exhibition purposes for years. The new birds weighed 5 lbs for the male and 4 lbs for the females. Stock was bred from them and, in 1930, a further importation was made, this time from the Parque de Avicultura which added extra vigour to the stock. The Brackenbury poultry farmer from Ickenham, who had arranged the original importations, entered some pullets at the Middlesex laying trials at Stanmore. In 1928 a pen of five pullets, bred from the first imports, laid a total of 999 eggs in 48 weeks, of which 406 were specials and 409 first grade eggs and were only beaten in the light breed section by White Leghorns.

To my knowledge there are no birds left in this country at the present time, as is the case with the Bresse. This suggests that for a breed even to survive in this country it must have excessive size or be decoratively adorned and certainly not be predominantly black in colouring.

There have never been any miniatures.

FIG 1. Shows a cockerel which was shown at the 1983 Hannover Show, and photographed by Josef Wolters.

94

FIG 2. Shows an illustration of the correct Castilian Fowls.

FIG 3 and 4. Were both shown by Mrs Lee from Middlesex at the 1934 Crystal Palace show. They were entered in the New Breed class and described as being Castellana.

CATALANA

The Catalana del Prat originated in the farming area south west of Barcelona in Spain known as Prat. Commencement of the breed began during the latter half of the nineteenth century. At this period Cochins were being imported to many countries around the world, which included Spain.

Here they interbred with the indigenous fowls of the area, which presumably would be the Castilian. The resulting progeny were developed into a breed which were not only capable of laying plenty of eggs, but carried a carcass of very succulent meat. The result was that surplus cockerels and females that had passed their economic laying period could be used in the rapidly developing poultry eating meat market.

Some of the birds still carried signs of the feathering on the shanks, but this was gradually bred out to leave the birds cleaned legged and singled combed with just a small white earlobe.

The extra size of the Cochin produced a bird with a deepish body and a full front. They carry their wings close to their bodies and well under their saddle hackles.

The tail formation has retained much of the Mediterranean characteristic of long and flowing sickle and side hangers.

Their combs are quite large for a medium heavy breed and are upright in the male bird and folded in the females.

The colour is what you would expect from a cross between these two breeds, producing a rich golden coloured male with a black tail and a certain amount of ticking to the hackle.

The female is usually buff coloured but can sometimes shade to a tawny partridge, she has a certain amount of black in her tail. In both sexes their legs are pale slate/blue.

A photograph of the Catalana taken in the 1920s, shows the hen to have a distinct little crest, which would suggest that some of the native fowls used originally were in the Brabanconne family.

During the 1920s Catalana were commercially bred in the Argentine, where they proved to be very successful.

In many ways the breed's development in Spain is equivalent to the Padovana in Italy, which again was intended to be used as a dual purpose breed, and this could very well be where the crest came from on the hen in the photo.

I understand that the Catalana has been made into bantam size, but I have no record of them coming into Britain.

Weights   Males 7.5lbs Females 5.5lbs

FIG 2. Is a female Partridge Catalana
hen, from the same period.

FIG 1. Shows a typical Buff Catalana
cock bird from 1930.

FIG 4. Shows a Buff Hen. These birds
were reputed to rival the White Leghorn
for egg production.

FIG 3. Is a Buff coloured, this time with a
neat forward facing crest.

97

CHANTECLER

This variety is Canadian in origin, and was developed at the Agricultural Institute in Oka. The work on it commenced in 1908, but it was 1921 before it was eventually accepted in the American book of Standards. The early creation of the breed owes much to Cistercian Monks, and especially Brother Wilfred.

The breed resembles a shorter tailed White Sumatra, but is much fuller fronted and of a stout build. The medium strong head has a Malay type comb, with a well curved yellow beak, which matches the bird's yellow legs and feet. It is possible that some of these birds were used in the development of modern day, medium sized table poultry.

Apparently, some of the stock were presented to the Prince of Wales in 1925. Little has been heard of the breed since before the 1939-1945 war, and I have no recollection of them since.

Five breeds were used in their creation. They were Indian Game, White Wyandotte and the White Rock. The other two mentioned were Rhode Island Reds and White Leghorns, which I suspect supplied their full tail furnishings.

The original colour was white, but, during the 1960s, a partridge coloured version has been developed. Both colours have now been successfully miniaturised and are listed in the American Book of Standards. As yet, I have no evidence of them being in the British Isles, but Linda Gryner, who is a prominent Canadian poultry fancier and has written a book on the Chantecler, would, I have no doubt, be interested in promoting the breed in this country.

The weights are not excessive being:-
Males 7.5-8.5lbs   Females 6-6.5 lbs
Miniatures
Males Min. 34 ozs.   Females 30 ozs.

Brother Wilfred and his White Chantecler

CH 1. Shows a pair of birds which were displayed at the World Poultry Congress in 1930.

CH 2. Is a painting by Arthur O. Shilling in 1937, depicting the ideal Chantecler.

99

CH 3. and CH 4. Were photographed by Hans Schippers at a show in Holland.

CH 5. and 6. These Miniature Chantecler were bred by Don Dearing from Ontario. They were photographed by J. Gryner, and are quite unique.

COCHIN

It would not be disrespectful to other breeds if I stated that the commencement of poultry breeding, where birds of different individual characteristics were separated into breeds, began with the birds which are now known as Cochins.

The period was during the late 1830s and early 1840s with an importation of birds from China. These were a present to Queen Victoria and assumed the name of Shanghais. There are slightly different accounts of the birds' description, especially in that a second importation were of a different style and type.

My assessment is that the originals were very much of a Malay type of bird, whilst the latter ones combined much looser, and more abundant feathering, some of which appeared to be single combed, whilst others still retained more of a pea type comb.

These birds were bred from, and, with the addition of further importations, were developed into the Cochins which we have at present time

Cochins were amongst the first breeds to be standardised but, even making allowances for this fact, there has probably never been a group of birds which have attracted the artist's brush and easel so consistently.

During the 1800s there were many excellent poultry artists. Amongst the best was Ludlow, and his vision of the ultimate development possible, to this bird of massive size and exotic curves, was quite remarkable. In fact it would be safe to state that the perfection in his paintings has as yet hardly ever been achieved in true life.

The possible ancestry of the originally imported birds has been discussed in one of the earlier chapters in the book.

The names which they originally assumed were taken from the areas in China where they were thought to have existed before being shipped to this country.

At present time there are six main colours of Cochins in the British Isles, and the birds should all be the same shape and style.

This is a bird of massive size and excessively feathered curves, especially in the areas around their thighs and cushion.

The frontal view of a correctly shaped Cochin should show a great width between the shoulder butts, with a well rounded front sweeping into a deep keeled breast.

The head and neck should be carried proudly upright with the abundantly feathered neck hackle covering the bird's shoulders and upper wing.

The back is short but clearly defined before moulding into the quickly rising cushion and main tail. This tail is carried almost vertical, but in no way must it be 'squirrel tailed'. The fourteen main tail feathers are completed into a flowing contour by broad feathered side hangers and rich quality cushion feathers which can extend right round and meet at the rear of the bird.

The wings should be carried parallel to the ground and be short feathered, which enables them to be tucked away under the cushion feathering.

The shanks should be moderate in length and of strong well rounded bone. The thighs should be well feathered but not having long feathers growing straight outwards from the lower part, thus being 'vulture hocked'.

With any bird of this massive size, the head piece should be in keeping with the body and therefore be of strong bone structure. However, this does not mean it can be excessively large combed and coarse textured.

The face and well developed ear lobes should be smooth skinned with a medium sized pair of evenly hanging wattles.

In all colours the comb shape is single and rich red in colour. The evenly spaced, wedge shaped spike should be on a strong base, keeping it upright at all times, and not being 'floppy combed' or 'hollow' and thus falling to one side. This fault is becoming more common, probably due to birds being kept in intensive conditions. The alert looking eyes should be prominently visible and not 'sunken eyed' caused by excessive skull bone structure.

Even though the breed is considered to be a purely exhibition breed, in their younger years the females are capable of laying a good quantity of beautifully textured eggs. Unfortunately, the strains of some colours do tend to lay rather small eggs for the size of bird.

Weights   *Males 13 lbs*   *Females 9 lbs*

The colours of Cochins are - Buff, Black, White, Blue, Cuckoo and Partridge, though there are now some variations being introduced, via the non-standard classes.

The *Buffs* should be one even colour throughout. Until recent years this was a golden shade of buff, especially in the male birds, but the introduction of American has created a paler version, which obviously contains Buff Orpington blood. This is very evident from their tendency to be short of feathering on the middle toes. Evenness of colour is probably more important than actual shade.

The standard does give you a wide licence, describing the colouring as Lemon Buff, Silver Buff or Cinnamon which I have stated in other breeds as being in my mind too flexible, believing that one correct colour should be stipulated, with others possibly being acceptable but on a points losing basis.

The male bird will obviously have darker and more lustrous colouring to his neck and saddle hackles, also his wing bar. His breast and thighs should follow the colour of his females.

Traces of black or white in the tail, wing and foot feathers are to be avoided. The under-colour in both sexes is to be of a sound buff colour, right to the skin, as should the shaft of the feathers be, especially in the flight feathers.

The eyes should be reddish, but can shade to orange and blend in with the bird's top colouring.

The *Black* can be a very handsome bird, but here, as with the Wyandottes and Leghorns, you have the yellow pigmentation which should be 'double mated', if the best show birds are to be obtained. However in Cochins the standard does permit 'dusky legs', even shading to lizard, which allows for a certain amount of tolerance.

In both sexes the top colour should be a rich green sheen black, with the under-colour preferably free from white and certainly not showing through to the top colour.

In male birds, especially, any signs of brassy, or red in the hackles or wing bow or wing bar is a definite fault, though a few spots of white in the foot feathering may be considered not too serious a fault.

I prefer the black to have red eyes, but the standard does list dark red or hazel as being acceptable.

The *White* should be pure silver throughout as again there is a tendency for male birds to have foreign coloured feathers in their hackles and mid wing areas. This faulty colouring usually relates to the back breeding where the white has been produced from another colour, very often the partridge, especially from cock breeding partridges.

There have been recorded cases where Blacks, Whites Blues and Cuckoos have all been bred from the same bloodlines. This breeding can encourage slate or willow coloured

102

shanks and feet instead of the rich yellow colouring which I consider to be a most important and striking feature of the White Cochin. The eyes are red but a paler shade is permissible.

The Blue is a most attractive colouring, and a different blue to the one in many other breeds. It is a 'pigeon blue' and is in some ways similar to lavender in other breeds. It is not a blue laced with a darker shade of blue as in the Orpington.

The Cochin Blue has also been described as 'powder blue' and should be evenly distributed throughout the bird's plumage. It should be free from lacing and any other foreign colours, especially in the tail feathering. Again the male birds can show signs of Red or Gold in their hackles, and wing bows etc. and is a bad fault. Both sexes should have blue legs and feet, but yellow is allowed to the underside of their toes. The eye colouring is described as being 'dark'.

The Cuckoo Cochin, as with other breeds, has less distinct barring than on the Plymouth Rocks, with the bars being a slate blue/grey on a background which is not pure white but 'Dusky' coloured.

This pattern should be evenly continued throughout the bird's feathering, and not be intermingled with either black, white or golden tinted feathers. The shanks and feet have to be a brilliant yellow, which contrasts with the bird's top colouring and gives them a different appearance from the Marans and North Holland blue with their white pigmentation. The eyes should be bright red.

When commencing to write this book on the breeds, I was tempted to use the principle whereby each basic colour was described and illustrated in great detail at the beginning of the chapters, and thereafter referred to for breeds where this colouring existed.

My reluctance to do so was largely influenced by the black-red colouring.

In some breeds the same colour pattern can be termed by a different name. In the case of Brahmas for instance it is called 'gold'.

In Cochins we have what are known as Partridge Cochins. The colour of these is based on the black-red colour pattern, but both male and female in the breed are called Partridge.

In the male bird, the whole of the under body, breast, thighs, footings etc. should be solid black in colour, as are the main tail feathers. The wing has also a band of black extending through the wing coverts (See diagram at the beginning of the book).

This black should be as rich as possible, and carry a green sheen to it showing no signs of grey or purple tinge.

The bird's striking appearance is supplied by the colouring of the hackle and saddle feathers.

These feathers should be broad, and of a bright orange red colour, with a black stripe running down the centre, but not to extend through the end of the feather.

The back is a solid colour, and a slightly darker shade than the hackles. This colouring extends over the shoulders, and completes the wing bow. The wing bay (diamond) is also reddish orange.

In the female, the colour is the one which most people would associate with the term Partridge. In the Cochin, the pencilling has been perfected to such a degree that it is possible to have three distinct 'V' shaped lines of solid black markings imposed on a pale brown background.

This feather pattern should extend to all parts of the body, with the exception of the neck hackle which is lemon coloured with the same distinctive black stripe as in the male bird.

To obtain the best show specimens double mating should most certainly be used as accepted procedure.

As with many of the breeds in the country at the present time, there is a growing inclination to develop them into a full range of colours.

When this procedure has been carried out to the extremity, around fifteen different variations are possible. Until the new colours have been approved by both the Breed Club and the Poultry Club, the birds have to be exhibited in non-standard classes.

Some of the colours which I have seen displayed include very attractive looking creels, which were presumably bred from partridge or buffs and cuckoos. A cross between buffs and blues resulted in a delightful salmon breasted blue pullet.

I understand that attempts are being made to perfect the equivalent of a dark as, in Brahmas which is really a silver partridge, or, as it is called in Wyandottes, silver pencilled.

A *Columbian* or light as it is called in Brahmas could also be easily created, but, as I have mentioned in the early chapters, until there are more conservationists in the country, there is an adequate number of breeds for them to choose from at the present time without creating more.

In the breed of Cochin the miniature version is open to debate. For many years reference has been made to Pekin Bantams being their small counterpart but it is not a theory with which I agree at all, believing that Pekins are a definite 'true bantam' much closer related to Japanese Bantams than the large Shanghais.

I do, however, believe that there should be a miniature Cochin, in a full range of colours, and hope that this will be accomplished and accepted in the not too distant future.

Buff Cochin Cock 1st at the Royal Show in 1935, Mr Williams, Middleton.

Buff Cochin, shown at Hanover in 1983, photo by Joseph Wolters

Is her counterpart from a much later date. This Partridge cock was bred and successfully shown by Captain Duckworth from Sussex, during the 1960s.

Shows a Partridge Cochin hen which was bred in 1924 by George Lane from Bristol, and was considered to be one of the best ever seen, and consequently won many top awards.

Shows a Black Cochin pullet which won first prize and Bronze Medal at the Crystal Palace, and Best Brahma or Cochin at the Dairy Show in 1925. She was bred and exhibited by Captain Whittaker.

Was bred by Colonel R. S. Williamson and won both the Crystal Palace and Birmingham shows in 1932.

This pair of Blue Cochins won the Poultry World Cup for the best pair of birds in the 'New Breed class ' at the Crystal Palace in 1934 for their dedicated breeder of Blue Fowl, Mr H. Whitely from Paignton Zoo.

Was also bred by Mr Whitely and shows a promising Blue Cochin cockerel which went on to achieve a series of good wins.

Shows a White hen with a great wealth of feather. She won the Cochin Club Show, and the Crystal Palace for her breeder Walter Warrilow, who was a Cochin expert.

Shows a White cockerel which won the Dairy Show in 1931. He was bred and exhibited by Mr Norman Grant M.B.E. from Sussex.

Shows a grand Buff pullet. She was bred in 1933, and won Champion Cochin at Birmingham, The Dairy, and Crystal Palace Shows, for her breeder Mr W. Kean from Manchester.

Is from 1923, and was bred by that Cochin veteran Mr G. H. Proctor from Durham and she won the Dairy Show for him.

Was also bred by a Cochin veteran, Robin Jackson from Ayr. This cock was a consistent winner for him during 1933.

Shows another of Mr Proctor's birds, this time the 1921 Dairy Show winning cockerel.

Illustrates a pair of Buffs which were bred by Lord Dewar in 1926. The Cock won Champion male Bird Any Variety, at the Crystal Palace.

Shows a well balanced Buff cock which won the Crystal Palace in 1936. He was bred by Mr. W. Kean.

Is very interesting. This Buff cock won three consecutive awards for Best Cochin at the Crystal Palace and Birmingham Shows in 1911, 1912 and 1913. Its breeder was Mr G. H. Proctor.

108

Shows a Blue pullet bred by Paignton Zoo, and was unshown at the time of the photograph.

Was bred at the Paignton Zoo, this time it is a Black hen which was a noted winner for them during 1935. It would be interesting to show this hen alongside today's birds and assess the comparison.

Illustrates a very attractive White cockerel, with two females, all of which were winners during 1930 and 1931 for their breeder, Mr. W. J. Warrilow from Croydon in Surrey.

COURTES PATTES and KRUPER

In most countries there exists a type of fowl, which has been specially developed to produce a breed in which the main feature is their excessively short thigh and shanks, which gives the birds a very squat appearance.

In France these birds are called Courtes Pattes, and, in Germany, Kruper, which is usually called Creeper in Britain, whilst our own variation is the Scots Dumpy.

Van Gink relates an interesting explanation of the Dutch name of Dachshuhn. Apparently it draws comparison between the bird's walk, and that of a badger.

Edward Brown states that poultry with short legs have been known to man from time immemorial, and could have come originally from the Far East. It is only with selective breeding that the birds have retained their short legs. Even though the gene is present in the birds, their general tendency is for many of them to revert to a longer leg.

The shape of both breeds is a long bodied bird, full in front, and capable of carrying a good carcass of very edible white meat. The wings are carried just below parallel, and the tail is held rather high, but is in no way squirrel tailed. There is a good flow of saddle hackle feathering, which continues into the well furnished tail, complete with a very wide and well pronounced pair of sickles.

The rich red coloured headpiece has a large single comb, standing upright in the male, and being slightly folded in the female. Their wattles are also well developed, being rather long, and hanging well down the throat.

The birds have stout but very short shanks, with four toes set firmly on the ground. Apart from this last point, their general description bears a close resemblance to that of the Dorking. I have made reference to this point in the summary of the Dorking breed's history.

Both breeds exist in several colours. Black is quite common, with variations such as White, Cuckoo, Black-Red etc.

FIG 1. Illustrates the birds as drawn by Cornelis Van Gink .

FIG 2. Shows a Black Kruper pullet from Germany, where she was photographed by Josef Wolters.

COVENY WHITE

Edward Brown records that the pioneer development of the breed commenced in the period prior to the First World War. This was done by a Mr. Unwin from Cambridgeshire. This gentleman's main occupation was in the growing of sweet peas, but, for some reason, he decided to create a different type of Leghorn. One of the aims was for the birds to have a more compact body, and therefore provide a better table bird.

The decision to replace the rather cumbersome single comb with a cup shaped one, as in the Sicilian Buttercup, was probably very practical. Many of the Leghorn cocks' combs became frost bitten during the winter breeding season, which obviously reduced fertility. Consequently it was common practice to 'dub' the stock male birds before the breeding season commenced.

In 1923, Stanley Street-Porter became involved with the project. This gentleman came from the same county, living in the Isle of Eley at the Coveney Manor. This obviously was the origin of the breed's name.

Street-Porter, as he was often referred to, was a man of both affluence and influence. He was a Justice of the Peace, Chairman of the NFU, a council member of several poultry advisor organisations and also involved with local government.

His clout and connections very quickly gained recognition for the breed and, by 1924, a standard had been drafted and approved by the Poultry Club Council.

The breed's description was of a bird with a medium depth of body with a longish and broad back moulding into a tail to be carried at approx. 45 degrees. The neck was long and abundantly feathered, as were the saddle hackle and tail coverts.

In general style the birds had an upright stance to create an appearance of activeness. Their main difference from normal is the comb which is a rather large version of the cup shape.

From photos of the birds, there appear to be two separate lines of single combs, rather than the more rounded crown of the Sicilian Buttercup. The female would also appear almost to have the Leghorn type of folded over comb. They had pure white earlobes, with the overall pigmentation of the bird being yellow, which obviously includes the shanks and beak.

One point in the standard which I consider debatable is the weights for the Coveney White. These are quoted as being up to 5 1/2lbs for Males and 4 1/2lbs for Females, which is half a pound less than the old standard for Leghorns, so how did the improved table qualities figure? The more recent weights for the British type of Leghorn are up to 7 1/2lbs cock and 5 1/2lbs the hen!

I do not have a simple explanation as to why the breed failed to become popular, but it would be constructive to comment that at one period a pure white version of the Sicilian Buttercup also failed to capture the imagination of the British poultry breeder.

At the present time a Mr Brocklesby from Derbyshire is developing a new breed of Bantam. These birds have a 'cup shaped' comb, and their body shape resembles a Rose comb Bantam. They have been described as being similar to a miniature Coveney. The main difference is that the Coveney had rich yellow coloured legs and beak, but the Brocklesby Crown is white pigmented.

I have seen the birds, and find a lot of their features to be appealing, though at the present time they have not achieved wide recognition.

The Brocklesby has a shortish back, with the tail carried well above the 45 degree level. The birds have an upright stance which is characteristic of a bird with a low wing carriage.

The main feature appears to be in their heads. The comb is of a full cup shape, as in the Sicilian. It is accompanied by a large pair of wattles, as in a Leghorn, and a thick white ear lobe. At the present time the birds are not fully standardised, maybe their popularity will increase when they receive the full seal of approval.

FIG 1. Is a pair of Coveney Whites, bred and exhibited by Stanley Street-Porter from Ely.

FIG 2. Shows a pair of Brocklesby Crowns, which have sometimes been called a miniature Coveney White.

CREVECOEUR

From the name it is obviously of French origin, and I must confess that I have never had any personal dealings with the breed, for no other reason than I have never got round to it.

When you come to analyse the breed, there is a striking resemblance to Houdans but minus the fifth toe and with a differently shaped comb. The birds have quite a large and full fronted body. They possess a characteristic V Shaped horn comb, and a full and well rounded crest.

The blacks are completely self in colour, including legs and feet.

The whites have a pinkie white pigmentation, whilst the self coloured blues have dark legs and feet.

Subconsciously I presume my preference for Houdans is because I find that totally black birds are not popular with new and enthusiastic poultry keepers, black being more of a specialist breeder's colour, as with Orpingtons.

There are no miniatures in this country at the present time.

Weights   Males   9lbs   Females 7lbs

Is a pair of Crevecoeur drawn by Ludlow.

A cock shown in 1921 by George Henwood, winning the Royal Agricultural Show.

CROAD LANGSHAN

The breed of Langshan has caused more controversy and bitterness between rival breeders than any other breed.

I do not intend to take up dozens of pages in the book reprinting old history but will briefly say that in 1872 Major Croad imported some black coloured, feather legged fowls from northern China and called them Langshans, after the region around the Yangtsze-kiang River in which they had been located, and where the birds had been bred for very many centuries.

The Cochin breeders in Britain rather stupidly claimed that these newly imported birds were actually Black Cochins. The leading poultry writers of that time Messrs Tegetmeier, Harrison-Weir and Lewis Wright managed to get themselves involved with the dispute. Major Croad persuaded his niece, Miss Croad, to assist with his fight to establish their pure identity.

A breakaway group of breeders commenced to create their own version which was to become the Modern Langshan. The Major passed away leaving Miss Croad to collect some fellow breeders into a group and, by 1904, a club was formed. It was called the Croad Langshan club in memory of the old Major.

The stupidity of all this commotion was that the true Langshan is a black bird with white pigmentation. It has a thin textured white skin and flesh. Even on the soles of its feet, and in-between the black scales on its legs a distinct pinkie white colouring shows.

The Cochin should be yellow legged, with the flesh and skin colouring showing a definite yellow cast.

Where the problems arose was that many of the so called black Cochins which were being imported as the genuine article were little more than Buff Cochin X Langshans, and, if you have paid good money for such dubious specimens, no doubt tempers do get raised to boiling point, which is what appears to have happened in this saga.

The turn of the century saw an upturn in the breed's popularity. A lot of the old bitterness had died down, and the breed was allowed to develop into an excellent utility laying fowl. One of its ambassadors was W Powell-Owen, who is highlighted in the Welsummer breed's summary. There were several changes to the original standard, an important one being the limiting of foot feathering to the side of the leg and outer toe, and not to include the middle one, which was another point to move the breed well away from the Cochin.

With the standard now well established, the period from 1913 was to see some Croad Langshans exhibited, which have probably never been improved upon, even to the present day.

I would say that the breed has several features which, when combined together, make it one of the most imposing breeds as yet perfected.

The Langshan has a wealth of feather but, owing to its ability to carry these feathers close to its body, the general appearance is one of sleekness combined with massive body structure.

When you take a good Langshan out of the show pen, the width of back and great depth of body is immediately apparent, whereas, in some of the loose feathered Orpingtons and Cochins, the feel of their body structure can be disappointing.

The Langshans have a long neck which is equally balanced by the massive tail, which again is deceptive in that the main tail feathers are spread, and it is adorned with an abundance of side hangers. The tails full contour is completed by an extremely long but well curved pair of sickles. The full tail is probably the largest of all the breeds, but with its high carriage, which is not quite fully upright, it moulds into the bird's other features of high wing carriage, well feathered, but not fluffy thigh feathering. One other big feature of the breed is the well rounded and long feathered neck hackle feathers, these really do form a massive cape. The saddle hackle feathers are shorter and quickly blend into the tail coverts.

The front of the bird should be wide and full chested, with a well rounded crop area, but the front is not carried as low as in the Cochins. The description of the legs can vary, the dilemma being that if they are referred to as long, one's thoughts immediately go to the Modern Langshan's extremely long reach; or, if the term shortish is used, the Cochin immediately springs to mind. My description would be that the thighs are quite long, but, owing to having plenty of feathering on them, they actually appear shorter than they are. The feathering must not show any signs of vulture hock feathering. The lower legs, or shanks, require a liberal distribution of not too long feathering which extends down the outer toe where it should increase in length. The length of the shanks I would again describe as being above average. The Langshan is a very upstanding and alert bird and should in no way appear 'squatty' looking. It should give the impression of being active and wanting to work for its living by going out in search for food, as should all the top utility breeds.

In keeping with most black breeds of poultry and waterfowl the sheen on the feathering of Langshans should be a rich bottle green which, when reflected in the light, does not show a purple cast.

The under-colouring should be dark grey, care must be taken that the male's under-colouring around the saddle hackle and tail roots does not drift into a much paler shade. This also applies to the neck hackle feathers; however a little white is allowed in the foot feathering.

The legs and feet are also black, with white toe nails. The soles of the feet should also be white, any sign of yellow or willow is a definite disqualification.

The eye colour is stated 'not to be black' but dark brown, with the comb face wattles and lobes to be a brilliant red colour. This red colouring is also required to be present on the skin running in-between the scales at the sides of the shanks. This feature is characteristic of Langshans, and helps to eliminate foreign blood lines.

One interesting point in the Langshan standard is the qualification 'A judge may penalise a bad fault to the extent of 25 points at his own discretion'. This or similar wording could well be added to all standards.

The breed in both large and small versions deserves to be more popular than it is. The birds have a beautiful temperament, with good table qualities, and are excellent layers of attractive tinted eggs, with a purple cast to them. Alternatively some strains have still retained the dark brown eggs of the original birds.

Possibly one reason for the breed's lack of support is that, during the 1990s, there has been a definite resistance amongst new poultry keepers to black breeds. The trend at present is towards the more multicoloured type of colouring.

There is a white version of Langshan; it is very rarely seen in this country.

These birds should be silver white throughout, with the same head and leg colouring as their black counterpart.

There are many excellent miniatures of the breed, most of which have been genuinely bred down from the large fowl.

Weights Large Males 9 lbs   Females 7 lbs

Croad Langshans were amongst the first breeds to be bred to a high standard of show perfection. Whilst choosing my selection of photographs I was spoilt for choice, especially amongst the male birds.

116

CL1. Illustrates a winning cockerel from 1913, which was bred by Mr H. P. Mullens, who showed him with great success. He was thought by many people to be as good a bird as any bred in later years.

CL 2. Represents the 1920s. He was bred by Mrs P. J. Hannon who was a very respected Croad breeder. During his showing career the bird collected many top awards.

CL 3. Shows a cock from the 1930s. He was bred by that photographic genius Arthur Rice. You can see the green sheen glistening on the bird's feathers. Again he was a noted winner at that period.

Harold Church from Hampshire was for many years amongst the top breeders of Croads. This cockerel in CL 4. is a typical example of his strain of birds. He won York and also the Club Show in 1933.

CL 5. Illustrates another of Harold's cockerels; this time bred in 1931, when he was second at the Club Show. This photo was taken at a later date when he had just won the Cup at Yeovil.

CL 6. Features an old cock which was bred by a friend of my father, Major Renwick from Richmond, Yorkshire. The photo was taken in 1947 when the bird had enjoyed a very successful showing season.

CL 7. Shows a cock bred by Lord Dewar. I have no records of him having been shown at the Club Show, but he accumulated a series of top awards at other events, and was highly regarded by the experts.

CL 8. Illustrates a change of colour. This white Croad won second prize at Birmingham Show in 1937. He was bred and exhibited by Mr A. Powell, who was chairman of the Essex branch of the Poultry Club.

118

CL 9. The first photo in my selection of females comes from 1911, when this bird was Champion Pullet at the Club Show. She was bred by Mr E. Crocker, and won many other prizes for him.

CL 10. Again we have a Harold Church bird. This time the 1931 Champion Croad at the Crystal Palace. She was described by the judge as being one of the best females he had ever seen.

CL 11. This time a pullet which won Best Croad at the Dairy and First at the Club Show, but only Third at the Crystal Palace. The year was 1933, the breeder, Harold Church.

CL 12. Shows a Blue Croad pullet. She was bred by Miss A. H. Gordon-Barrett, who was later to become Mrs Hannon. The bird was only shown twice, and won First on both occasions.

CROWING BREEDS

Crowing competitions add a new dimension to keeping poultry as a hobby. On the European continent, the Bergische Crower has had a reputation surrounding its excellent vocal chords for centuries, the bird's main habitat being the districts of Rhenish Prussia, where its voice could be heard echoing around the mountainous regions.

Recent information researched by the Reverend Trudgian, informs us that, in Japan, the art of developing and perfecting a cockerel's historic warning sound has been transformed into something more in keeping with the local Operatic Society.

The European birds were thought to be closely related to the Schlotterkamm and probably from the same family. There is only one colour of Bergische.

It is similar to the Mottled Schlotterkamm with the exception that the Bergische has two or three greenish/black bars across the wing in addition to the wing bay .

To my knowledge there have never been organised crowing competitions in either the British Isles or America. Germany and Japan are the countries where the art has been developed and has created the most interest. However, Russia, China, Brazil, Indonesia and the Balcins, are also developing Crowing Breeds.

I am grateful to Rev. Ray Trudgian and his Japanese friends, Messrs. Imamura, Sasaki and Tsushima for supplying the detailed information about the Japanese Crowers.

There are three main breeds. One of them is similar to our Yokohama Miniatures. This bird is called a Totenko, and crows in the tone of a tenor.

Another variety resembles the Shamos, which have recently arrived in this country as an exhibition breed. These birds have a deep toned bass voice.

The breed which fascinates me is a very distinguished looking character. He is self black in colour and, in some ways, looks like a Sumatra with a large single comb. However, a deeper study of the breed reveals a bird which is different from any other I can recall, and I believe it could be made into an interesting showman's breed. These baritone singers are called Tomaru.

The organisation and procedure for crowing contests begin with the competitors being placed on a ladder like stool, standing roughly chest high to their owner. There must be no touching or communicating between the bird and its owner once the contest has started. Prior to the starting signal, the owner can get his bird 'wound up' by his own crowing impersonations, which is similar to showing a Norwich Cropper Pigeon.

Assessment of the bird's crow is based on 100 marks, 40 for volume, which must be low, strong and clear. 40 are for the rhythm of crow which is separated into five divisions, Start, Take off, Middle Section, Run Down and Finish.

Once the birds repertoire begins it is given five minutes to make it's first crow. Failure to do so results in immediate disqualification.

It is allowed up to l5 minutes to make its three crows upon which the contest is based. The length of crow is allocated 20 marks. It must not be shorter than 15 seconds, which the Totenko, and Tomaru can achieve with ease, sometimes up to 25 seconds. The Keoyoshi crows for over 18 seconds, apparently with its beak almost closed.

FIG 1. Shows a drawing by Kramer of Bergische Crower Fowls. Their wing clearly illustrates the double line of markings.

FIG 2. Is one of the photos supplied by Ray Trudgian and his Japanese friends. The cockerel is a Totenko, and clearly shows a relationship with the Yokohama family.

121

FIG 3. Is the Japanese Tomaru, the Baritone Crower.

FIG 4. Shows a pair of Koeyoshi. An additional photo of this breed is included in the colour section of the book.

122

DOMINIQUE

The Dominique is a breed, the history of which creates more questions than answers.

Harrison Weir in his book 'Our Poultry', when writing on the development of the Barred Rock in America, refers to a letter received from his friend mentioning the use of the Dominique. Harrison is quoted as saying, 'What's a Dominique?'

There is no mention of the breed by any of the early historians or poultry experts, either here or on the European continent.

It has been recorded that poultry with barring to their feathers, were common in the Eastern United States as long since as the mid eighteenth century. They were described as being reasonably small sized, with a mixture of single and rose combs.

I offer you my own conclusions. America is a recently occupied continent only 300 years old and all the poultry bred there have originated from stock which has been imported mainly from the European Continent. There does not appear to be any poultry indigenous to the USA.

All the breeds associated with the country have been developed there in the last 150-200 years. This breed creation has often been conducted in association with the Federal State and Provincial Departments of Agriculture, with most of their breeding programme well recorded. Most of the breeds developed were designed to be used for commercial and practical use and quickly provide food for the rapidly increasing population, either as solely egg producers or table poultry. But in the case of Rocks, which were the first new breed to be completed, both qualities were coupled to create a 'dual purpose' breed. In the barred version of Plymouth Rock, the bird's ancestry refers to the Dominique being used to supply the barring factor.

At one time it was thought that the Dominique entered the states via Canada, where it may have been taken by French sailors. This seems to me a long way round. I would prefer to theorise that the very early imports to America from Europe were the Leghorn/ Bresse type of birds for egg laying, and amongst them were some birds with Cuckoo markings.

For centuries there has been in Southern France, especially around the area of Rennes, a cuckoo marked bird, known as the Coucou de Bretagne, which has a large rose comb carried well to the front of the beak, and with a spike sticking out behind the head.

It was thought that these birds were the result of crossing with the Hamburgh fowl, or possibly the Campines which were also capable of breeding some rose combed stock.

The main characteristics of the Dominique are the combination of cuckoo coloured feathering and rose comb plus the big difference from all other European cuckoo coloured breeds in that it has yellow pigment, which could have been inherited from the Leghorn genes. This feature of yellow legs and skin colouring is also a feature on all the American breeds. It is present in all the table poultry breeds, where the population accept and prefer it, unlike their European cousins. They also prefer white shelled eggs instead of brown, unlike we in England at the present time.

So, we have the Dominique described as a cuckoo coloured, rose combed bird with yellow legs and feet with close fitting feathering typical of the Mediterranean light breeds.

Later in the nineteenth century, the poultry expert and author Lewis Wright in 'Lewis Wright of Poultry', illustrates a fine pair of Dominiques in a coloured print by the top class artist Ludlow, who clearly shows the breed to be very close in type to the Hamburgh, which would be consistent with the French Cuckoo assumption.

The birds were first nameless, but around 1850, when the first poultry show was held in Boston, they assumed the name of Dominique.

Where did they get the name Dominique? I think the name itself would finally squash any possibility that the breed was indigenous to the states.

Anyhow, if it was, I am sure that it would have been given more status and recognition, and certainly been better preserved in their history, as the Scots Dumpy became the emblem of Scotland.

Working on the theory that the birds followed the route taken by Christopher Columbus, who is widely accepted as discovering America, it leaves us with two possibilities:

A) The word Dominic, when translated, means 'King', and it may be that one of these cuckoo marked cockerels, with an importation of White Leghorn females, looked to be superior, i.e. the king.

B) Christopher Columbus was by religion a Dominican monk. Could it be that the birds included in part of his earliest explorations and consequent imports to the States were thus named Dominiques? I leave you to form your own conclusions.

It is interesting to note that Robert Henderson who bred Dominiques and supplied the adjacent photograph describes them as being, 'One of the first breeds to be produced in America', which adds weight to Harrison Weir's and Lewis Wright's assessment that they were merely 'crossbreds'. He further states that there are no records to state which breeds were used in their creation, but most fanciers believe there to be Hamburgh blood included. This adds weight to my theory that the breed should be sleek in feathering, not loose feathered and Wyandotte shaped like a few specimens in Britain at the present time. To me they are an attractive breed which has been allowed to decline in America and have never really been accepted in Europe. To me this is very strange.

A painting of American Dominiques depicting what I believe to be very representative of the breed.

124

Another painting from America, this time showing traces of barred Wyandotte blood.

One of the very few photographs of a live Dominique. It was taken by Robert Henderson from Ohio, and shows a cockerel bred in 1934.

A more recent illustration of the Dominique, in which the bird has still retained the breed's original type, unlike the ones which have been developed into resembling a Barred Wyandotte.

DORKING HISTORY

The Dorking is quoted in some sources as being a truly British breed, whilst others believe that it came to these shores with the Romans. That is only half the debate, the other part is which came first, the Sussex or the Dorkings.

I have no doubt that there will be readers who say 'Does it matter?' Just get on and tell us about the breed at present, not what it might have been 2,000 years ago', which is fair comment. However, my nature being what it is, I am afraid that I will have to conduct a short debate on both the breeds' history, in an attempt to reach a conclusion to the question.

If the Dorking was indigenous to the British Isles, why is the original colour quoted in some historians' view as being white? In most species of wild fowl the dominant colour is black-red/partridge pairing which offers a natural camouflage; that is unless the bird lives in arctic conditions.

In most cases white is simply a sport out of blacks or cuckoos, with the blues being created later.

If the Romans did bring the Dorking to these shores, why did they not leave some behind for themselves? The only breeds they had in Italy were the light breed Leghorn types which were called the common fowl of Italy, and one called the Polverara which looked like a crossbred Creve-Coeur, and there is certainly no mention of any Italian breed with five toes. France has some of these and they are referred to as the common five toed fowl (see Houdans and Faverolles).

However, reference to Edward Brown's excellent recordings leads us to Belgium where we find the Ardennes, a five toed 'breed' which is distributed throughout the Ardennes. Its appearance and wild nature suggest that it has descended from a game type fowl. The history of the Ardennes is that it can live wild in the heavily wooded areas and does not adapt well to confinement. It is an excellent table fowl, especially if hung long enough to soften.

This is interesting. The Dorking was for many years reputedly Britain's top table fowl.

One point which has intrigued me for years is, why do we have as standard single combed Red and Silver Dorkings, with the Whites and the Cuckoos only accepted in a rose combed version, and, to confuse the point even more, that Darks can be either single or rose combed?

If you study the list of breeds which have been common in the British Isles during the last 150 years or so, you will notice that the bulk of the rose combed ones originate from the northern parts, e.g. Hamburghs, Redcaps, Pheasant fowls. But, again consulting with Edward Brown, the history for the Scots Dumpy quotes that a Mr Cluny Macpherson recorded that they were brought into Albain, which is apparently an old name for Scotland, by Phoenician traders long before the Roman invasion. If this is correct they could state a good case for themselves as being the common fowl of Scotland. The shortness of leg which we now associate with the breed I have no doubt is basically a modern showman's creation by selective breeding, and, as with Japanese Bantams, the few really short legged birds are nearly freaks. A high percentage of the birds bred each year are longer legged and obviously trying to revert back to their original form. The next interesting point is that in the earliest colour description for Dumpies, they are listed as being black, cuckoo, grey, plus dark with white legs and a white skin. It also states that there were both single and rose combed birds.

My memory of history is that the Romans were very active in the northern parts of

England and over what we now know as the borders, so if they collected some Ardennes from Belgium and took them to Scotland, where they crossed with the local 'Dumpies' you would immediately have Dorkings, as we know them now, and always associate with the town of Dorking. However, the original term for the breed was Darking, which may have been the old name for Dorking, but an old dictionary quotes the word dark as meaning to keep secret i.e. to be kept in the dark.

The earliest pictures of the Dorking show it to be a short legged bird showing little if any thighs, and even the current standard quotes 'legs short and strong, the thighs large and well developed, but almost hidden by body feathering, shanks short, moderately stout and round in bone'. The original weight quoted for Dumpies was 7.5lbs males, which I believe is far greater than nowadays, where they probably contain either Courtes Pattes or creeper blood and are quoted as being 4 lbs for the male bird's weight.

If you accept my theory around the Dark Dorking, the Silvers were accepted as being bred at a much later date, with some excellent specimens always being bred in the north of England, Ralph Alty being a prime example of a top class breeder from Lancashire. It may not be a coincidence that a writer in the Gardeners' Chronicle in 1848 praises the Dorkings bred in Cumberland, known as the 'Jew Breed' and also the Silver Pheasant breed. This suggests that they have been in the areas for many centuries especially around Keswick and Ambleside which were large Roman stations. He also mentions that over the borders they are known as the Scotch breed.

Assuming that the Silver Dorkings descended from the Darks, it would be feasible to suggest the introduction of Duckwing Old English Game blood, of which there would be plenty readily available in Cumbria. Presumably the Cuckoos came from the Dumpy theory, and perhaps the original Whites, but there is a beautiful coloured print in Lewis Wright's book illustrating a pair of currently winning white Dorkings. It is not painted by an artist whose name I can distinguish. It is certainly not Whippel or Ludlow, both of whom were usually spot on with their work , but this painting clearly shows the birds to have Hamburgh combs and even a clearly defined white lobe. It may be that the lady who bred them was recreating the colour in an attempt to improve the breed, otherwise it suggests one of my original points, about north country blood being used in the creation of rose combed Dorkings.

This leaves us with the Red Dorking and where I commenced the chapter. Many writers have stated that the Reds were the first colour of Dorking, and that they were tighter in feather. From the photographs available I would observe that they are also longer in the leg and thighs as well, so, presumably, they were from a different line of breeding.

An association with the Sussex or Surrey Fowls, as they were often called, must be correct. It is quoted so many times in history.

Presumably there was more than one boat load of Romans who invaded our island, and equally certain is the assumption that those arriving in the northern parts entered via the eastern ports, presumably using the River Tees or the Humber, where the original stock to create the Lancashire and Yorkshire Hamburghs was alleged to have arrived at these shores. The ones entering southern parts would do so via the English Channel, which is adjacent to the counties of Kent, Surrey and Sussex, all of which have been noted for their Sussex type fowl, since the earliest of writings and recordings.

My last question still remains debatable. Was there a four toed bird in these parts before the Romans brought their five toed wonders and cross bred them, or did they bring over a version which was both four and five toed?

At this point in the debate I will suggest that the only fowl that could have been common to the area was a form of game bird, but I will attempt to reach a more definite

127

conclusion in my summary of the Sussex Fowl.

Until then I must accept that the Red Dorking, certainly in its original form, was a five toed Brown Sussex.

Dorking Breed Summary

The Dorking exists in five different colours, all of which should be the same shape and style.

The birds should have a full and well rounded front and reasonably long and very flat back, (for some reason the breed is prone to being round backed).

The tail is well furnished and carried almost straight out, and certainly should in no way be approaching a 'squirrel' tail. The two main sickles have a feature of being rather longer than in many breeds, a feature which is mentioned in the Ardennes, Du Mans and CouCou de Bretagne breed summaries.

The thighs should be short for a bird of such size and are powerful and well muscled, with the legs a reasonable length, not too strong in the bone, and carrying one of the breed's main features, the very well defined five toes. These must be well divided with the top one of good length and pointing upwards.

There was a period when these fifth toes were strapped into position during growth, to ensure that they matured at the correct angle.

The single combed birds are noted for having large sized combs and strong heads, and, as with the thighs, the neck is short and thick, being well covered with a flowing hackle.

In recent years the birds have lost some of their size, possibly due to wanting a change of blood. The breed is now in the hands of very few breeders. For a long period after the last war A. J. Major (Jack) bred them in large quantities and sold them all round the British Isles, so the blood lines will be very similar in many instances.

During the later part of the era, George Isherwood was the semi-retired poultry man for Jack. They also bred and showed Scots Dumpies.

In the various colours of Dorkings the Reds are different to the Rhode Island, in that the males and females are not self coloured. The male's top colouring is two tone red, the back and wing bows being a darker colour than the hackle and saddle hackle, with a black tail and breast.

The females are typical Old English Partridge Game colouring of a gold hackle striped with black, body feathers a Red/Brown, tipped with black and having a yellow shaft, as in Welsummer females.

The White is a pure white colour, and the Cuckoo is a typical dark grey barring on a bluish ground colour. Both these colours are in rose comb versions only, the leader of which is slightly upturned.

The Darks and the Silvers have proved to be most successful showbirds. In colour they could loosely be described as Duckwing Old English Game coloured.

The Darks were the first to be perfected, and the male bird has a solid, jet black breast and wing bar. The whole of the tail is also black, but is allowed some white in the roots of the main sickles.

The hackles are white, which can drift to a straw colouring, with the saddle and neck hackles showing a slight black striping, which may without any detriment extend to the wing bows and across the bird's back.

The Dark female's colour is allowed quite a bit of variance; basically the hackle matches that of the male bird, with a reddish brown breast, tipped or laced with grey/black colouring.

128

The rest of the plumage should be a brown/black, with the shaft showing whitish in colour.

The colouring of the Dark Dorking is not the easiest to describe owing to the large amount of latitude allowed in the standard, the emphasis being on the bird's shape and meat potential. Size and type are allocated 48 points, and, the colour being just 12, these figures speak for themselves.

The Silver Dorking was reputed to be the last colour developed. It obviously is descended from the Darks, and is a very good example of the showmen adjusting a breed's standard to be very clearly defined, and not complicated with 'either/ors', and the allocation of points is also altered to be more realistic.

In Silver males, the neck and saddle hackle, the back and external part of the wing, except the wing bar, are stated to be pure silver white, free from any sign of straw colouring or markings of any kind. The breast, thighs, wing bar and the main tail should be a solid black, free from mottling or white ticking on the breast.

The female is again Duckwing coloured, with a silver neck hackle striped with black. Her breast is a reddish brown fading to fawn. The rest of her plumage including the thigh feathers, is silver grey, finely pencilled with a darker shade and free from any red, brown or black stipplings. The main tail feathers are black.

All this is straight forward, sensible and easy to read, and even if the ideal is hard to achieve, it gives you the ultimate ambition. The points award for the Silver were altered to read 30 for type and size, with the coloured doubled to 24. The head points are also increased from 10 to 16.

I admit the original standard was designed around a bird renowned for its table qualities, and many points were allocated to highlight these features, much the same as my comments regarding the Sussex standard. It is in need of being brought up to modern ideas.

There is one point which I have highlighted. Because of the breed's reputation as a table bird much emphasis is put on the bird's requiring a straight breast bone. This is a point which I consider to be essential in all breeds of poultry, believing that a crooked breast is a sign of weakness in the bird's breeding.

You may have a certain amount of damage to the breast bone through faulty perching, but this usually takes the form of a hollow or flat section, not, as the old saying was, 'as crooked as a dog's hind leg'.

You will also notice that the Silver Dorking is restricted to being single combed, not given the choice of rose or single, as in the Darks.

To give a quick summary of the Dorking, they are a breed I admire and have kept, mainly the Silvers. They have a lovely temperament and are great to look at when walking around a grass paddock. At the close I list the standard weights, but it is a long while since Ralph Alty and his friends showed birds which would be approaching these weights, whilst most of the modern day birds are much smaller.

There has been Miniature Dorking for longer than some people imagine. We were showing them 40 years ago, and they were quite good replicas of the large Silvers.

Once again they are beginning to increase in numbers, and hopefully will continue to do so.

Weights   *Males*   *10-14 lbs*   *Females*   *8-10 lbs*

Illustrates the breed of Dorking beautifully. It is a Silver Grey cock bred by John Dewar in 1933 and won many Championship Awards.

An interesting photo. It was taken in 1906 when it was described as being a Silver Grey. Whatever his colour, he is a useful looking bird.

Bred by A. J. Major in 1933 and was described as a Dark Dorking. He had a very successful show career, winning at The Royal Counties, Ayr and Oxford during the summer season.

Another useful looking Silver cockerel, which was a noted winner in 1931.

An attractive Rosecombed Dark Dorking. He was bred by Jack Major and won Birmingham in 1926.

A great bodied Silver Grey pullet. She was bred by John Mechie from Auchtermuchty in Fife, and won the London Dairy Show in 1926. She also won the Scottish Royal Highland.

Another of Jack Major's Silvers. Bred in 1926, she was a consistent winner for him.

A pair of Red Dorkings from the early 1930s, bred and shown by Mrs M. A. Grant.

My final two photos for Dorkings are by way of a comparison. Left picture shows a grand bodied and well balanced Dark cock, which was a noted winner during the 1930s. Right picture illustrates the 1927 winning bird at the Maddison Square Gardens in New York. He was described as being a Silver Grey, but he looks to be heavily striped in both his hackle and his saddle. He has a good head and a grand pair of back toes.

DRENTE

The Drente fowl is of Dutch origin, and, I believe, was one of Van Gink's favourite breeds. His marvellous paintings of the birds illustrate them in the most detailed perfection.

Birds of their description have been recorded in Holland for several centuries. Basically they are in the 'Continental Leghorn' category, though perhaps a little smaller in size.

One of their great appeals is the wide range of colours in which they can reproduce themselves, even when left to their own breeding programme.

In the history of the breed, Mr M Houwink, when discussing the Dutch breeds in his book, written in 1900, says that he believes them to be the nearest to the original type of Gallus Bankiva, than any breed he has encountered. The birds were originally found in the area of Drente, which is noted for being poor quality land, but the birds run free there, and can thrive on their meagre diet. They are good layers, with a small but tasty carcass of meat, and they are capable of sitting their own eggs. All of which sounds to me consistent with a very old and original breed of poultry, which I am sure has been responsible for the development of other breeds.

The Drente is drawn by Van Gink to have a well rounded front, which is not too deep, but very prominent.

They have a short back which then moulds into a full flowing and well spread tail, which is furnished with plenty of side hangers.

The neck and saddle hackles are also abundantly feathered, with soft textured and flowing feathers.

The female also shows to have the same body shape, again, with her tail in a fan shape.

Both sexes have medium sized single combs, carried upright by both of them. They have a neat pair of round hackles and white ear lobes.

Their legs are of moderate length, and quite stout in the bone for such a small framed bird. To me, a feature of the breed is its proud and defiant stance.

As aforementioned, the colouring within the breed is comprehensive, and circulates around the basic black/red partridge pattern extending into Pile Black, Blue, White and Cuckoo.

Edward Brown relates that the breed also exists in both Gold and Silver Pencilled and Laced versions. There is also the one mentioned in the Ancona breed, which had a spangled or speckled colouring.

One of the reasons for me to put the breed into my choice of the top hundred soft feathered varieties, was the unanswered question, as to whether the birds we have in this country at the present time, and call Dutch Bantams, are actually miniature Drente Fowl, or really are a different race of what we refer to as 'True Bantams', meaning that they have no large counterpart.

It was during very recent times that the first Dutch Bantams arrived into this country, and I, along with many others, without doubt, accepted them as being attractive and extremely diminutive Bantams. They were very small and equally proportioned, especially in their head and legs.

It was at a much later stage in life that I noticed the paintings of Van Gink and immediately recognised that his illustrations of the Drente Fowl and the Dutch Bantams were almost identical apart from their size. I was then able to locate some of Van Gink's writings on the breed, and read with interest his beliefs as to the beginnings of Dutch Bantams. His theory again centres around the area of Drente and their local fowl, which had been allowed to cross with various breeds of Bantam type fowl. The result of these crosses were known as Partridge Bantams.

One of the breeds which had been involved with the early crossing was the Japanese, which is fully accepted as a genuine 'True Bantam'.

These crossbred Bantams were allowed to breed in the area, until the beginning of the twentieth century, when their potential was recognised. Selective breeding was commenced, and, in 1906, they were admitted to the Official Poultry Standards of Holland.

In 1911 the White, Black and Silver Partridge were also accepted. The birds were exported to the United States of America, where, at the present time, there are now 10 different colours standardised.

Why it took until the 1960s for the birds to be fully recognised in this country remains one of the unanswered mysteries of life, especially when, once here, their immediate attraction catapulted them into one of the exhibitors' favourite Bantams.

During the early development of the breed in Holland some of the birds spread into the adjoining areas of Germany, where once again they continued to flourish.

There is at the present time a continental breed called the German Bantam. These are extremely popular, being capable of attracting over 500 entries at the Championship Shows. These birds bear a resemblance to the Dutch Bantams, and I would not be surprised if there was some initial connection between the two varieties. The development of the German Bantam has created a bird with very fully furnished tail, suggesting the introduction of Phoenix Yokohama blood.

Whether or not you can officially call the Dutch Bantam a miniature Drente is debatable, but the birds are certainly very attractive, with their red coloured upright combs highlighting a neat white earlobe. Their proudly displayed full front and low wing carriage is additionally emphasised by a short back and well furnished tail which is carried fairly high.

In spite of their very small size the birds are very hardy and reasonably easy to hatch and rear.

There is a photograph of a Drente in the colour section.

Weights   *Males*   *5.5 lbs*   *Females*   *4.5 lbs*

A pullet which was shown at Utrect in 1984. In this country she would be described as being Silver Duckwing coloured.

Again shown at Utrect, with her colour being 'Gezoomd Patrije'. Both photos were taken by Josef Wolters. A painting by Van Gink appears in the colour section, and illustrates a beautiful pair of Pile coloured Drente Fowl.

DRESDENER

One of the most popular breeds on the continent is the Dresdener. The birds are displayed in both large and miniature versions in four different colours.

I cannot find any recordings of a similar type in the early recordings of the breeds, so I presume that they have been recently developed. Fred Jeffreys states that the large fowl of the breed were developed in Germany by interbreeding Rhode Island Red, New Hampshire Red and Wyandottes. This would appear to be the British type of utility White Wyandotte, rather than the much softer feathered exhibition birds. These utility Wyandottes were extremely popular as a laying bird prior to the creation of what is now called the modern hybrid. It is interesting that there appears to be a trend amongst new starters in the keeping of poultry almost to accept the various strains of hybrids as being 'breeds'. People often refer to them as Warrens or Ross.

The Dresdener has a definite appearance of having the ability to lay a large quantity of eggs which, when coupled to their range of colour pattern, obviously makes them a very appealing breed.

The shape of a Dresdener is one of a long backed Wyandotte. All the Wyandotte curves are present, but in an elongated outline. Their tails are carried at a lower angle and slightly spread. They have a rounded front, but, with the bird's shape being longer than deep, it is not as prominent as in the Wyandotte.

The breed has a rose comb, which is not too enlarged and is in keeping with the bird's body size. This I would put into Powell-Owen's favourite description of 'light heavy', as opposed to a full blown heavy-weight.

There are four different colours, all of which have yellow pigment. Firstly the White which is pure coloured throughout. The Black, carries a most lustrous green sheen to its top colouring and, interestingly, the males do not appear to show any signs of white under colour. The Black-Red Partridge colour is very similar to the Welsummer, which is a darker shade than the Brown Leghorn pattern.

The last colour is apparently a favourite one. It resembles the New Hampshire shade of Chestnut Red, through to Golden Bay.

The tail on the male bird is solid black, and, as with the self-black variety, it carries a beautiful green sheen to it.

The Dresdener is available in miniature version with a full range of colours available. The popularity of the breed in Germany is demonstrated by the statistic of there being over 400 of them at last year's classic event.

A colour photograph of a Dresdener can be seen in the colour section.

DU MANS AND COUCOU de BRETAGNE

This breed is common around the town of Le Mans, and is described as being a rose combed La Fleche, either of which could be interesting. The bird's colouring is like Henry Ford's, 'Take your choice providing that it is black'.

There are many breeds on the continent which I have not mentioned in this book; some of them because I was of the opinion that they were simply variations on a theme of localised cross breeds. Tumbler Pigeons appear to be similar in that every district seems to have its own version of the breed.

Some of these poultry breeds I have never even seen a picture of. The Du Mans was one such case until recently, when I was shown a painting and asked to comment on the breed's origin. My first reaction was to say Rosecombed Minorca but, on further deliberation, I formed the opinion that it was a pair of Du Mans.

Even though little is known about the breed, there is a belief that the birds have been in that area of France for longer than was at one time assumed. The point which interested me was that the region in question is straight across the English Channel, and there was a possibility of birds being intershipped to some of the southern ports of the British Isles. Maybe our Black Hamburghs supplied the rose comb to the birds in France. Maybe some of these black coloured fowls crossed to the southern counties of Kent, Sussex and Surrey to form part of their meat producing birds because the Du Mans has a fine reputation for its flesh qualities and commanded high prices for its beautifully white coloured and succulent meat.

Although black in colour, the birds do not have a green sheen to them; a point which set me wondering what might be crossed into them. If you study a map of north west France, a few kilometres away from Le Mans lies the region of Bretagne which has been known to have cuckoo coloured fowls living there for centuries mostly with rose combs, whilst the area more to the south has cuckoo birds with single combs.

For either version, breeding with the blacks would tend to dull the colouring, and would almost certainly produce some white coloured specimens, again with both types of comb.

These birds could easily have made their way to the British Isles with the Phoenicians. If so they probably have more involvement with our poultry heritage than I ever suspected.

CouCou de Bretagne is described by Edward Brown as being of medium size, with a good frame, which is well developed in the front, and around the breast area. It has very fleshy limbs and the neck is short and thick and well covered with abundant hackle feathers. The head is strong in structure and has a short and strong beak. The head is surmounted by a large comb, which is usually rose shaped. Their wattles are medium in size and should hang evenly. The tail on the male bird is well furnished, with the main pair of sickles very long. The legs are short and strong, but not sufficiently to give the birds a dumpy appearance, and are pinky white in colour. The ground colour of the cuckoo is steel grey barred with blue black. This extends to all parts of the body.

Much of the breed's shape and conformation appear to have a lot in common with the description of the Dorking, and in some ways the Scots Dumpy. Maybe in future years D.N.A. laboratory testing will have developed to a point where we are no longer speculating how breeds were created. The computer will tell us at the touch of a key. The Bretons regard the CouCou de Bretagne as one of the most useful of domestic fowl. This of course

137

offers another theory on the birds which the Romans allegedly brought to the British Isles, and which were to become Dorkings. The crossing of CouCou and some of the five toed Houdan type fowls, which were minus a crest, would be very similar to the Dorking.

Weights   Males   7lbs   Females   5.5lbs

A print showing the old type of Du Mans.

FAVEROLLES

My summary for the Faverolles breed is quite short, the reason being that the British Faverolles Society produced, in 1995, an excellent handbook on the breed. This publication was printed to celebrate the centenary of Faverolles in Britain. It was compiled by John Craft in association with Jesse and Sue Bruton, who gathered help and information from many other fanciers and sources. Consequently, the book gives a very informative description of the breed, including its history, from various countries of the world. It is well illustrated, both in colour and monochrome.

I therefore now use brief extracts from the book, and include in the photo section many of their selected prints. Faverolles are recognised as being of French origin, being developed in the village of that name. They were considered to be a meat producing breed, which was also capable of laying an adequate supply of good quality eggs, especially during the winter months. This point was thought to be assisted by the birds being covered by rather loose fitting and soft textured feathering.

The type of fowl used in its creation is not fully known, which is consistent with many other breeds. The theory is that many of these birds were really crossbreeds, and the eventual development of the birds into a uniform standard was done by selective breeding.

It would be safe to assume that the breed's five toes and abundantly feathered full beard were inherited from the Houdans, which were bred extensively in the neighbouring district of Houdan. These birds would also be responsible for some of the early Faverolles having combs other than the approved single type.

The English Dorkings have been freely mentioned as being part of the equation. These were presumably the Reds and they would assist in developing the Salmon Faverolles, which have always appeared to be the dominant colour. Again, the Dorking would supply the characteristic fifth toe. Most of the breeds developed and created during the second half of the nineteenth century contained some form of Shanghai/Cochin/Brahma type of fowl. These birds possessed great size, and appealed to many poultry keepers. The Antwerp Brahma version would have been the ideal choice because of having a single comb, and white pigmentation. These birds also provided the leg feathering which extends down the outer toe, but not on to the middle one. The 'Light' or 'Columbian' coloured Brahmas would also be responsible for the development of 'Ermine' coloured Faverolles.

Other breeds which have been recorded as being involved with the original stock included the continental cuckoo coloured fowl.

These breeds also include the French Rennes, the Flemish Cuckoo and also the Maline. Cuckoo Faverolles have been reported since before the turn of the century, but, curiously, they were not a standard colour until 1990, even though they were shown at the Club Shows in 1911 and 1915.

John Craft devotes many pages of the book to investigating the breed's ancient history. This makes very interesting reading for anyone wishing to learn more of the breed's origins. He also traces the breed's progress in this country for both Large Fowl and Miniatures in every recognised colour.

The shape of a Faverolles should be of a strong looking bird, with a broad and flat back. It should have a well developed chest and breast area, be wide between the shoulders, and have a smoothly rounded and deep keel. All these points are associated with a meat breed, but the birds should also retain the qualities of a utility laying fowl, being neither coarse nor cumbersome.

The points mentioned so far account for half of the total points allocated to the perfect bird.

One of the striking features of the breed is the very prominent beard, which is fully muffled. This point is very noticeable in the Salmons, especially on the male bird with his black beard extending well past his ear lobes and contrasting with his straw coloured hackle feathering. This is not so prominent in the female, where the beard is creamy white against a hackle of darkish wheaten brown.

The evenly serrated single comb should not be over large, but must be of the smooth texture which is associated with a utility laying fowl. The ear lobes and wattles should be very small and covered by the beard. The perfect head shows one of strength and character, without being coarse, or showing 'beetle brows'. The whole headpiece receives a total of 20 points.

Legs and feet are allocated a total of 10 points, which includes their shank feathering. I feel that this total is rather low for a breed with a fifth toe. Dorkings for example have 10 points for the fifth toe alone, with additional points for the shanks etc.

In Faverolles the front toes are long and straight, with the rear two being well separated, and the extra toe facing upwards. The wings are short, and carried well up under the saddle hackle. The thighs should not be long but have sufficient length to avoid the bird's having a square appearance. The shanks are, again, moderate in length, built of strong round bone, and free from being 'knock kneed'.

One feature of the Faverolles' general appearance is their tail carriage. The tail should be carried well up, but not squirrel tailed. The tail itself is constructed with broad feathers and is only of medium length, which balances the short and thick neck. A long feathered and low carried tail is considered to be a serious fault.

Faverolles are now recognised in a range of colours but, to me, the Salmons are the ones instantly associated with the breed. A correctly marked Salmon male bird is a very handsome 'gentleman', which is hard to equal by any other breed.

The whole of his underbody and tail should be a rich coloured black. This extends into his leg feathering and is also prominently displayed in his beard and muff, which again is solid black.

The male's hackle and saddle hackle are an even colour of straw which is free from other foreign colours or striping. His back and wing bows are described as being a 'bright cherry mahogany', which contrasts with the block wing bar and white diamond of the wing bay formed by the outer edges of the secondaries.

The Salmon female is basically wheaten brown which shades into lighter and darker variations in different parts of the body. The head and neck are striped with a darker shade, whilst the breast and thighs shade to cream and their beard and muff should be a creamy white.

In both sexes the legs are white, the beak can shade to horn, whilst the eyes can be orange to yellow, grey or hazel.

The colour for Whites is straight forward, in that the bird has to be a pure silver white, free from any form of black ticking or red/brown feathers. These can appear on the male bird's wing bar and hackles. The legs are white, the comb, wattles and ear lobes a rich red, with the eyes as described for Salmons.

The Blacks should have a solid colour throughout, showing a green sheen free from purple tinge or dull colouring. The legs, feet and beak are also black, and the eyes as dark as possible.

I prefer to see the under colour as dark as possible and certainly with no signs of white showing through to the outer feathering.

Faverolles are a breed which I have admired since being a teenager. I first judged their Club Show some thirty years ago, when Mr Milner was the Secretary and one of the breed's keenest enthusiasts.

My selection of photographs will, in many instances, duplicate those used by John Craft in his excellent handbook of the breed. I commence with Salmons which are my favourite colour, and I believe the most popular.

The aim in any breed summary should be to illustrate to newcomers photos of birds showing the height of perfection as attained. Additionally there should be a diagram or painting of their ultimate aims. In this case I reproduce from John Craft's Handbook two photos taken from the American Faverolles Club's Standard. I especially like the female's type.

A cock from 1928 when he won the Club Show. He then went on to win at Birmingham in 1929. This fine specimen was bred and exhibited by a very successful breeder Mr. H. W. Biddlecombe from Gloucester.

From a slightly earlier period. This cockerel won the Dairy Show in 1921. He looks to me as if he could be a better bird than the photo suggests at first glance. He was bred by Mr. C. H. Bradley also from Gloucester. I wonder if there was a relationship to the birds shown in later years by Mr. Biddlecombe.

Demonstrates a deep bodied cock, which won the Dairy Show in 1931. He was bred and exhibited by another keen breeder Dr. T. W. E. Royden from Norfolk. The doctor was also a keen breeder of Sumatras.

A rangy bodied cockerel, which won Birmingham in 1935. I believe that, when matured into a cock, he would look a useful bird. He was shown by Mr. T. G. L. Alexandra from Salop.

A pullet from 1922, when she won the Dairy Show. She was exhibited by Mr George Tomkin.

Again bred by Mr Biddlecombe. She won both the Dairy and Birmingham Shows as a pullet in 1929.

The pullet which won both the Dairy Show and the Club Show in 1931. She was bred by Mrs Huntington from Warwick.

A pullet with a useful looking beard. She won the Dairy Show in 1932 and was bred by Dr Royden.

This is one of my favourite Faverolles photos. It depicts mother and daughter. The old hen on the right was never shown, but bred many winners, one of which is shown on the left. These birds were from the early 1920s, and bred by Miss Sedgwick. Moving forward to more recent times, to illustrate the breed's progress.

The 1972 Club Show Champion. She was bred by Mr. J. L. Milner.

Advances to 1979 with a hen bred by Mrs A. Cason. She was Best Large Fowl at the Club Show.

A hen bred by Norma Critchlow. This hen was Best Large Fowl at the Club Show in 1988 and 1991. In many ways, she shows a resemblance to Miss Sedgwick's hens. I wonder if they could be related?

Another of Mr. Milner's Club Show winners. This Cock won in 1971 and again in 1972.

A great bodied cock which won Best Large Fowl at the 1989 Club Show. He was bred by John Craft. Miniature Faverolles have improved greatly in recent years.

The cockerel which won the 1982 Club Show for Mrs Sue Bruton.

In 1994, this Bantam male was Club Show Champion for John Craft. Many of once less fashionable colours of Faverolles have improved greatly since the 1930s.

A 1920s winner for D. Shakeshaft.

Returning back to the old photos of Large
Fowl, an interesting one is this Large Fowl
Blue hen which won the Birmingham
Show in 1935 for Mr. A. B. Memmory from
Littleover in Derbyshire.

Won the Dairy Show in 1934. She was
only a pullet, but appears to be lacking in
body structure. She was bred by Dr
Royden.

In 1938 this cockerel won at Birmingham
for Doctor Royden. The judge George
Tomkin expressed his view that he was
the best White cock he had ever seen.
From the amount of feathering to his legs
and feet I would suggest that he contained
some Cochin Blood.

146

An Ermine pullet from 1933, when she was described as being the latest creation in Faverolles. She won the Dairy Show for Mr. Biddlecombe. Unfortunately she tends to look like a Light Sussex with a beard.

Won the best A.O.C. Cup at Birmingham in 1935. He was bred by Dr Royden and, I would say, was very representative of the colour at that period.

A great example. This Ermine Bantam female was bred by John Craft in 1991 when she was awarded Best Ermine at the Club Show.

A grand White Bantam hen bred by Cliff Lowe. She is from the 1970s when she had many good wins for him.

FAYOUMI

The Breed's History

The Fayoumi fowl is rather a mystery. These birds have been in existence for possibly longer than any others and yet in many ways little is known about them.

During recent years the birds have captured the imagination of several people, none more so than Lana Gazder, who after a great deal of research and investigation has provided the greater part of this breed summary.

One of the unusual points about the birds is, that even though they are well recorded in Egyptian history dating back to B.C., it is not until very recent years that they arrived into this country, and not until 1995 were they accepted as a fully standardised breed.

One possible explanation is that they are so similar in shape and markings to several other long established breeds that they have been overlooked.

It would be very easy to state a case which established them as being the progenitor of many of these breeds, possibly being originally termed the Turkish fowl, or by the name of Bigawi fowl, during their transportation to European countries.

On the European continent, there are several countries with a breed which is considered to be native to that country. There is no doubt that the birds have been in each of the south eastern countries for a long time, in certain cases, centuries, but they are so similar in style and markings, that there is presumably a common bond.

One of the breeds which I have in mind is the Bresse from France, where the original colour was the grey, but prints of them illustrate a bird which is actually similar to the British Pencilled Hamburgh.

In Belgium we have the Campine-Braekel combination, whilst Germany and Holland have the Groniger and Assendelft Breeds, and there are other variations all very similar.

This is one of the points raised in the earlier chapter in the book, 'Origins of the Breeds', where I suggested that D.N.A testing would be the only way to prove positively the relationship between different breeds.

The Fayoumi is charming little bird, which warrants the greater following which I am sure will eventually develop.

The Standard

In shape and style the Fayoumi proves a very interesting bird. Two main characteristics are a long neck and unique tail carriage. The tail is carried vertical, with the main feathers spread wide open, in a similar style to Japanese Bantams.

This is different from most other breed standards, though many of the utility breeds, when bred purely for egg production gradually revert back to this type of tail carriage. White Leghorns and R I Reds are perfect examples of this feature.

In the Fayoumi, these long necks and high tails balance each other, to create an active looking bird capable of searching for its own food, which is one of the breed's features back home in Egypt.

The legs and feet are of strong bone for such a small bird, as are also the muscular thighs. The legs and feet are slate blue in colour with their skin also having a tendency to show a dusky blue shade to it.

The comb on a Fayoumi is of the single upright type with evenly cut serrations. It is not too large in size, with the end following the contours of the head. The wattles are medium in size and should hang evenly. The whole headpiece should be smooth in texture and in

148

a rich red colouring, as are the earlobes.

The female's comb is similarly cut but is not over enlarged as in the Minorcas.

The shape of the bird shows a high carried pair of wide shoulders. The body is not too long and has a neatly rounded front with an upright stance which again portrays an active looking bird.

The feather markings of the Fayoumi are of the pencilled type of barring with the black being three times the width of the ground colour. In the females this pencilling pattern should extend throughout the bird's feathering with the exception of the neck hackle which is pure silver/white.

The male's colouring is rather more complicated. I believe the ambition is for show specimens to be bred from a single mating, as opposed to pencilled Hamburghs where double mating is definitely required.

The male's neck hackle, back and wing bars are solid silver, but his saddle hackles can show a slight black ticking. His main tail should be solid black with the furnishing showing a silver edging.

The pencilling on the female's and the male's breast and thighs is, at present, described as being coarsely pencilled, finishing with a silver tip.

The standard in Britain has only just been completed and I have no doubt that in future years slight alterations will be made to it as the breed develops, and allow good quality show birds to be bred from the same breeding pen. At the present time there is a wide variation in the male birds' marking pattern. Some of them are almost pure silver and very close to a cock breeding pencilled Hamburgh.

Unfortunately, the standard does not state a definite amount of marking for the male bird's breast and thigh areas. I would suggest that it should be evenly distributed.

In the wings, the flights and secondaries have a definite barred pattern; this applies to both males and females and again is broader in the black than in the ground colour.

There is also a gold version of Fayoumi which is identical except that the ground colour is an even shade of gold as opposed to silver/white.

To my knowledge there are no miniature Fayoumis in Britain but America has developed them. There they exist in the traditional Silver and Gold pencilled types. A variation has also been produced which is black tailed white and black tailed buff.

This new pattern suggests to me that Japanese Bantams have been used in the procedure to miniaturise the breed, and additionally create a bird which appears to be very attractive looking.

Weights	Large Males	4.5 lbs	Females	3.5lbs
	Miniatures Males	16 ozs	Females	14 ozs

EGYPTIAN FAYOUMI
- My Observations by Lana Gazder

Short History

Fayoumi have been in this country for only a short period of time, having been imported into the UK in 1984 by the Domestic Fowl Trust. They have been bred pure for generations in the Fayum district of Egypt, solely for their qualities of vigour and egg production. Nevertheless, they have remained true to type and display their own plumage pattern and breed characteristics, despite lack of selection in that area.

It is very hard to find information on the Fayoumi, probably because they used to be referred to as the 'BIGAWI'. However, there is a mention of them in an article entitled 'Poultry Keeping in Egypt' by Mohammed Askar Bey, written in the 1920s for the World Poultry Congress. Here the author states, 'In the Bigawi, a pure breed in the Fayum, the colour is fixed and is characteristic of the breed'.

Later he gives a description of the Bigawi and ends his article by suggesting that it should be officially standardised. His 'Description of the Bigawi' fits today's birds very nicely, and I am sure the breed has remained unaltered for hundreds of years. I have been involved in compiling a present day standard for the Fayoumi fowl, and look forward to its inclusion in the new British Poultry Standards Book.

There is an American Fayoumi bantam standard but this describes birds not typical of the Egyptian fowl, and gives their origin as the USA!

In 1981 Ian Eastwood wrote an article entitled 'Fayoumi - the Smallholders Layer?' In his first paragraph he states that he read an extensive account of the breed in 'Misset's International Poultry' written by Dr E. Hossary. I am still trying to locate a copy of this article.

Make, Shape, Temperment and Colour

At first glance one could mistake a Fayoumi for a Campine or Braekel, to which they are probably related. All three may be offshoots of an ancient Turkish fowl. The Fayoumi may be indigenous to Egypt, or may have sprung from Turkey and been traded abroad, adopting the nationality of the country it became established in. Whatever the story, the fact remains that the plumage pattern is very similar in all three breeds. However, the Fayoumi sports a red ear-lobe unlike the other two.

It is basically an upright, wedge-shaped, neat 'small' large fowl with a stamp of its own, being rather long in the neck and short in the thigh and possessing a very high tail carriage, verging on vertical when excited or alarmed.

Compared to some quieter breeds, the Fayoumi appear rather aggressive and pugnacious. They seem to have a very strong hierarchy instinct, and the pecking order within a flock in constantly being challenged. Given occupation and a reasonable amount of space, the Fayoumi can live in harmony with any other breed, even other males, without bloodshed as long as ground rules are adhered to!

Fayoumi keepers to whom I have spoken are all in agreement about their birds' characteristics. They are lively, amusing and fascinating. Females are typical of all good layers, active and busy. Males are born showmen, constantly trying to impress the girls with cocky struttings, yet protective and vigilant. I have never known a Fayoumi of either sex to show aggression towards people and, although they hate being caught, once the initial panic is over, they are easy to handle and tolerate all normal procedures.

Pen training and show preparation can be undertaken with little fuss. But be warned, they will never be 'tame'. If regular handling ceases they will quickly revert back to their flighty selves! This is their nature and it should not be changed.

There are two colour varieties in the Fayoumi, Gold and Silver Pencilled. They are genetically a pencilled and not a barred breed. In the Silvers, pure white ground colour is barred with beetle-green black, bars being coarse and irregular, not refined and accurate. In males, neck-hackle, back and saddle are pure white with lacking in saddle coverts and a solid green-black tail. Females have a pure white neck and the rest of the body is barred like the male's with a darkly barred and solid black tail.

Both sexes posses dark brown eyes, an upright medium single comb, red ear lobes, slate blue legs and horn toe nails. Most Fayoumi conform to the above plumage pattern but, because they have never been selectively bred for colour, natural variations do occur. These 'sports' appear to be over marked or under-marked birds in varying degrees of light and dark.

The over-marked individuals are heavily barred, the ground colour nearly obliterated on neck and back by dark striping. I have seen some specimens verging on 'birchen'. The under-marked birds have a ground colour that predominates and barring is sparse, faint or non-existent except on wings and tail. Most under marked birds retain a black main tail and almost resemble the colour of the exhibition Silver Pencilled Hamburg male.

Although I am ignorant about genetics and colour, I intend to do some experiments by using an over-marked male on an under-marked female. I will note with interest the resulting chicks' colours. I have also noticed variations in the Fayoumi pencilling. Some barring curves around the feather and resembles lacing. Some barring becomes rounded and resembles spangling. I am sure birds showing these plumage tendencies could be selected to create new varieties.

Perhaps this is how the American Fayoumi Bantam colours of 'black tailed silver' and 'black tailed buff' have been created from under marked silver and gold pencilled specimens.

An interesting feature of the British population of Fayoumi is the appearance of golds. Only the silver pencilled variety was imported, yet a recessive gold gene has popped up to produce gold pencilled chicks from silver parents. Not many breeders have produced golds but those who have seem to be getting only female chicks. I know of only one gold male ever bred, and sadly he is dead. I would be delighted to hear from anyone who has a well hidden gold Fayoumi male in his or her pens, or who can shed any light on the subject.

I know it is possible that the Fayoumi has been crossed with other breeds along the way. This was one of the reasons why I investigated the origins of all the stock I keep, and the birds in my pen now have been obtained from bona-fide breeders, who have kept Fayoumi unadulterated for many years. The three gold females I have at present are every inch 'Fayoumi', in make and shape and all I can do in the future is to try to breed for type. Like all breeders, I have a few problems in my breeding pens, such as partly white ear lobes, deformities in combs and colour irregularities but, given time, I intend to rid my stock of all these undesirable features. In the hope of importing fresh blood and, given the interest being shown in this historical breed, a bit of publicity could secure a rosy future for the Fayoumi in Britain.

Fayoumi Trigger Childhood Memories

I have been keeping the Fayoumi chicken for several years. They are not everyone's cup of tea, having some peculiar habits and a very strange temperament.

However this flighty nature and alarmist attitude to life is only a product of hundreds of years having to survive in a harsh environment where danger and deprivation are an everyday fact of life. When one appreciates this aspect of the Fayoumi development one can forgive them their quirks and start to understand what makes them tick.

As a race they have managed to evolve unto a useful, tough and typey little fowl of fairly fixed plumage and unmistakable characteristics. Not only have they survived but they have thrived, and for that reason alone I take my hat off to them.

As I make my daily rounds to feed all my stock I take time, leaning on pen doors, to check this and that. I gaze fondly at them, mentally assessing each one and dreaming about their future exhibition potential, as I'm sure everybody does, but I make a point of feeding my Fayoumi last of all so I can sit on my upturned bucket and spend some time with them. Studying their behaviour I find that I am transported into another world.

I spent a lot of my childhood in India where these sort of fowl were abundant. After all, the Fayoumi is basically just a back-street chicken hailing from Egypt, and semi-feral chickens from hot countries are probably the same the world over!

I feel they fall into the same slot as the ubiquitous Pariah dog, the cur of the Middle and Far East. Both pi-dog and village chicken live a symbiotic existence with man. Both scrape a living on the fringes of society, tolerated as scavenging opportunists, nevertheless, fulfilling a useful role.

As a child in India I used to spend hours watching in fascination the comings and goings of street life from the safety of our compound garden gate. The municipal dustbin, a huge container filled with household rubbish, was positioned on the corner of the street. Here was a living lesson in hierarchy. Villagers and their children, beggars, crows, cattle, pi-dogs, feral cats and the village chickens would all gather in an organised rabble to sift systematically through the waste. I could never work out who was ultimately boss in the pecking order but it struck me that the chickens always came out best! They were the winners by sheer tactics. Feigning fear at the threats of others, they would be ducking and diving in and out to secure the best morsels! Nip and tuck, dart and dodge. How like my Fayoumi at home, with their quicksilver reactions, outwitting all the larger breeds at scrap time!

The Indian rural chicken always seemed to look so well, glossy and in hardy condition, as were our garden or compound flock. They 'belonged' to us but ranged freely. In truth I had often recognised one or two of my garden favourites in that awful dustbin gang! When at home they avoided the well aimed kicks of our cook, for daring onto the kitchen step. They lined up awaiting scraps and again beat all opposition, leaving the pi-dogs reeling. They were practically uncatchable too. Children of all countries have made a national sport of 'catch the chicken' and the Indian fowls have evolved an equally brilliant escape routine in defence.

Our little flock laid delicious eggs for our table but every now and then an unfortunate individual would end up tethered to the kitchen balcony, awaiting the knife - as we awaited our lunch. My English horror at this fact of life had to be smoothed over by my Eastern acceptance, in the knowledge that no food could be fresher.

All these village poultry were of Jungle Fowl type, being small, economical in body needs, frugal, hardy and self-sufficient.

They were a vocal bunch, squabbling amicably amongst themselves as they scratched and searched, forever on the go. The description of 'active foragers' suited them perfectly. Whenever they had to be caught up, all hell was let loose, raucous screams of blue murder emitting from their throats! How very similar they were to my Egyptian flock in every way. Perhaps an in-built survival instinct had taught them that they would rarely ever be handled except for slaughter! Could this be why my Fayoumi are so panic stricken when first caught? I am always left feeling embarrassed and apologetic when I catch my birds to show to friends. Fayoumi keepers seem to be instantly labelled as eccentrics without having to explain fanciful theories or make excuses for their fowls' demented behaviour!

As I sit and watch, my Fayoumi seem to be in their element as they busy themselves in the dust, totally oblivious to my other birds' open-winged gasps. I have been plagued with mites this summer, sprays and powders have been utilised to the full, my birds have the 'dusted' look about them and this brings back vivid memories of the DDT powder used in India.

All our stock was liberally doused in the stuff, in fact our mali (gardener) would sprinkle anything that moved in the compound! A weekly round-up of all stock was quite a high-light. The chickens' screams could be heard a mile away. They would all emerge sheep-ishly from the mali's shed surrounded by a grey haze of DDT powder. That smell would hang in the air for days. Perhaps the amount used was some strange yardstick of stockmanship amongst the malis.

I harboured an unreasonable hatred for our poor mali, as he had the unenviable task of culling anything that was unproductive or over-productive, including our dogs and cats. Puppies and kittens were regularly drowned in our well. Hens that missed too many lay-ing days would end up beheaded, running their last lap of the yard to flutter and twitch in their final dust-bath.

All very disturbing for an English child to witness, but a good lesson on the harsh realities of the East. Anything that could not earn its keep had to go, but the 'good doers' lived to produce more of their ilk. This type of selection was essential for the survival of all concerned, and I am sure the rural fowl owes its continuing existence to generations of men like our mali.

The shrill voice of my Fayoumi cockerels have just jolted me back to reality. Poor neighbours! I do feel guilty about the noise, but how can I expect them to appreciate the significance in that wild and piercing call of the village chicken. In India they say the cock crows to shatter the evil of the night, and herald the new day to safety. In England we seem to have lost that romance in our need to sleep!

153

The illustrations for Fayoumi Fowl are interesting, in that the photos and drawings trace the birds' progress since their earliest recordings.

A drawing of the allegedly now extinct Turkish Fowl.

Drawn by Aldrovandi in 1599, depicting Gallus Turcicus. This drawing was hung in the University of Bologna, in Italy; unfortunately it does not give any more detail as to the type of Jungle Fowl it was representing.

A Fayoumi cockerel waiting to be washed in Lana Gazder's sink. The bird's style, especially his well spread tail carriage is almost identical to that of Gallus Turcicus.

Again taken at Lana's. This time showing a breeding pen of birds. The hen standing on top of the ex-bee hive nesting box again shows this upright tail setting which is a feature of the breed.

FRIESIAN

This breed is a native of Holland, and is sometimes referred to as the Dutch everyday layer, a name they would not have earned themselves by lazing around and going broody every few weeks.

They, or at any rate a similar looking fowl, were extremely popular in many countries on the continent as general farmyard laying birds.

I would assume they have been in existence for many centuries; certainly they are credited with being brought to the shores of northern England and being the basic breed used to develop the Gold Hamburghs, which in turn were used to produce the Pheasant Fowl.

They have a certain similarity to the Braekel and, as is often the case with the 'original' breeds, Friesians exist in both single and rose comb versions. Their basic feather markings are similar to those of pencilled Hamburghs, with the male birds more or less self coloured except for their tail which is self coloured, with the outer edges laced with the same colouring as their ground colour. This obviously varies between the Gold, Silver or Yellow variations of colour. The females have an even pattern of barring to their plumage, including their tail and wings.

There are many different colours within the breed, one of my favourite being the red mottled. Others include one where the pencilling is white, as opposed to the normal black. Both males and females have upright standing single combs. These are reasonably small as are their neat little ear lobes, which are white in colour. Their basic leg colouring is slate blue and they have the standard number of four toes. The male birds have well furnished and flowing tails, whilst the females carry theirs well spread and quite high without being squirrel tailed.

The breed is noted for having a very alert appearance and for being very active. Being of a hardy nature the birds are capable of living semi-wild in farm buildings and cattle yards, using all the hours of daylight to scavenge around for their food, thus being very economical to keep. This is a very similar statement to the one made by Lana Gazder when describing her Fayoumi Fowls.

Friesians do not take very kindly to being in a confined space, and will certainly require high fencing to prevent them roosting high in the rafters and, in the morning, escaping to their freedom.

Certainly they have what I call the appearance of a natural breed made by Mother Nature, not developed by man.

There have been some of the breed in England recently but I am a little confused with their appearance. The ones I have seen are small enough to be classified as bantams, yet I was assured they were large fowl.

Somewhere I believe we had our wires crossed. The standard weight for the breed on the continent, was quoted originally as males 5.5lbs, females 4.5lbs, which is quite a reasonable size for that type of small light breed.

I consider both the large and miniature fowl would be a very useful addition to our list of breeds, especially the yellow pencilled variety, which is a most striking contrast of colours.

Other colours include Cuckoos, Mottles, self Blacks and Whites (which unfortunately start to look a little similar to Bresse, and lose the breed individual characteristics.)

A painting of a Friesian is found in the colour section.

A very typical Friesian pullet. The photo was taken in 1984 by Josef Wolters at the Utrect Show, with her colour described as being Citroenpel.

A young Friesian pullet, her colouring is a very attractive shade of Blue pencilling.

FRIZZLE

In some ways I do not describe the Frizzle as a breed of poultry, rather more a feather variation. This I am told is the case in some continental countries.

In Britain any colouring is acceptable, with the usual colouring following the pattern of the Old English Game Fowl.

The breed is classified as being in the heavy breed category, a fact which often surprises breeders who are new to the fancy.

The basic standard requirements are for a deep bodied bird with a full front and a high carried tail, the wings being well tucked up under the tail i.e. Wyandotte fashion. A single comb is mandatory in all colours.

The legs and feet which have four toes should be coloured to blend in with the body's colour pattern, and it is here that a question arises with the Blacks, which type of black is it, the one which carries black under-colour dark legs and feet with white toe nails and a black eye as in the Australorp and Minorcas etc., or the one with red eye colour, and yellow legs and consequently has the problem with white in the under-colour and at the root of the tail feathers, i.e. Black Wyandottes and Black Leghorns?

The great feature of the breed is in its feathering. Not only must the feathers curl backwards towards the head but that curl must be present on a good quality broad feathering. This quality feathering disappears if fully frizzled feathered birds are mated together for too many generations. This results in a loss of curl and a narrow spiky feather which is short of wealth.

To correct this, a flat feathered version has to be used, or alternatively a comparably shaped bird from another breed has to be used. Wyandottes are a favourite, the colour matching the one which you are keeping as frizzle feathered, and it is usual to introduce a flat female.

The Frizzle is well represented in miniature form, and it is in this form that most people visualise the breed. The feathering certainly seems to be more in keeping with a small bird rather than the large version. Referring back to the commencement of the breed, I suggested that the Frizzles should not be considered as a separate breed. This point is endosed by the Japanese and Poland clubs, both of which cater for a frizzle feathered version of their breeds.

Weights	Large Fowl	Males	8lbs	Females	6lbs
	Minatures	Males	24-28ozs	Females	20-24ozs

A blue Frizzle hen from the 1930s.

A white Frizzle bantam hen bred by Fred Entwistle, the son of W.F. Entwistle.

157

A Buff Frizzle cock which was bred by that connoisseur of Frizzles, Major G. T. Williams. The bird was awarded first prize at the 1923 Dairy Show.

Again from 1923 and was described as being a Frizzled Orpington.

Won the Crystal Palace in 1933 for its owner, Sir Claude Alexander, from Sussex. The colour would appear to be Black Spangled.

Again bred by Colonel Williams, and was the 1922 Birmingham Show winner.

158

A very attractive Spangled Frizzle miniature female. She was the winner of the Great Yorkshire for Miss W. Gott from Leeds.

This White miniature pullet won the 1922 Dairy show for Mr A. Hobson from Yorkshire.

Taken in the early 1930s, when this miniature white cock must have been one of the best, winning at the Dairy Show in 1932, first at Virginia Water in 1933. In 1934 he won at the Crystal Palace, and Birmingham, then in 1935 he won the London Bantam Club Show. He was bred by that expert of the more glamorous breeds Sid Butler.

A very attractive Blue Frizzle cock. He was bred by Major G. T. Williams from Cornwall, and won the Cup for Best Frizzle at the 1933 Crystal Palace Show.

GERMAN LANGSHAN

This breed is very new to Britain and, to me, shows little resemblance to either the Croad Langshan or the Modern Langshan. It has been suggested that with the German version having long legs, there is a connection with the old time English Moderns, but I find the rest of the bird's structure and feather formation entirely different.

The German Langshan is in keeping with several other more recently imported breeds in which the miniature version of the birds has proved to be more accepted by the fanciers.

The shape of both versions should be identical but I also find that, in the bantam form, the bird's style looks more attractive.

In Germany the breed goes under the name of Deutchman and its shape has been described as resembling one of the long stemmed wine goblets. I suppose that it would be fair comment to say that the main feature of the breed lies in its extremely long legs. The birds have short backs and a very high rising tail which is balanced by the bird's long neck being carried well upright in a jaunty manner.

Their body shape is deeper than long with the closely feathered thighs neatly moulding into it. The breed really does have a style all of its own.

Their feathering fits closely to the body, but is of a softer texture than that of the Modern Langshan. The breed has three main colours, black, blue and white, all of which have very neat single combs with not too enlarged wattles and earlobes in a rich red colour. It is a breed which I can find very appealing but in a different way from my old favourite Modern Langshans.

For many years I pondered over the breed which might have been used to alter the shape of the original Langshans, which were called 'Croads'. The problem was eventually solved when reading an article which was written by Cornelis Van Gink some sixty years ago. Apparently, no other breed has been introduced. The shape of the German Langshan has been obtained by selective breeding from the original Chinese Langshans which were imported into Germany in 1879. They were bred for clean legs with the tighter feathering which we now associate with the birds.

However, there is one point which I find intriguing. The original birds were blacks, followed by whites, blues and cuckoos. Where did the genes come from to create these extra colours if no other breeds were involved? The English Modern Langshans were bred in blacks, whites, and blues, whilst the Croads were only in black and white versions.

This statement by Van Gink does, however, substantiate the claim often made by the English breeders that their Moderns were created by selective breeding, even though some of them did appear to contain Malay blood. My guess would be that some of the originally imported Chinese Langshans contained a long legged, hard feathered bird as well as the true Langshan. Possibly my old friend the Raiza Game.

The great popularity of the bantams when they were first introduced to this country, appears to have declined in recent years, a point for which I can offer no logical explanation.

A drawing by Van Gink, showing a pair of Large Fowl German Langshans in white.

A pair of German Langshan Bantams, in black, and, as with the Van Gink portrait, they were drawn around 1928.

The breed in Germany during 1982. This cockerel was photographed by Josef Wolters and shows the bird to perfection.

A lovely pair of miniatures taken during the 1970s.

GOLDEN ESSEX

The Golden Essex is a breed which, to many people, would simply be described as a single combed laced Wyandotte. In fact the birds are very similar to many of the ones shown at the Lancashire and Yorkshire shows in their famous 'Cross Bred Laying Hen' classes .

The breed was created by Mr F. W. Sorrell and passed by the Poultry Club Standards Committee in 1933. The main aim in developing the breed was to produce a bird capable of laying good quantities of dark brown eggs whilst retaining a well fleshed carcass.

Their origin was a cross between a Croad Langshan cock and Rhode Island Red hens. The resulting progeny was then mated with a Barnevelder cock to add extra brown egg potential. The chicks from this mating came in a wide range of colouring with the ones showing single lacing being selected for future inter breeding. However, the main priority was in selecting the ones laying dark coloured eggs.

In colour the male has a black stripe to his hackle but a red/gold saddle and a laced body. The female should be evenly single laced throughout.

Weights   Male   7 lbs   *Female   5 lbs*

A pair of Golden Essex, bred by their originator Mr F.W. Sorrell from Essex.

A photo taken by Arthur Rice, showing a hen in the later stages of development. This shows the greatly improved lacing and body shape.

163

HAMBURGH

Profile of Harold and Norma Critchlow

Norma was born in Leek, and Harold was born in Copesdon, a village close to Leek where they have lived all their married life as farmers, in partnership with Harold's parents, then taking over the farm in 1974 upon the retirement of his father.

Norma and Harold were married in 1962 after Harold's completion of an Agricultural Degree Course, at Staffordshire Agricultural College. They have two children, Sharon who is married to David and a son who now take a leading role in the farm.

Harold's interest in poultry started as a schoolboy, when he obtained a trio of Hamburghs, a breed he still keeps today, and still one of his favourite breeds. Over the years he and Norma have kept, bred and shown numerous breeds, and still keep several breeds, Norma's favourites being Japanese and Faverolles, with which she has won Club Show and Best of Breed on many occasions.

Harold first started showing poultry in the mid-seventies retiring from his other sport of Motorcycle Trial Riding, after achieving considerable success. Norma started showing her own birds, consistently winning 'True Bantam' and 'Ladies' Awards'.

They keep other types of Livestock with Norma showing her Rhodesian Ridgeback dogs, and Harold showing their horses with the same dedication and success.

Harold & Norma Critchlow

One of the most beautiful and attractive breeds of poultry has to be the Hamburgh. It is also one of the most prolific layers. The name of the breed goes back to the early 1840s and was listed in the Birmingham Show schedule for 1848. No one seems to know why they were called Hamburghs as they show no traceable contact with the city in Germany of the same name.

Prior to this, the different varieties were known by several names. The spangled were called 'Moonies or Pheasant Fowl'. The blacks were known as 'Black Pheasant', the pencilled were called 'Bolton Greys', 'Bolton Bays', 'Chitterpratts' and 'Dutch Everyday Layers'. These varieties are generally accepted as coming from two sources. The blacks and spangles originate from England, from the counties of Yorkshire and Lancashire to be more precise, although, I have to say, there may be some connection with a Spangled Turkish Fowl with a rose comb , as described by the Italian naturalist Aldrovandi in 1599.

The pencilled variety appears to be more documented, with Moubray making a statement in his book about a small variety of fowl imported from Holland called 'Everyday Hens', which are every day layers, and then, in 1852, B.P. Bren wrote about the 'Dutch Everyday Layers' being widely distributed over England and noted for their egg laying ability. In all cases you will find the spangled and blacks are larger than the pencilled colours.

Bantam versions were introduced around 1900 in England. Prior to this they only existed in large fowl with bantams originating around the 1900s.

Officially classed as a light breed, they are one of the smaller large fowl. However this does not stop them topping the league as egg layers of decent sized white eggs. The range of varied feather patterns and colours in this breed makes them an obvious choice for the fancier looking for something attractive and different.

Markings range from Spangled (this is where the feather has one large round black spangle on the end of every feather, giving a contrast to the ground colour of either Silver or Gold) to Pencilled (this is where all the feathers on the body of the hen have numerous black barrings equally spaced by the ground colour of either silver or gold, with the neck hackle completely free of black markings). The cocks however have no barrings, only the ground colour all over, and a flowing black tail, and edging on all sickle feathers of ground colour, either gold or silver. The other main variety is the Black Hamburgh. This should have very good green beetle like sheen on all feathers.

All the colours of this charming breed have a common leg colour of slate blue and a neat head with a red rose comb and white lobe, which certainly adds the final touches to an already attractive breed.

The colours mentioned are the ones standardised in Britain but on the continent there is a wide variety of colours such as blue, pencilled, buff pencilled, cuckoo, blue, as well as a few other odd colours.

In supplying the photographic illustrations for Harold Critchlow's excellent summary of Hamburghs, I have selected birds from several different countries. The main feature on any Hamburgh is the head piece, which receives a massive 45 points in the Black, and 25 in the other colours.

HAM 1. Was taken from the front cover of Feathered World in 1931 and shows a collection of winning birds bred by Mr. J. King from Silsden in Yorkshire. Joe was one of the breed's greatest ambassadors. He bred and showed excellent birds in all colours for a span of over fifty years. All of the four birds had won in the strongest of competition, the Silver Spangled hen having been made Best in Show on several occasions. The Gold Pencilled cockerel shows a good comb and a wonderful flow of tail feathering, whilst the pair of Blacks illustrate their green top sheen, even in monochrome, the cock bird in particular showing a beautiful comb and leader.

HAM 2. Shows a Silver Spangled cockerel from America. The photo was taken in 1925.

HAM 3. Offers a comparison to an English cockerel from the same era. This bird was bred by Mr. J. S. Pickles, whilst the American ones were by Doctor Wolfe, and were noted winners for him.
The points allocated for markings in the Spangle and pencilled colours account for over fifty percent of the total. Joseph King had bred many Silver Spangled females, which were great examples of birds with the moon shaped markings.

HAM 4. Shows a hen which was famous during the mid 1920s, with wins at the Scottish Hamburgh Club Show, where she won a clock for being the Supreme Champion and was also awarded Champion Female in all breeds at the 1926 Ayr Agricultural Show.

HAM 5. This hen won the English Hamburgh Club Show in 1932 and 1933, plus many other Classic Shows.

Large Fowl Silver Pencilled are not very often seen. HAM 6. Shows a very attractive pullet from 1920 when she won the English Club Show. She also won the Crystal Palace in 1921. She was bred by Mr W. H. Avery from Birmingham, and, even from this old photograph, you can see how beautifully pencilled she is all over her body. The colouring on the Gold Pencilled males is hard to illustrate in black and white photography.

The cock in HAM 7. was again bred by Joe King, and in 1924 was awarded Champion Bird over all breeds at the Crystal Palace, which was a magnificent achievement for the breed. He illustrates a very characteristic Hamburgh comb and lobe with a beautiful width to his flowing tail.

If you were judging Hamburghs strictly to the points allocated by the Club Standard, you would find only 10 or 15 points for type, style and condition, with Blacks receiving the most. I believe that, subconsciously, more emphasis is laid on these points than the standard suggests.

HAM 8. Shows a cock which was a winner for 'Uncle Bert Anthony' in 1936. To me he lacks the correct Hamburgh style and reminds me more of a Rosecomb Minorca, a point which is emphasised by his almond shaped lobes.

HAM 9. Shows a typical style of Black cock, bred by Joseph King in the 1920s and his many wins included Ayr, Great Harwood, Hebden Bridge, Keighley etc., all of which had strong Hamburgh competition.

HAM 10. Shows another of his Blacks, this time a hen with a massive lobe and a very pointed and straight leader, which is carried slightly upwards to highlight the feature.

Miniature Hamburghs have been very popular for longer than some people may imagine. HAM 11. Shows a neat little pullet from 1934. She was bred by Mr. R. Wright from Coleshill, and won second at both The Dairy and Birmingham Shows.

HAM 12. Shows a hen which appears to be well spangled, but perhaps could be better in her comb. She is from 1930, and won the Crystal Palace in that year for Mrs Howes from Gosport.

HAM 13. Illustrates a change of variety, and shows a Pencilled pullet which was bred and exhibited by Peter Parris from The Isle of Wight. She was from the 1970s and won many awards for him.

HAM 14. Shows one of David Kay's Spangles. She is an excellent pullet and was Champion of the 1970 Birmingham Club Show.

HAM 15. Shows a cockerel which was bred in the 1960s by Mr. J. D. Kay from Blackburn. During his life the bird won 31 First Prizes, and many Champion Exhibit and Breed Championships. These include the Dairy Show twice, and male Champion at the Club Shows, three years in succession. He was never beaten and was considered by many to be the Best Bantam ever bred.

HAM 16 and 17. Two excellent photographs taken by Hans Schippers in Holland, and reproduced by Shirley Murdoch in Fancy Fowl. The first print shows a very attractive Silver Pencilled pullet. She is finely marked, with a beautifully clear silver neck hackle. The second bird is a Gold Pencilled pullet, which again is neatly pencilled.

During his writings Harold has referred to 'moonies'. These are hen feathered male birds, and HAM 18. clearly illustrates one such cockerel, heading a very attractive breeding pen for Mrs Mitchell from Manchester in the 1960s.

HOUDAN

A visitor to the local poultry show could be excused for confusing Houdans and the Poland. However, a Houdan breeder would soon be able to enlighten him as to his mistake. The first obvious difference is that the Houdan has five toes not four. The birds also have a beautiful muff which is absent from the white crested versions of Poland. The crest on a Houdan may be quite large but it is tight feathered enough for the birds to be able to eat and drink without having their vision obscured by an over developed 'top hat'. As with the Poland this crest should be full, compact and well rounded on top without being split into two halves.

This slightly smaller crest allows the comb to become part of he bird's features. It is a very attractive strawberry leaf type and should be prominent without being excessively large.

Their body shape is one of quite well developed shoulders, a reasonably long back and a well rounded breast, all of which is carried more or less horizontal. The males have a fully furnished tail which is carried well out and slightly spread. The general appearance of the birds is one of being active and alert which suits their ability to range free and they are excellent layers. They were very popular in Lancashire and Yorkshire for many decades as the ideal farm yard laying bird.

Their main body colouring is rich green/black, which is then evenly mottled with white and, as with other white marked breeds, these markings tend to go lighter coloured with each moult. The face and comb are red and their very small lobe is slightly white coloured. The legs should be white, mottled with black spots and, as mentioned at the beginning, they have a double hind toe. These two should be clearly separated and be of good length and well divided.

One of the breed's instant attractions is its large beard which is in addition to its face and ear muffling. This beard can be very pronounced, especially in the females where it is allocated 12 points. Size and type get 30 points with 15 each for crest and colouring.

The origin of the breed is thought to be the town of Houdan in France where it has existed for centuries before coming to Britain around the boom period of importing, i.e. the 1850s.

It may at first thought seem strange, but the early history of the Houdan is probably associated with the Ancona. To my knowledge they are the only two breeds in this country to have legs where the scales on the front of their shanks are mottled in a black pattern and become a feature of the breed. The Du Mantes in France has a similar feature. These birds were single combed with a beard but no crest. They only had four toes, and were probably the middle version of the original spotted fowls which were discussed in the breed summary for the Ancona and the birds which we now know as Houdans.

The early imports of Houdans were a mixture of four and five toed birds, with many of them only having very small upright standing crests. The Houdans which I recall from my early days were imported from France and had a much larger body size than the present day birds. In fact, some of the male birds showed a resemblance to a Dorking type of fowl.

It would therefore appear that the Houdans were developed from the long established 'Spotted Fowl' from Beuce, and took their name from a small town in that area. Some of these were reported to carry a fifth toe and when these were crossed with Padoue/Poland types of bird, the Houdan was created.

The birds had a great reputation, not as a laying bird, but for their meat qualities so, presumably, a heavier type of bird was also introduced to their development, probably a five toed Faverolles or Dorking.

I have bred the large fowl for many years and can recommend them to anyone. They are of an excellent nature and can be very successful in the showing world. With their crest not being as abundant as the Poland they do not require as much personal preparation, though they still must have their heads free from Northern mite or there will be serious problems. As with the Poland their crests require careful washing. When they are thoroughly wet you can see the top of their skull only has a thin layer of skin to act as protection and if too much pressure is exerted in an attempt to remove a stain the birds can quickly become exhausted.

Weights   Large   Males   7-8lbs   Females 6-7 lbs

FIG 1. Shows the winning pair of birds from the 1922 show at Olympia.

FIG 2. Is a rather unusual White Houdan. He was shown at the Crystal Palace in 1924.

FIG 3. Shows the Bath and West winner in 1933, bred by R. S. Carter from Cambourne.

173

FIG 4. Illustrates a pair of Houdans from 1933. They were especially selected from Mr F. W. Goodwin's flock of 100 breeding birds. Fred Goodwin obtained his original stock from Mesdames Hill and Maconchie in 1903, and by 1933 had a total head of 500 Houdans.

FIG 5. Shows a hen which won all the major shows during 1923 and 1924. She was shown by Mr R. M. Thomas from Swansea.

FIG 6. Is a great crested hen which won the crystal Palace in 1935 for its breeder Mr G. Henwood from Cornwall.

IXWORTH

This breed can truly be described as being 'Made in Britain'. It was created by Reginald Appleyard, who also developed a new breed of laying duck. These were called Silver Appleyards, after himself, whilst the poultry breed was named after the village in which he resided. It was Ixworth in the county of Suffolk.

Reg commenced work on his poultry project in 1931 and continued it for seven years before he considered the birds ready for public display. The style of the breed is best described in his own words. He said that he wanted to establish a bird which was white feathered and was also white pigmented in both bone and flesh. The bone was not to be too heavy and wasteful, which also made the male birds more fertile.

Reg very sensibly left us with details of the breeds used in his project, which are different from most of the breeds I have summarised. These breeds were White Old English Game, Indian Game, both Dark and Jubilee, White Sussex, White Orpingtons and, interestingly, White Minorcas. I draw attention to the Minorcas, because they were also used by William Cook in the development of the Orpingtons. Presumably in both cases they were used for their egg laying qualities.

One reason why the Ixworth's development was successful is that all surplus birds could profitably be sold into the dressed poultry market. He did actually quote one shilling and two pence per pound live weight at 16 weeks old. This converts to approximately 6p in today's money!!!

Subsequently, he was confident to mate up to ten different breeding pens, which obviously gave him a wide choice of genetic variations and permutations.

In shape, the Ixworth is much longer in the body than an Indian Game, whilst still retaining a great width of shoulder and a broad flat back. The wings are carried well up and are not excessively long. Their tails are compact, with the male birds having only short sickles and side hangers. In both sexes they are carried quite low without being straight out.

The thighs are very muscular and only medium in length. The shanks are constructed of strong but not excessively thick bone. A great feature of the breed is their deep breast, which must have a straight breast bone. The legs are set well apart which highlights their breast development.

The comb is described by Reg as being 'double combed' which is usually taken to mean similar to the triple pea comb, associated with Indian Game or Brahma. This should be a rich red as are the wattles and earlobes. The eye should be prominent and not beetle browed and as near to red as possible.

Great attention is drawn to the laying potential of the females. The intention was that not only would both sexes carry a well meated carcass at all stages of their life but the pullets would be capable of laying sufficient eggs to be commercially viable as well as reproducing further stock.

Another feature which he emphasised was their feathering. This had to be close fitting but also retain sufficient texture and quality for the growing stock to become quickly covered, which reduced rearing costs and assured an even body growth in the chickens.

Many of these thoughts were well ahead of time. There were several other people who attempted to create a commercial table breed; Mrs. Jenkins with her Wherwells and, later, the Surrey; the York Fowl produced by Mr. Rain; the Buckeye and Jersey Giant in America; Styrians from Austria and the North Holland Blue from the European continent. These are all examples of breeds which have failed to live up to their creators' high hopes.

Probably the answer lies in the modern day production of table birds. In most cases these are bred from two separate lines. The males are bred to supply the excessive quantity of meat, whilst the female is capable of good egg production combined with a reasonable body of flesh. The crossing of these two types of white coloured birds is an improvement on the old fashioned method of breeding. Indian Game cocks were mated with Light Sussex Females producing good table fowl, but were coloured in their feathering and also carried yellow pigment which is not as acceptable to the British housewife.

After Reginald Appleyard's death, Peter McKenzie from Dunmow in Essex continued with the breed. Peter also developed a White Indian Game, basically from continually breeding Jubilee coloured birds together until the colour became almost washed out. I believe that there may also have been an introduction of Sussex because Peter also bred some top quality commercial Light Sussex right out of the old McEntire mould.

At the present time there would appear to be very few breeders of Ixworths, and the birds which I have seen are more in keeping with a White Indian than with the original concept of Mr. Appleyard.

There are a few miniature Ixworths about, which again show a resemblance to the Indian Game Fowl, especially in their feathering.

Weight   *Males*   *9lbs*   *Females*   *7lbs*

A fine pair of Ixworths, bred by their creator Reginald Appleyard. These birds were exhibited at the London Dairy Show in 1937.

JAVA

This breed was thought to have come originally from the East Indies with a reputation for massive size.

My investigations conclude that the breed is not what I describe as an original, but more of a man made creation, though probably more by accident than calculated planning. Much of the breed's history is discussed under the heading of Raiza Game.

Certainly, in more recent times, the Java Fowl has been used in the creation of many new American breeds such as the Plymouth Rock and Rhode Island Red and, certainly, the Jersey Giant.

There is one point regarding the Java Fowl which I cannot understand. They are mentioned throughout many breed histories and also as a separate breed by certain writers, but you rarely see a photograph of one! Why? Indeed I am not sure if they have been standardised world wide as a recognised breed. They have certainly not been in Britain.

The American standards book included them during the 1890s which is 60 years after they were first recorded in the States.

The description which we have for the Java illustrates a bird of large size with great width across its long back, a very deep and well rounded front and crop area and with a neatly feathered tail, carried well up with the male bird and showing a long pair of sickles. The wings fit closely to the body and are carried well under the tail.

All of this sounds very similar to the description of the Croad Langshan!

The birds, however, had three very noticeable features; firstly, their feathering was quite hard in texture and very close fitting to the body. This was accompanied by the most superb 'beetle green sheen' as in the Modern Langshans. The last point was according to Lewis Wright one of only two characteristics of the breed; the other is their combs.

This is a single version, the difference being that, at the front, there is a part of it above the nostrils without any spikes. They commence farther back, more in a line above the eye. There is also a tendency for the comb to finish well clear of the head in what is often termed 'fly away combed'.

This characteristic is very hereditary in Modern Langshans I have also seen the feature in some Croad Langshans and even Rhode Island Reds. From experiments I have carried out I believe that this feature on the comb is originally created by the crossing of a single combed breed with a breed having a triple pea type of comb. You also produce some birds which are starting to develop the Buttercup type of comb.

The comb, wattles, ear lobes and face should all be a rich red colour. The strong legs are being quoted as being black, with the soles showing a tendency towards a willowy-yellow colouring, as are many of the present day Sumatras'.

Much of this description is identical to that of the Jersey Giant which I believe could be called the modern day version of the Java.

My conclusion about the so called 'Java Fowl' is that the original birds were the result of Langshans being crossed with a heavy weight Game Bird, this bird probably itself being a cross between the Sumatra and a wild Gallus Giganticus Jungle Fowl.

Regarding the possibility of a miniature version Fred Jeffry says that attempts have been made to create them in America but the birds have failed to arouse much interest.

Weights   *Males*   *10lbs*   *Females*   *8lbs*

A drawing of Black Java, looking very similar to Jersey Giants.

A photograph of a very elusive actual live Java. It was bred by Henry Turck, and won the 1927 New York State show. Interestingly, he was called 'Romeo The Second'.

JERSEY GIANT

This breed was not officially standardised in America until 1922 but work on its development commenced some 50 years previously. The breed obviously has strong connections with the Java Fowl and, in the modernised version, birds were reported to weigh up to 16 lbs.

The whole aspect of the bird revolves around massive size and the ability to carry large quantities of meat on its bone structure, this being inherited from one of the early heavy weight game birds, often described as being descendants from Gallus Giganticus.

The Jersey Giant is described as a bird with a deep body and a long back which is carried parallel to the ground. It has a well rounded front and carries its wings up under the tail. The tail itself is neat and definitely not of the full flowing type. It is carried at an angle of 45 degrees. The whole bone structure of the bird has to be strong with well rounded shanks and toes which are firmly on the ground. The head has also to show great strength but the comb is quite small for a bird of such size. It is of the single upright type.

Every breed has its own individual character and in this case it is in the distinctive leg colouring. This is a greenish black shading to willow-yellow on the soles. The white variety has a paler shade of leg colouring, which is more towards greenish yellow.

There appears to be some variation in the standards between the British and those in some other countries, especially regarding the correct tail structure and carriage which can be quoted as being at a much lower trajectory than 45 degrees, which is nearer to my interpretation of the breed.

The feather structure of the birds is of the close fitting type, in many ways resembling the Croad Langshans, with the black variety having a lustrous green sheen to its top colour. The white is to be pure white throughout.

The comb, wattles, etc. should be bright red with the eye colour only required to be dark brown or hazel, not fully black as in the Australorp.

I have not kept the breed because I have never been able to obtain birds which I considered to be good enough to excite me. I have considered making them from scratch, but felt that, with the Java no longer available, the tendency would be to end up with something approaching yellow footed Australorps.

If anyone is interested in attempting to make them, I would suggest using the commercial broiler females. These are supposed to contain American White Plymouth Rock blood which was originally created from the Java.

It is a breed which intrigues me and it seems a shame to see it decline in popularity but it has also lost favour in America, probably due to the arrival of the commercial broiler birds which replaced it in the meat markets. There are reports of miniature Jersey Giants in America but I have never heard of any over here.

To create them in correct form you would have to use some type of heavily meated bird such as an Indian or Malay Game, with the Australorp providing the shape and colouring. There is one point in favour of the exercise. The surplus birds would make some excellent curry. The feature of Jersey Giants is identical to the North Holland Blue, in that as soon as you handle the birds and feel the weight and excessive meat on the birds' bones you appreciate the difference between them and the Marans. The same applies with 'Giants', as opposed to Langshans, Australorps or Croads.

Standard Weights   *Males*   *13 lbs*   *Females*   *10 lbs*

Sketched in the United States of America. It was depicted to be the ideal Jersey Giant, the artist having utilised the best features from the top winning birds in the USA.

A White cock which won at Birmingham in 1934 for Mr J Cowans from Northumberland.

A Black cockerel which is not yet fully mature, but looks to have the potential to become a good bird.

A Black cock from 1935. He was shown by Mr E. H. Rose, and won at all the leading shows collecting along his journeys 16 cups and silver spoons.

Illustrates the breed from Europe in more recent times. This Blue cockerel was photographed at Utrect in 1984 by Josef Wolters.

A winning Black pullet from the 1930s, bred by Mrs Allen from Skipton in Yorkshire, who was one of the breed's greatest enthusiasts. She bred hundreds of them every year.

This white pullet was again bred by Mrs Allen, and won the Birmingham Club Show in 1935.

KIWI AND KLONDYKE

In the past many writers have dismissed the breed of Kiwi as being a cross between Silkies and Wyandottes.

It was suggested that they were introduced as birds which were capable of laying well and at the same time having a different appearance and extra appeal.

However, deeper investigation into the breed reveals a rather more complex history and possible origin.

In the section of this book relating to the breed of Silkies references are made to many of the early historians and writers having records of birds with soft fluffy feathers and little tail or wing feathers, some dating back to the thirteenth century.

The general information surrounded a bird having dense black pigmentation which extended into the flesh and even into their bones. These were often call Gallus Morio or Negro Fowl.

This black pigment was very dominant, and transferred to the offspring when crossed with a conventional bird.

In 1867, Tegetmeier quoted a Mr. Edward Blyth, curator of a museum in Calcutta, who was convinced that there were at least two original types of 'Silkie feathered' birds, one having the black pigment, with a rosecomb and feathered legs. The other variety had a single comb which was a rich red colour and its pigment was yellow.

During the nineteenth century when many new breeds were being imported from India and China there were reports from both Cochin and Langshan breeders of birds arriving with extremely loose and fluffy feathering. Indeed some of them actually bred from these birds which were fully 'Silkie feathered'.

This would suggest to me that the excessive feathering on many of our present day breeds did originally trace back to a cross between the traditional Asil/Malay type of bird and one of these Silkie Fowl. When the cross is done in present times the Silkie feather is immediately converted onto conventional feathering. This can easily be extended from a flat feather to the 'cup shaped' feather which is associated with breeds such as Orpingtons.

The Kiwis in New Zealand again show this extremely soft and long silky plumage. There is also mention of a similar bird in Australia known as the Emu Fowl, which is presumably from a resemblance to the wild Emu. The Emu is not exactly Silkie in the feathering but is certainly very loose in the barbs of the feathers.

The fact that birds of this description are spread over Australasia raises the question, are they native from those parts or were they imported, possibly by accident, from the areas around Singapore and Malaysia? This is the region in which Edward Blyth says he has seen the white pigmented birds.

This theory stands up well under scrutiny. The Kiwis have single red coloured combs and wattles etc., yellow pigment to their legs, no crest or beard, only four toes which are on legs clean of feathering and quite large bodies.

Conversely, the birds we now know as the Silkie have a unique type of rosecomb (with blue ear lobes), black pigment, a crest, and, in some cases, also a beard, five toes, feathered legs and are small in the body, which does illustrate quite a difference between the two!

Some Kiwis were imported to Britain during the 1920s and the 1930s and created quite a favourable impression. A pullet shown by Bruff Jackson won second prize in the new breed class at the Olympia Classic Show. A trio of them was shown at Ulverston show as utility birds; there were 13 entries and they again won second prize. The judge was Arthur

Snowden, who was at that time a well known authority on Utility Poultry, and he was very impressed with their laying possibilities.

The feathering on these birds was described as being different from that of the Silkie breed. The base of the feather appears to be much stiffer and quite 'spiky' before branching out into the broad silky feathering. The wings and tail are again constructed of this strong spiky feathering with only a sparse scattering of webbing.

There has been mention of a similar breed in America under the name of Klondyke. As with the Kiwi, the birds were dismissed as simply being a cross between Silkies and, in the American case, White Leghorns. This would suggest that they were not as robust as the Kiwi which was quoted as being in the heavy breed category. The fact that Leghorn was mentioned would definitely indicate that the birds were of yellow pigmentation. There is also no mention of five toes, crests and all the other differences which are associated with the Silkie. The breed did not appear to catch on and, as far as I am aware, is now extinct in the USA.

One other interesting point, and I am sure that there is no connection, is that in the waterfowl species there is the Sebastopol Goose which has long streamer like goose feathers. These are constructed of much softer texture than the normal goose feathering. This curly type of feather can also extend to their breast feathering. In some ways it could be described as 'Frizzle' feathers in poultry. This connection between Frizzle and Silkie feathering has often been mentioned by the early historians and is probably correct in that they are only one step removed from one another.

The same variation occurs in other species of animals. Dogs and cats for instance can, in certain breeds, be either short coated or in a longer haired 'Silkie' version, with another variation being the 'curly coated', with the woolly hair forming ringlets as in the human Afro-Asian equivalent.

Cattle have their own variations with the long haired Highland Cattle and the Galloways.

In conclusion, the Kiwi is obviously a bird which is different from almost any other and it seems a shame it has not been more carefully preserved.

The Kiwi pullet shown by Bruff Jackson in the new breed class at Olympia in 1938.

A two year old Kiwi cock owned by Mr C. Van Dionant from Brussels.

KRAIENKOPPE

Periodically a breed appears which is far enough apart from existing ones to be individual. Such a breed is the Kraienkoppe. The breed is credited with coming from Germany and the first birds which I encountered were miniatures during the 1960s. They were silver duckwing, and very attractive. They quickly caught the public's and breeders' eye but unfortunately appear to have lost some of their initial popularity. The large version quickly followed but at the present time they are limited to a few enthusiastic breeders. That very clever Dutchman, Van Gink, records that the breed was developed both in Holland and Germany, at around the middle of the nineteenth century and the breeds used in its creation were Malay, Duckwing, Leghorn and, as usual in these historical recordings, those elusive birds appear. Here they are mentioned as 'Country Fowls', which makes a change from 'Native Crossbreds' or 'Local Barnyard Fowls'.

In Holland the breed is known as the Twentse Hoender and until more recent times was only bred in the silver colouring. The breed now includes the black-red/partridge colouring. A spot of research quickly uncovered that the first birds arrived in Britain as long ago as 1928, with another importation in 1930. The styles of the two strains were quite different, with the first birds very similar to the ones of the present time.

The breed style is one of its own, with the birds having a very 'gamey' appearance and the ones which Tommy Holland has can't half fight. If you don't get the cocks out of the show pen first time they will tear lumps out of you. Maybe there was some Bruge blood involved originally; otherwise the birds quoted as being Malay were the old fashioned type, before they were developed into a showman's creation.

The birds have an upright stance and a longish back, with a well furnished tail carried at around the 45 degrees angle. They have a strongish head, with a curved beak which is strong at the base. Their wattles and lobes are small to match the close fitting comb.

A feature of the breed is that, even though they have a hard game feel to their body, they have long and full feathering to their neck and saddle hackle. Their bone structure is strong and well rounded. This point is highlighted by their very distinctive yellow shanks, which very often have dark brown toe nails. This feature is, I believe, inherited from the Malay blood in Holland. Welsummers and Barnevelders also have the feature.

In colour the Silver males carry the usual duckwing pattern of neck hackle, saddle hackle, wing butt and wing bay being silver, whilst the body and complete tail should be solid black. In the female the hackle is silver with a black stripe in the centre of each feather. The front part of the breast is chestnut, with the rest of the body colouring being a stippled grey, with the feather shaft showing a paler shade. The black/red partridge colour being as usual with the silver replaced by a reddish/brown in the males and a soft brown in the females.

There are some beautiful miniatures in the country which really do resemble the large version, especially in the silver variety, which with their black background and rich yellow legs, look very striking. The effect is highlighted by their rich red headpiece, and well furnished tail. To summarise, it is a breed well worth considering. It has a character all to itself and is attractive to look at as a potential showbird and Tommy says that the ones which don't make it taste great in a curry!

Weights	L F	Males	5 1/2 - 6 1/2 lbs	Females	4 - 5 1/2 lbs
	Miniature	Males	30 ozs	Females	26 ozs

A pair of Silver Kraienkoppe which were shown at the 1928 Crystal Palace.

This pair of birds came from a different importation and this photograph was taken in 1930 at the World Poultry Congress. This particular event was held every 3 years at different locations all over the world, with the 1930 venue being London.

These two pictures are from recent times. They are a pair of Silvers, bred by Brian Sands from Boston. Both birds have been consistent winners at the major shows.

186

LA FLECHE

As the name suggests, this breed is of French origin. It is a very large bodied bird with tight feathering and stands fairly upright on long legs. Its body shape is wide at the shoulders with a very prominent breast. Its back is fairly long and is finished with a well furnished and fully curved tail.

One of the main features is the twin horned comb which is similar to the Crevecoeur's but the La Fleche is plain headed, though it is said that some birds do show signs of feathers at the back of the head. It has white ear lobes and long wattles hanging well down its throat, both of which suggest a relationship with the Du Mans. The colouring is black, which includes the legs and feet.

The breed's origin is not really known, but it is thought to have been in existence for centuries. La Fleche is a town north of the River Loire and birds of this type were mentioned during the fifteenth century, but the writer believed them to have been there for centuries previous to that date.

My own observation of the breed is that it appears to have the Asiatic Game look about it, possibly obtained from the Bruge, or Belgium Game, sometimes called the Combattant Du Nord in Northern France. Basically they would all be of the same origin. The La Fleche has a reputation for excellent tasting flesh, but is a slow maturing breed, a point which hints at the relationship with these aforementioned game birds, as does the breed's ability to free range over large areas before returning home to roost.

We have never kept the breed, not for any adverse reason. It is simply that none ever came our way which looked to be the right sort. They are a breed which I have often admired in paintings.

I have never heard of any miniatures in this country but, I would think, there could be some on the continent. If not, they would be a glorious challenge.

Weights   Large Fowl   Males   8-10 lbs   Females   6-8 lbs

This illustration by Harrison Weir shows the strength and robust body of the La Fleche.

A pair of La Fleche as drawn by Ludlow.

187

A painting by 'Roz', and taken from the Rare Breed Society calendar. It illustrates the potential beauty of La Fleche.

A pair of La Fleche as exhibited at the 1921 World Poultry Congress.

188

LAKENFELDER

This breed is credited with being originated in Germany, though there are some doubts about it. The breed or a similar breed dates back over 150 years in other parts of the world. At one period the term Jerusalem was included in its name suggesting (possibly quite wrongly) a connection with that part of the world.

The history and development of the breed are also rather sketchy, but a relationship to Campines is almost certain. There is a strong resemblance in head features, especially in comb texture. Which other breeds were used I can find no definite proof of, but the original grey coloured Bresse would be my most likely candidate.

That great Dutchman Van Gink believed the birds had originally been developed in Holland. In 1934 he writes, as far back as 1727, a gentleman had travelled through a village called Lakervelt, situated in the Eastern corner of Southern Holland, and recorded seeing local fowls which had a reputation for being excellent layers, with delicious tasting meat.

The description of the fowls bears similarity to the present day Lakenvelders, as the Dutch spell the name. The fact that this traveller was impressed with the birds' appearance would suggest they were far different from the common fowls of that period.

The birds themselves are a very striking combination of black and white with slate coloured legs, a neat red coloured single comb and wattles, with a small sized but well defined white ear lobe. Lakenfelders have a medium sized body with a flowing tail. The general feel of them is similar to a Bresse in that they carry a lot of meat on a fine boned structure.

I have enjoyed keeping them for a number of years. Actually they are one of my daughter's favourite breeds. They can become friendly and docile, but initially are very cautious.

The one possible hindrance to their popularity is the standard. The points allocated for the colouring are nearly half the total for the whole bird, but the colour is described in the standard of perfection by using 28 indefinite words and not mentioning the difference of markings for both sexes, also completely ignoring under-colour and wings. The situation as I understood it some years since was a conflict of opinion centring on the amount of black or otherwise on the male bird's back, along with the seemingly impossible task of being able to breed the colour as outlined without having slate blue under-colour. The completely clear white wing sides are also very difficult to achieve in combination with a completely solid black hackle and tail. Not only should a standard be clearly defined but it must also have been proved to be, within reason, obtainable.

Many of these standards are compiled by the committee, and do not forget that a camel was designed by a committee, but originally set out to be a horse!

The breed itself is very striking and attractive, so would it not be better for the breed's popularity if we settled for a standard which is reasonable to achieve and allocated more points to the style of the birds, which at the moment receives only 10, the head also being 10 and the legs 5.

I offer this as a constructive suggestion about a breed I find pleasing to look at, useful to keep and popular with customers who are looking for a bird suitable to decorate their garden and at the same time provide poultry produce.

Miniatures are now in this country and again are very attractive.

Weights   Males   6 lbs   Females   4.5 lbs

A drawing by Van Gink in 1934 based on a German bred male, and a Dutch female to illustrate the ideal requirements of a Lakenfelder.

A pair of Lakenfelders which were imported from Holland in 1927 by Mr A.T. Organ from Somerset, who then showed the birds with much success.

LEGHORN

Writing about this breed immediately reminds me of another Mediterranean breed, the Ancona, and all the confusion surrounding the origin of that breed.

Here I can confidently state that the common fowl of Italy was exported to many countries of the world, including the USA and Britain from the port of Leghorn, and consequently these birds were so named.

These Italian light breed fowl, if not indigenous to that country, have certainly been there for over two and a half thousand years, which to me is certainly long enough to have established at least a few steps up the ladder to that status.

Apparently the Italians had not been concerned with segregating colour or markings, but simply allowed the birds to multiply as they wished, in any colour pattern selected by themselves.

The careful colour selection and controlled breeding programme were carried out in other countries. Here in Britain we have at the present time 14 different colours of Leghorns.

I do not propose to describe each colour individually, as many of them follow the standard of O. E. Game or, alternatively, the breed used to create a Leghorn version of that breed, e.g. Sussex to make the Columbian Leghorn.

The browns were amongst the first consignment and they proved to be very popular for close to 100 years, only declining in the 1950s when the appearance of the modern hybrid started to replace the old fashioned first crosses, two of the favourites being Brown Leghorn X Rhode Island Red and Brown Leghorn X Light Sussex, this being a sex link which added extra appeal.

The exhibition type of Brown Leghorn created by the showmen was a different proposition. Being developed during the latter part of the last century, it was claimed that black-red Game blood, was used to increase the intensity of colouring. This also increased the length of leg and created a change of style from that of the original laying type birds. Brown Leghorns were at one period a very popular and successful showing breed but have declined dramatically in recent years.

The reason is probably due to the birds requiring double mating if you wish to obtain the best results. This situation has arisen in other breeds where extra patience is needed in their breeding programme. The colour of a brown male is described as having the hackle feathers orange-red in colour, but earlier standards quote the colour as being golden-bay, whilst I would suggest that the most successful showbirds in the past shaded to much more of a lemon tinge, with the saddle hackles a darker shade, especially on their feather ends.

The neck hackles have a black stripe in the centre. This is especially prominent at the head end with the markings diminishing towards the lower part as it approaches the shoulders. This hackle colouring is also on the females. Their body is an even colour of partridge type markings, on a rich brown base. This colouring has often been described as that of a fallen oak tree. The breast is salmon red.

The two main points which create the need for double mating are that the females should have wing sides which are perfectly free from red colouring or what is often called 'foxiness', whilst the male requires a solid black coloured breast, completely free from any signs of red coloured feathering, or even with the black showing a dusky grey tinge to it. The male's tail should also be a rich green sheened black. Any sign of white in the root of the sickle feathers is considered quite a serious fault.

Winning showbirds possessing these correct points, if mated together, will not repro-

191

duce correctly marked specimens. Both sexes require to be mated with a partner carrying the necessary markings to balance their own colouring.

This situation has often led to a breeder concentrating his efforts into just one sex of a particular breed, where they are termed 'cockerel' or 'pullet' breeders.

The black version was also very popular with commercial egg producers, being a very hardy and excellent layer. The bird's colouring is of the type which has yellow pigmentation to the beetle green black colouring, meaning that, for show birds, double mating is required.

The White Leghorn, especially in the British Isles, was developed into two separate categories, the first being an absolute egg laying machine, being slight in body and high in tail carriage which was often fan shaped. It had no excessive development in head piece features with everything about it retained in its concept of being simply the best laying bird, which it proved to be by setting new records at the laying trials.

The other version was the showman's version, which had great length of body and was vastly larger in body size having a single comb developed into the size of a sirloin steak with pendulous wattles and a lobe which was the size of a half-crown. And that was on the females, (more details on the comb etc. are under Minorcas).

The show Leghorn in all colours stood well up on strong legs, with a tail carried well outwards and tightly 'whipped' in the female, the males being well furnished with long sickles and side hangers. The decline in the popularity of large fowls merely stimulated the rise in numbers of the miniature Leghorns, with the breed club catering for both types. This club was formed in 1876 and has the distinction of being the first independent breed club. The club is still going strong and gives encouragement to new breeders of both large and small Leghorns.

The type for the miniature version follows the one set by the breeds of exhibition type Leghorns rather than the commercial or utility birds.

All the colours have been developed in the miniatures, or Bantams as they are still often referred to and, as with many other breeds, they are nearer to perfection than the large fowl ever achieved. Head points are of paramount importance, followed closely by type and style. This last point is sometimes overlooked in the quest for a perfect head piece, with many of the Bantams showing a bit short on the leg and losing that desired look of being wide at the shoulders, with the wings carried well up under the tail, emphasising their long back. Their feather texture should be tight and not loose or soft, which gives the bird a firm feel when handled.

The Leghorn is a top class, highly competitive breed for anyone wishing to be involved with a breed which is capable of being Best in Show and yet is capable of keeping the household well supplied with good quality eggs.

If it has any drawback it is that to breed the best birds dual mating is required, not only for the colouring factor in browns and blacks, but also because to produce females with sufficient fold in their combs, a male bird is needed which is excessive in this feature.

The other point is that the show life of a Leghorn can be short. They either go white in face or become over developed in the combs. The weights for large fowls are printed below, but many of exhibition type which were highly successful show-birds were far in excess of these, especially the females.

Weights	Large Fowl	Males	7.5 lbs	Females	5.5lbs
	Miniatures	Males	32 ozs	Females	28 ozs

To photographically illustrate the breed of Leghorn correctly, each of the colours should be shown in both males and females. This is not practical for some of the minor colours, but a reference to that colour in another breed will illustrate their colouring; Partridge being an example, where Wyandottes could be used. Additionally, the difference in type between the old fashioned exhibition and a more recent 'utility' version requires highlighting. Consequently my coverage of the breed extends to some forty seven photos.

I commence with Whites from the 1912 era when the partnership of Messrs Whitaker and Tootill was breeding White Leghorns of the highest quality.

The Champion of 1912.

The top bird in 1913.

A great bodied hen which was bred by Walter Bradley when he farmed for himself in Yorkshire before joining Lord Dewar. This photo was taken in 1920, by which time she had won over one hundred prizes including all the Major Shows.

The 1924 Crystal Palace winner. By now Walter was manager for Lord Dewar, and had obviously taken his strain of birds with him. Consequently the name on the winning ticket was Lord Dewar.

Another famous name amongst Leghorn breeders was Mr J. Finch from Bolton. The cockerel shown was unbeaten during 1923, and fully illustrates the style of bird which Johnnie was to show for the next twenty five years.

The 1922 Dairy Show Champion Leghorn. This pullet was exhibited by Harry Derbyshire who was, in my youth, the driver for Billy Hamnett's team of birds. This winning white pullet was claimed at the catalogue price of £25 pounds, which would have been a good price in those days.

The 1925 Crystal Palace winning White pullet. She was shown by a man called J. Hazel from Essex who does not appear to have continued his success in the succeeding years.

Lord Dewar won both the London Dairy Show and Crystal Palace in 1926 with this white pullet.

The cockerel above enabled him to complete the Crystal Palace double. The name of Ian Gow was now becoming prominent. He was President of the White Leghorn Club and had an excellent manager in the young Michael Harrison. Many of their birds were of the more 'Utility' type.

Utility Champion at the Great Yorkshire. He was bred from the bird which came second at the 1925 Crystal Palace. His sisters competed at the Lancashire laying trials, finishing in a very creditable position, despite having a bird die in the early stages of the competition.

The 1927 winning utility cockerel at the Crystal Palace.

The utility aspect of the breed was now becoming more popular, and Messrs R. & E. Charteris built a reputation for the laying type of Leghorns. Above is a bird very typical of their stock in the early 1930s.

At the same period, Johnny Finch continued breeding his 'out and out' exhibition type birds, as shown here.

Lord Dewar won the Utility Leghorn pullet class at the Crystal Palace with this very attractive bird above.

The Champion Utility bird at the 1933 Dairy Show was a White Leghorn cockerel, bred and shown by W. Binnie and Son from Scotland. Willie was to breed many more Champions during the next three decades. This bird shown above bears quite a resemblance to one of Lord Dewar's winning utility birds shown below.

The 1928 Dairy Show winning pullet, shown by Ian Gow and clearly illustrates the difference between the two types.

I cannot remember seeing many top quality Black Leghorn male birds, However, I have selected a few from the archives which are very presentable.

The winning bird at the 1906 Black Leghorn Club Show. It was shown by Harry Hall and looks good, but I am not sure how much artistic licence 'Lydon' took when drawing it.

The cockerel here won both the Dairy Show and the Crystal Palace in 1924, and looks pretty good to me. The bird was shown by Walter Hurst.

Rosecombs are allowed in the Mediterranean breeds, but are rarely seen. This bird won second prize at the Crystal Palace in 1923.

The cockerel here was a noted winner in 1921. He was bred and exhibited by Mr J. Searle from Surrey.

A good hen which was bred by Mr J. B. Salmond in the 1920s, He then emigrated to Australia taking his birds with him, where the hen continued to beat the opposition.

A very attractive pullet from the 1930s. She was bred and successfully shown by Mr Searle.

Black Leghorns have always been a favourite Utility breed, and in 1932 the pullet here gained the award for Champion 'Utility Bird' at the London Dairy Show. She was bred in Lancashire by Samuel Brooks.

The hen which won the 1934 Club Show. She continued her winning ways in 1935 including the Royal Cornwall. She was bred by Mr J. S. Appleton from Coventry.

Blues are very attractive, but have never been bred in large numbers. In 1923 the Dairy Show winner was the pullet shown above. She was exhibited by William Cook, who was more noted for creating the breed of Orpington.

Another good Blue pullet. She was from the 1930s, and I believe bred by Billie Wilkinson when he was manager at Paignton Zoo.

Another colour which is rarely seen, especially in Large Fowl, is the Cuckoo. Here is a reasonable specimen which won the 1923 Crystal Palace for Mrs C. E. Parke from Dorset.

Depicts a much rangier bodied bird, which is also free from white in the root of its tail.

A Golden Duckwing cockerel. This bird won many best of breed awards during 1927. He was bred and exhibited by Harry Brazier from Buckinghamshire.

Duckwings are another attractive colour within the Leghorns, and again not frequently seen. Above is a Silver Duckwing cockerel which won the Crystal Palace in 1926.

The pullet shown here won champion Duckwing at the 1923 Club Show. She then went on to win Birmingham, and was second at Olympia, proving herself another successful bird for Harry Glazier.

A good Pyle is highly attractive, and the cockerel here illustrates this point. He was bred by Jimmy Waugh in Northern Ireland, where he won many first prizes.

Exchequer Leghorns have always had a reputation for being a good laying bird, but have never been too popular in the show pen. Above shows the 1932 Dairy Show winner.

Whilst this bird won the Dairy in 1933. Both birds were bred and exhibited by Messrs Lee and Drake from Yorkshire.

Buff Leghorns went through a period of great popularity. This was continuing the interest created by the arrival of Cochins, when Buff became the fashionable colour, even in clothing. Recent years have seen only a limited number of them at the various shows. Above shows the pair of birds which won the 1921 Crystal Palace. Both were bred and exhibited by Arthur Fish from Preston.

That well known poultry authority, Harry Fox from Matlock, won the 1932 London Dairy Show with the cockerel above.

Whilst the bird above shows the 1923 Crystal Palace winner. I consider this bird's spikes and serrations to be equal to any of the more established colours.

The bird here won the 1934 Dairy Show for Mr A Jaques.

Another of the Arthur Fish specials won the 1928 Crystal Palace and is shown above.

Brown Leghorns were always a very popular utility bird, whilst the exhibition version was developed to a high standard of perfection in both males and females. Unfortunately, the Black-Red/Partridge colour is difficult to portray when using black and white photography. However, readers will be able to appreciate the birds' head points and style, if not their beautiful colouring.

The cockerel above won the 1931 Club Show. He was bred and exhibited by Mr E. L. Simon.

The cockerel here was bred by Thomas Finney, and won many of the Championship Shows in 1924.

The same breeder won the Crystal Palace in 1932 with the bird shown above.

In Brown females, the pullet here won the 1935 Crystal Palace for J. C. Dixon from Doncaster.

The pullet above won the 1931 Crystal Palace for Alex McLatchie.

Whilst the bird here had a very successful showing career for George Elliott.

A breeding pen of Exchequers, which were bred commercially on Stanley Hutchinson's farm at Thirsk in Yorkshire. This was one of several pens which were mated for the 1923 breeding season.

LINCOLNSHIRE BUFF

These birds are, from their name, obviously associated with my adopted county. They are recorded in several books and really exemplify many of the breeds mentioned in the late nineteenth and early twentieth centuries. They were never standardised by an official body and are actually a type of fowl associated with a certain locality.

When running in a flock, they bore a close resemblance to each other and developed a reputation in neighbouring counties for their ability to live and lay well.

From the pieces of information still available, the nucleus of the breed was the Shanghai (or Buff Cochin as it was to become known), mated with several different breeds which included Dorking and Wheaten Old English Game. Both were easily available and could be beneficial in adding table qualities to the rather large framed and sparsely meated Cochins. They would also give the Lincolnshire Buff the white pigmented skin and leg colour necessary for the British meat trade in which it had a good reputation.

Their ability to produce a good quantity of eggs would also develop from the hybrid vigour resulting from the cross breeding.

The result of all this was that the Lincolnshire was a 'breed' well in advance of most others at that period of the late 1800s, but controversy arose when William Cook introduced the Buff Orpington in 1894, and claimed to have developed it without the use of Lincolnshire Buff blood. Many people doubted his statement but, nevertheless, the fact was that with Cook's publicity skills a buff coloured bird, if sold as a Lincolnshire, was worth four shillings (20p), but if sold as the revolutionary Orpington would fetch ten shillings. The Lincolnshire breeders objected to the ruling body, but the Poultry Club decided that the name of the buff coloured fowls be Orpingtons, and from then on they were the standardised breed, resulting in the decline of the Lincolnshire version. It was a great pity because buff coloured birds are still very popular and, with a little bit of negotiating, two different breeds could have been developed.

However, Brian Sands, in conjunction with the Lincolnshire Agricultural College is remaking the birds and progress is very sound. The original project started some ten years ago when they crossed a Red Dorking cock with some Buff Cochin type females on which the legs were white and only half feathered, these birds resulting from an introduction of Buff Orpington blood to increase vigour in my Cochins.

A club has now been formed and the members are again pressing for official standardisation of the breed.

The standard for Lincolnshire Buffs has been carefully drafted to emphasise that there is a distinct difference between them and the Buff Orpington. The male birds are to be longer in the back and carry their tail at a lower angle which is described as being 'well out'. The feathering of the birds is to be much tighter to the body than the loose cup shaped feather on the Orpington.

The legs show an obvious difference. The Lincolnshire has an extra claw, making it a five toed breed as in the Dorkings. This extra toe must be well separated from the conventional rear toe and be carried pointing upwards.

In colouring the Lincolnshire Buffs are described as having a shaded pattern, with the neck and saddle hackles being a rich orange, as is the back. This colouring then increases in depth to form a chestnut/copper wing covert. This colour would, I expect, also extend into the wing bar.

The main tail feathers are black with the side hangers having a chestnut outer edging.

The body plumage is a ginger buff, as is the under colouring, right down to the skin.

The females' colouring is the same, allowing for the sexual differences and feather structure.

The beak is described as being buff coloured, whilst the legs and feet remain white, all of which is well removed from the Buff Orpington and Buff Cochin standards.

I just wonder, though, if there is now a tendency for the breed to be creeping to a point where it could be accused of being a pale coloured New Hampshire Red with white legs and five toes.

A colour photograph of a Lincolnshire Buff can be seen in the colour section.

A pair of Lincolnshire Buffs, drawn by Harrison Weir in 1891.

MALINE

Here is a breed not seen in this country for many years. It was originally credited as being of Belgian origin. It is a massive sized cuckoo coloured bird, carrying a vast amount of meat, which suggests that at some period there has been a connection with the Belgian Game Fowl and possibly some Antwerp Brahma involved as well.

The Antwerp Brahma was different. It had a single comb and white legs combined with what could be described as Light Brahma colouring. The bird built a reputation for developing enormous size. This was possibly achieved as a result of having been crossed in India with the Hyderabad. The colour of the Malines came originally from the Flemish Cuckoo, or French Cuckoo which was probably from the same stock anyway.

The Maline exists in two types, the standard single combed version and the more interesting one which has a flat type of comb, combined with a large and feather free gullet, with very little if any wattles as in the original Brahmas. This is termed as being single lobed.

Both versions have very deep and full fronted bodies, a high carried tail, legs and feet white in colour, and a scattering of feathers down the sides.

The breed was obviously used in the development of the North Holland Blue, and possibly the Marans as well.

There are no miniatures of the breed at the present time.

Weights Male 12lbs   Females 10 lbs

This photo by Josef Wolters shows relation to the single combed Maline. This Mechelner cock was shown at Hanover 1982.

208

FIG 1. This hen was Third in the A.O.V. class at the 1932 Crystal Palace. She was bred and exhibited by Mr Seys from Sussex.

FIG 2. Shows a big bodied which was imported from Belguim in 1926. After breeding here for Richard Terrot she was exported to Australia in an attempt to revive the breed in that country.

FIG 3. This rather unusual White Maline cock was owned by Ken Atterby from Lincolnshire.

FIG 4. Illustrates the single wattled version of Coucou de Malines.

MARANS

This breed is one of the last to be introduced to this country, arriving in 1929. Since then it has created for itself a fine reputation as a layer of very dark coloured brown eggs but has never been accepted by the exhibition poultry breeders as a show bird.

When the birds were at their height as show birds during the boom period just after the 1939-1945 war, the breed was present in several distinct and attractive colourings, e.g. the silver cuckoo and the golden cuckoo, but even these have dwindled away until virtually all the birds nowadays are straight forward dark cuckoos.

The Marans was developed originally as a dual purpose breed and still carries a good body of flesh, though not as abundant and firm as the North Holland Blue.

There are many breeds quoted as being part of the breed's original creation but I would suggest that some of them were quickly discarded, the basic ones being some form of the continental cuckoo for markings, and very definitely the Langshan for the brown egg factor. This breed would obviously introduce the leg feathering which was present on the earlier birds. I cannot see any reason to use other breeds if you wish to produce a brown egg laying cuckoo bird.

I have just mentioned silver and gold versions. Now this might require additional breeds but I also stated that these two colours have almost become 'rare breeds', presumably by breeders selecting their sitting eggs on darkness of colour, which have proved to be the ones containing the most Langshan blood, and not the attractive coloured hens.

This style of breed could easily be described as being a cuckoo marked Croad Langshan, i.e. short in back, high tail carriage with a full and well rounded front, all set off with what should be a smooth textured and evenly cut single comb which is free from double spikes and side sprigs. Unfortunately, the heads on many Marans males leave a lot to be desired, but presumably their mother and grandmother laid good coloured eggs.

The point regarding feathered legs warrants further mention. Over here we have selected clean legged Marans and feathered legged North Holland Blues, but the continent have done the reverse for some reason.

There are some excellent miniatures which are genuinely bred down from the large fowl, thus retaining the brown egg qualities, not having been made by crossing similar types of already developed bantams, which may create birds with the breed's standard appearance, but lose the dark egg factor.

Weights Large Fowl Male 8 lbs   Females 7 lbs
Miniatures   Male 32 ozs   Females 28 ozs

FIG 1. Shows a typical Dark Cuckoo Marans cockerel.

FIG 2. Was bred by Ken Bosley, who has been a stalwart of the breed for many years. This hen was Champion Marans at the 1954 National Poultry Show.

FIG 3. Shows a young cockerel bred by the breed's earliest supporter, the Hon C. K. Greenway from Stanbridge Earls poultry farms. The bird won the new breed class at the Crystal Palace Show in 1937.

FIG 4. Illustrates a grand bodied pullet, which was again bred by Ken Bosley. She won Champion Marans at the 1973 Nottingham Championship Show.

FIG 5. Shows a grand pair of Miniatures. They were bred by Ken and formed part of his winning trio at the 1995 National Show. (Photo by John Tarren).

FIG 6 This Large Fowl pullet is a winning bird from the 1940s. She is illustrating a silver coloured hackle, which was popular in those days.

FIG 7. Gives you two for the price of one; the Reverend Trudgian displaying an excellent miniature Marans cockerel. The bird was bred by him and was a very consistent winner for several years.

212

MARSH DAISY

This is a genuine British breed, and for once we have Edward Brown's detailed account of its creation. It is as follows:- A Mr G W Scott who was secretary of the Marsh Daisy Club supplied the information, and without this detail I would have to say the breed was created from a mixture of cross breeds.

In the 1890s John Wright from Southport Lancs., kept some rosecombed white coloured fowl for laying eggs. These were a cross between a black Hamburgh cock and white Leghorn hens.

He obtained a sitting of Cinnamon Malay eggs, and managed to rear a couple of pullets. These were mated to an Old English Game Bantam cock, and they bred a black-red/partridge coloured cockerel which was mated to the rosecombed white females, and this produced a rosecombed white cockerel, which was again used on to some of the slightly different generation of rosecombed females. These were then bred together until 1913 with no outside blood being used, simply alternating the same stock at three to four year intervals.

In 1913 Charles Moor bought two old hens from Mr Wright, who was by now 80 years old. He had not bred any stock for several years and had lost his only remaining male bird.

Charles Moor bought a Pit Game cock, and mated it with the two hens. A cockerel from this pairing was put back to the same two hens. The procedure was again repeated with the next generation. Sicilian Buttercups were then introduced with the intention of fixing the Willow Green coloured leg and white ear lobes.

By now it was 1921 and the story can soon become boring, but I found interesting the careful recordings of a procedure which has been completed many times in the past, not always by calculation, in the evolution of a new breed.

Unfortunately, I have never kept the breed myself, so I contacted Maureen Case who, along with her husband, runs the Long Ash Farm Park at Milton Abbas in Dorset. Maureen lists the Marsh Daisy as being amongst her favourite breeds and she considers them to be ideal for anyone wishing to keep a few birds in an orchard or small paddock.

Apparently they love to be on free range and are excellent searchers for their own food. They are good layers of very tasty eggs and, when required, the hens will sit their own eggs and be excellent mothers, no doubt due to the Game blood in their ancestry. They are very hardy and any surplus cockerels make very rich tasting table birds. The breed standard has no outstanding feature to its shape but is a very pleasant looking bird, with well proportioned shoulders, a longish back and a well furnished tail carried at an angle of 45 degrees. The breast is well rounded and full at the front, giving the bird a blocky appearance, even though its carriage is slightly more upright than horizontal.

The main features are its attractive willow coloured legs and feet which should have horn coloured toe nails. This feature, as I mentioned in the Barnevelder and Welsummer, is inherited from the Malay blood.

The breed's head is also very distinctive with the bright red rosecomb full of working but not excessive as in the Redcap. It has a neat leader following the curve of the head and not upright as in the Hamburgh.

The lobes are described as white but usually carry some of the willow pigment from the legs and actually show to be a lemon shade. The eye should be red.

There are several colours, but the one which sticks in most people's minds is the wheaten, so described for both males and females.

In the male bird the top colour should be a rich gold whilst the breast and under parts are dark stone coloured. The red in the saddle hackle shades to black as it progresses toward the black sickles and side hangers.

The female is basically stone coloured, shading lighter towards the tail of the bird. The neck hackle is deep chestnut with a slight black edging at the end of each feather.

The birds have a gamey appearance, with fairly tight feathering, and in the show pen have style about them. As with some other breeds the birds should be more popular than they are. There does not seem to be any outstanding reason why they are only in a few breeders' hands, but it is certainly a scarce breed.

There has never been any miniature version.

Weights Male 6-7 lbs   Females 5-6 lbs

FIG 1. This photo was taken in recent times and illustrates a cock which was bred by Mr and Mrs Case at their Farm Park in Dorset. He was one of Maureen's favourite birds, winning many first prizes for her.

FIG 2. Shows a charming pair of Marsh Daisies, bred and exhibited by the Hon. Alice Hawke during the early 1930s, and this photograph illustrates birds which were typical of that period.

FIG 3. Is the 1932 Crystal Palace and Club Show winning Black Marsh Daisy cock. His style shows the inclusion of Black Hamburgh blood in their creation. He was bred and exhibited by E. C. Parsons from Somerset.

FIG 4. Is a pullet clearly showing the attractive Wheaten colouring and alert gamey appearance.

MINORCA

A statement that Minorcas are the showman's 'development of the Castilian' is readily accepted. The Castilian is the common black fowl of Spain, the name Minorca being derived from the port of that name from which most of the birds were exported. Minorcas trace back in British history certainly to 1780, and maybe before. But until the early part of the nineteenth century, the breed's popularity was still confined to Devon, Cornwall and south of the Thames, where the breed was being used for successful egg production. It is easy to assume that the Spanish, as we now call the breed which has its face completely covered with an extension of the white ear lobe, and the Minorca to be of the same origin, but I have to agree with Harrison Weir that this may not be the case. The fact that the Spanish have been used to increase the lobe size on the Castilian/Minorca will be correct and there was a period when the Minorca was referred to as the red faced Spanish. But way back there could be some other breeding with the Castilian type of fowl, which added the white face etc., probably from a near neighbouring country, thus creating a different variety.

The breed gradually spread itself around the British Isles and increased in popularity to a point where, by 1888, six classes at the famous Crystal Palace Show attracted 120 entries, and the Minorca was one of the top rated breeds at the exhibition.

The original birds increased in body size, possibly by the use of Langshan blood and, by selective breeding, their head features were developing into ones which were to become famous during the twentieth century.

The breed is actually classified as a light breed. This is by feather formation not, as someone new to the fancy might believe, associated with the birds' weight. This weight can be very misleading in a fully fit adult bird, especially in the females.

The possible inclusion of Langshan blood would certainly improve size and vigour. It is possible that the Minorca blood which William Cook said he used in the making of the Black Orpington Breed was actually from some of these crosses which had taken the Langshan characteristics and were not suitable to use for Minorca breeding, but would add some clout to his new project of creating a large bodied well rounded black fowl.

The breed's characteristics are two fold; 40 points are allocated to the head which is the main feature, but 32 are awarded for body size, structure and, what is to me a great feature of the breed, its style. The best birds have long legs and thighs, which give them the ability to stand in the show pen and display an upright stance with a long back, moulding into the male bird's tail feathers and furnishings. It has a pride bordering on arrogance, and the female has the same stance, but with a tightly whipped tail. They are not a nervous bird. They have a great temperament and seem to have a close affection for humans but maybe this varies within strains. For a long time one which we have continued to breed was originated by David Barriskill, and shown successfully at all the shows in Northern Ireland.

The head piece should be the same for all the main Mediterranean breeds, but the Minorca has the one which is the most developed, especially in the lobes. These should measure 2.75 inches by 1.5 inches according to the standard. Many birds far exceed these figures, which is fine by me, but they must have thickness, the more the better, not as Billy Blackburn once said to a fellow exhibitor, 'Your Minorca hen's lobes are like tissue paper.' The surface of the lobe must be smooth and level, not lined with ridges. It should also be soft to touch; the old saying was 'feel like a kid glove'. Now, to what I suppose is the main feature, the comb. For a start, the bird must have a strong beak and head to be able to carry the heavy weight of comb which, in the male bird, must be wide at the base to enable the comb to stand upright without falling to one side.

The serrations on a comb are the gaps in-between the spikes and this point can confuse people but, whichever way you describe the comb, the spikes must be wedge shaped and not narrow or 'pencilly' and they must be deeply cut into the base, not like the teeth on a saw simply situated along the edges. If you measure the famous McNab's comb the spikes are almost half the depth of the total height of the comb.

These spikes must be free from 'side sprigs' or blemishes, with the largest one situated directly over the eye. They then fan outwards, slightly decreasing in size. The number of spikes is not mandatory; providing they are evenly distributed, five is acceptable, but six were always considered acceptable in a Minorca.

The front of the comb is also important. This must be flat on both sides, the surfaces being smooth and level, not having what are known as 'thumb marks'.

The female's comb, instead of being upright, should fold neatly over to one side, either side will be acceptable; ideally, when in its natural position, it should not obstruct the bird's vision.

If you hold a female's comb upright the formation and distribution of the spikes should be identical to the male's comb.

The face on both sexes should be smooth and as free from feathering as possible. It must also be solid red and not have any sign of the lobe starting to creep into the face and becomimg what is known as 'white in face'. This raises a point of interest in some judges' eyes. The back of the lobe should also be white, as is the front side, but I consider that, providing the red backing to the lobe does not show around the lobe's edges, not only is it acceptable, but a very good deterrent to a bird's lobes spreading into the face, i.e. Spanish style. The standard quotes that the lobe should fit close to the head but you will find that the thickest lobes always stand away a little. This I do not mind providing they are flat surfaced and not creased or folded.

Again referring to the standard, the lobes are quoted as being almond shaped but you will find they are much nearer to round on the females. The eyes, legs and feet need to be black but, on older birds, you will find that they lose some colouring, and this is acceptable. I have given the Minorca's head a very detailed summary, knowing that nearly all the comments are also applicable to Leghorns, Anconas, Andalusians and, except for the face, the Spanish.

The description is also applicable to most other single combed breeds simply by substituting the pronounced white lobe for a conventional red lobe. As with most of the Mediterranean breeds, the Minorca can also be in a rosecombed version. This comb should fit closely to the head with the leader following it round to the top of the neck without touching it.

The surface of the Rosecomb is evenly covered with small points, the whole appearance being one of symmetrical contour, rather than something which was simply thrown on.

The breed has been very successfully miniaturised; by this I mean actually bred down from the large fowl not, as with some breeds, a small version created by using a mixture of existing bantams with similar characteristics. I can recall seeing David Barriskill's birds when they were in the process of being diminished in size and they certainly contained some of his best large fowl blood lines.

Blacks are the main colour in Minorcas. Blues and Whites are also standardised but have never really caught the showman's fancy.

Weights	Large Fowl	Males 7-8 lbs	Females 6-8 lbs
	Miniatures	Males 34 ozs	Females 30 ozs

When selecting the birds to represent the breed of Minorca, I have deliberately omitted a photo of the famous 'McNab', which was considered to be the most perfect specimen ever bred. His photo has been widely used, and I hope to illustrate the breed by using less fashionable prints. I will commence by showing a cockerel which was bred by Walter Bradley when he worked for himself, before becoming Poultry Manager for Lord Dewar. This bird is shown in MIN 1. He has a great body shape and length of limb and a useful headpiece. He won the Challenge Cup for Best Minorca at the Crystal Palace in 1920.

Moving on to 1922, you will see in MIN 2 a very similar stamp of cockerel. This bird won the Trophy for Champion Minorca at Olympia. By now this strain of Minorcas was being shown in the name of Lord Dewar. If you take a close look at this bird, you will notice a great resemblance to McNab who did all the winning during 1924. I believe that they were father and son.

MIN 3. Shows a cockerel with a great lobe and a neatly cut comb. He is different in style to the Bradley cockerels just discussed. This cockerel won the Challenge Cup for best Minorca at the 1923 Crystal Palace. He was bred and exhibited by Mr A. Millen from Ashford in Kent.

MIN 4. Illustrates a very similar style of bird. He was only ever shown once when he won the Dairy Show in 1932. He was bred by Mr W. Fisher, whose strain was more associated with breeding top class females, so presumably this cockerel's comb went over before the Crystal Palace show.

218

MIN 5. Shows a rather more utility type of male bird. He was bred by Fred Seed from Blackpool, who for many years consistently produced this type of Minorca, one of their features being that they did not quickly go 'over the top'. This bird was successfully shown as a cockerel at Birmingham and Olympia during 1933, and Olympia again in 1934. This photo was actually taken in 1935 when the bird was going into his third year.

The rangy cockerel in MIN 6 was bred by Mr Alf Dodd from Crewe, who continued showing Minorcas well into the 1950s. Alf's birds always had great quality lobes, as this bird illustrates. The cockerel won Altrincham, before moving on to successes at the other major shows.

MIN 7. Shows a similar bird which was again bred by Alf Dodd. He won the Dairy Show and was second at the Birmingham United Minorca Club Show in 1927.

MIN 8. Shows a cockerel from South Africa. He was bred there during the early 1930s and won Champion Minorca at Cape Town. He was bred by Mr H. Pitts, whose brother also bred Minorcas in Britain.

219

The selection of photographs for Minorca females takes a similar pattern to those of the males, in that one strain of birds achieves great success. In this case it is the pullet breeders of Mr W. Fisher from Surrey.

MIN 9. Shows a great pullet which was also bred by Mr W. Fisher in 1922. In that year she won 6 Firsts, 17 Specials and 3 Championships, which was nearly a clean sweep, the missing one being at Olympia, where Lord Dewar's cockerel was champion.

MIN 10. Is another grand bodied bird, with a strong lobe. She won the Cup for Best Pullet at the British Minorca Club Show held in Birmingham. However she was only Third at the Crystal Palace United Minorca Club Show. She was bred in 1928 by Alf Dodd.

MIN 11. Shows another excellent pullet, this time bred in 1933, when she won First prize and two cups at the Birmingham Club Show. She was charmingly named 'Lady Selsdon'.

MIN 12. Was bred in 1934 and takes the title of 'Lady Selsdon the Second'. She won Supreme Champion of the United Minorca Club Show held at Olympia for her owner W. Fisher, who was the Club Secretary.

MIN 13. Once again illustrates that the birds bred by Fred Seed were capable of lasting more than a single season. This bird won Champion Minorca at the 1921 British Minorca Club Show. She went to the Dairy Show in 1930 and was Third, and then in 1931, when this photo was taken, she won the Cup for Best Hen at the British Minorca Club Show.

MIN I4. Shows a pullet bred by Messrs Goodman Bros. She was shown seven times in 1935, and her only defeat was by her own sister.

MIN 15. Was taken in 1919, and illustrates a pullet from Western Australia. She was bred by Mr R. Marshall, who bought a breeding pen of Minorcas from Willie Binnie in 1916. During her show career she was unbeaten, with wins at all the Major Shows, including Perth where she was awarded the Gold Medal.

MIN 16. Shows a hen from the great Willie Binnie himself. During her life she won at the British Minorca Club Show, The Crystal Palace and York.

221

MIN 17. Shows a pullet which is rather more on the Utility lines. She won Best Minorca at the 1929 Dairy Show and was bred by Alf Dodd.

MIN 18. Is again an ideal looking Utility pullet. She was shown at the 1932 Birmingham Show and was champion at the Minorca Club Show. She eventually was awarded Champion Female in all Breeds. Her Breeder was Tom Sedden from Staffordshire, who christened her 'Lady Brena'.

MIN 19. Shows a Rosecomb Minorca bred by Mr B. G. Moore from Ebbw Vale. He won both the Crystal Palace and Birmingham in 1933.

MIN 20. Is another variation. This time a Blue pullet which won the 1934 Crystal Palace. Bred as you might have guessed by H Whitley from Paington Zoo.

MIN 21. Shows an extremely old print drawn by Gladys Price. It was used in 1920 to illustrate an article outlining the breed's great potential as a top class egg producer, with the females expected still to be economical when in their third laying year.

MIN 22. To conclude this chapter on Minorcas, I have chosen, as I did at the commencement, two photos of the great Walter Bradley's birds. Both are from the period around 1918. The cockerel swept all before him at the London Shows, including 'Best Bird, Any variety'.

MIN 23. Shows a tremendous hen, which in her time had been Champion Minorca at The Crystal Palace, Birmingham and the London Minorca Club Show. The final clip is one showing Walter Bradley's mating list for Minorcas for the 1920 breeding season.

223

MODERN LANGSHAN

The breed of Langshan was surrounded by controversy after its introduction in 1872. It became known as the Croad Langshan, taking the name from one of its original importers, the Croad family.

The type I am now discussing is the Modern Langshan which was evolved at a time when it was fashionable to have long legs and upstanding birds in both the Old English and Malay Game fowls.

The over heated arguments with the Croad family and other Langshan breeders between themselves and the black Cochin exhibitors prompted the creation of a breed which was so different as not to be confused with either of them. This was to become known as the Modern Langshan. I have a very soft spot for the breed, having been involved with them since childhood. They have never been bred in large quantities but there were sufficient of them at one period for them to have their own breed club, the details and records of which are in my possession, having been passed on from Tom Pickerill who was the last secretary, the club folding on his death. Tom was a great friend of my father. He lived near Crewe and was the last large breeder of Moderns, often mating up to three separate breeding pens which were quite a sight to look at.

There are now only a very few breeders of them, and at one period we lost our only male bird to a fox so we used a Rhode Island Red cockerel, with very good results. Both of the breeds contained Java blood originally so they were quite compatible and gave us extra vigour without losing too much style.

The German Langshan is very different in type and feather conformation. It has the required long legs but they are clean, not sparsely feathered as in the Moderns.

The breed has never been considered for utility purposes, even though they are capable of laying plenty of good sized eggs which are a delicate pink shading. The Croad looks to be more of a utility fowl and there has always been the problem that if you get poor specimens of either breed they tend to look too much alike, which probably explains why the Moderns have never been the most popular of breeds. But given good specimens of either breed and place them side by side, there is a lot of difference.

The beetle green sheen on a true Modern Langshan is probably not equalled in any other breed of poultry. Indeed it is comparable to a Cayuga or Black East Indies duck.

When the original controversy got out of hand, the influential Lewis Wright was adamant in proclaiming that all black birds possessing feathered legs were descended from the same species. Consequently, the Modern was developed to have a long body with a sloping back and a low carried tail. Its neck was also long and carried almost vertical. The long but strong boned legs were to have a slight feathering down the sides and extend along the outer toes. The legs and toes were to be black with white toe nails and very definitely white soles to the feet.

The feathering was to be tight fitting, giving the birds a very gamey feel. This was highlighted by the fact that they were capable of carrying plenty of flesh and could easily weigh well into double figures.

The history of the breed's development is said to have been based purely on selection from the imported Croad Langshans. Because of the breed's style and carriage, many people assumed that Malay blood had been introduced directly. I have my doubts regarding this point. During all the time we have bred the Moderns I have never seen one with any sign of a pea comb. However, there is a difference to the single comb on many of the Modern Langshans.

This difference in comb shape is, I believe, connected with the Black Raiza fowl (for more details please refer to the chapter on their breed) which I suspect was included in the blood lines of the original Langshan/Cochin birds, and by selecting to a tighter feathered and longer backed bird would be quite possible.

Eventually this long legged version was perfected and continued in the same form for another 80 years, but I am afraid that it is now very close to extinction, which is a shame for such a docile, friendly and useful breed, and I ask for new breeders to assist with the project of saving this truly British creation. No doubt some people will comment that the breed is too close in appearance to the Croads and was simply just a localised version. If this is so, then I am biased by a breed of which I have fond memories.

Maybe one of the reasons for the breed's lack of support is that its main colour is black which does not appear to have great appeal to new breeders. The other less common colours were blue and white. It interests me why the colour black does not appeal to the general public when displayed on poultry, but has great appeal when illustrated on ducks.

There have never been any miniature Modern Langshans, but the German Langshan Miniatures are proving to be quite popular, so maybe we can alter the style of them and create some with feathered legs etc. to be Modern Langshan Miniatures. It would be beneficial to have more emphasis on the colours other than black.

Weights Males 10 lbs Females 8 lbs

Many of you will have gathered that, amongst my old time favourite breeds, the Modern Langshan is high on the list. I therefore have no conscience in illustrating more photographs of the breed than their present time popularity would suggest.

ML 1. The two Langshans won at the Club Show, held at York. The Hen was owned by the Club President, Mr Howe, and was Best in Show. The Cockerel by the oldest member, Mr John Stirzaker.

225

ML 2. Was bred by John Ayrton from Brighouse in Yorkshire, and is one of the best Modern Langshans I have seen. During 1932 and 1933 he won the Club Show twice, the Crystal Palace and Birmingham, and was never beaten.

ML 3. Shows a pen of White Moderns, which were sports, (an early throwback from their genetic make-up) from the Blacks. They were bred in 1926 by Mr B. W. J. Wright, who had bred the same blood line of Langshans for fifteen years, and had never previously hatched a white one.

226

ML 4. Is a cockerel again bred by John Ayrton, and was the 1934 Birmingham Show Winner.

ML 5. Won the 1934 Birmingham Fatstock Show. She was bred by the old Club Secretary, John Pickerill from Crewe.

ML 6. Shows the hen which has the unique achievement for a Modern Langshan of being Reserve Supreme Champion in the whole show at the 1934 Crystal Palace. She was exhibited by the famous H. S. Anthony.

ML 7. Shows a Blue Modern Langshan pullet. She was bred by Mr S. T. Ashton, and in 1913 was second at the Club Show. The Blue Langshan Club was founded in 1906, but the colour is now very rare in Britain.

NAKED NECK

This breed is one of Nature's freaks. It is thought to originate from the area of Transylvania in Hungary, and the breed's main characteristic is that virtually all the neck and even part of the crop area is naked of feathering, just rich red coloured skin, giving the birds a revolting yet fascinating appearance.

When first introduced into this country around the 1920s, there was speculation that the birds were the result of a cross between fowls and a turkey, and for a period they assumed the name of Churkeys.

This was a story quickly taken up by the press and the breed gained much publicity, but after their original appeal as novelties faded the breed was left in the hands of just a few stalwarts.

In recent years the breed has once again gained world-wide publicity for its ability to withstand the extreme heat of the eastern countries and is consequently being used as part of the breeding programme for their commercial table poultry industry. Naked Necks had been used in France for centuries as a free ranging meat bird, and they had a good reputation for their ability to convert the pickings from the wild into tasty roasting chickens.

They are classed as heavy breeds and, when crossed with other breeds, the bare neck factor is quite dominant.

The basic shape of the Naked Neck could be described as similar to that of the Sussex or Rock families, with a wide shouldered well rounded front but not so long backed. Its wings are carried fairly high up. It has a single comb, medium in size and a rich red colour, as have the face wattles and the front of the crop, with the almost obscene long neck bare except for a 'cap' of feathers on the rear portion of the bird's head.

The breed exists in a wide range of colours, basically built around the traditional game colour pattern.

The breed has been successfully miniaturised in all the colours and they are more popular than the large birds, certainly in this country.

Weights   *Large Males   5.5 - 6 lbs*   *Females   4-5 lbs*

A White Naked Neck bantam hen fostering her happy family.

228

A typical Naked Neck from the 1930s, when they were often referred to as 'Churkeys'. He was bred by Mrs Colbeck from Wakefield.

Again from 1933, an unusual Rosecombed White. The bird was shown in the non competitive class at the Crystal Palace by his breeder James Hayden from Basingstoke.

From the 1980s, miniature Naked Necks bred by Brian Sands from Boston. Both birds have proved to be very successful in the show pen.

An unusual white cockerel. He was exhibited by Herr Richard Greif at the 1930 World Poultry Congress.

Again illustrates the old fashioned Rosecombed version. I believe this cockerel was from American stock.

An excellently clear necked Large Fowl pullet, photographed by Josef Walters at the 1983 Hannover Show.

230

NEW HAMPSHIRE RED

This breed was developed in the American state of New Hampshire, being their version of the breed created by the neighbouring state of Rhode Island.

The breed was admitted to the breed standards in 1935, so it must be amongst the very last to be introduced.

The breed was at one time claimed to be pure R. I. Red simply bred into a different version over a period of 30 years. This may be so, but I have a feeling that someone has been slightly economical with the true facts. We kept the breed for many years as a commercial proposition, often crossing these birds with R. I. Reds and finding them to be excellent layers. The type of bird we had was much longer in the body and slimmer than the ones seen at the present time. These birds appear to be more Wyandotte shaped, with high carried tails and rather softer feathering. The standard says that the tails should be carried at an angle of 45 degrees in the males and 35 degrees in the females, which is in keeping with my memory of them 40 years ago.

Under-colour is one point which I am quick to refer to. I would prefer this to be sound to the skin, as in a Rhode, but the N.H.R. allows a little smoky tinge to be present. This to me does not mean blue under-colour as is often seen on today's birds.

The general top colour shades between reddish bay and chestnut red according to the standard. It is very attractive to look at and could be described as a reddish buff shading.

The wing markings are different from those of the R. I. Red, in that instead of one side of the secondaries and flight feathers being black and one red, the N. H. Red only requires the black to extend as a broad stripe, which leaves the outer edge medium red coloured.

The main tail and sickles are a green sheen black, whilst the side hangers have a chestnut red edging.

The comb is the standard type, a medium sized, evenly serrated, five spiked version, rich red in colour. The eye is bay coloured and the legs are yellow with a slight horn colouring to the front scales.

There are some very attractive miniatures around but, as I have just mentioned, many of them require greater detail paid to their under-colour to satisfy a Rhode Island Red breeder like myself.

I consider the New Hampshire Red to have a very promising future. The breed combines laying qualities with meat producing potential and I am sure that many newcomers would find the colouring more attractive than the very deep red coloured Rhode Island Red.

On the continent, there is now an additional colour pattern to the breed, with blue replacing the original black markings.

I have not as yet seen the birds, but I am told that at the main show in Holland they looked very attractive. I have no doubt that they will eventually prove to be just as appealing in the British Isles.

Weights	Large	Males	8.5lbs	Females	6.5lbs
	Miniature	Males	34oz	Females	26oz

A superb drawing by Cornelis Van Gink showing the beauty of New Hampshire Reds.

A New Hampshire Red cockerel which was shown by Mr C. C. Ernst in the New Breeds section of the 1934 Crystal Palace Show.

Again bred by Mr Ernst in 1934 and was one of the first New Hampshires to be entered for the National Laying Trials.

NIEDERRHEINER

This breed is in most ways a duplicate of the Bielefelder, with the one major difference that the birds are white pigmented as opposed to yellow. The birds' style and shape are very similar, with a well proportioned body shape, including a full and nicely rounded front.

They have the same characteristic of being a good table fowl, combined with egg laying capabilities.

With the Niederrheiner you have a wider range of colours to chose from. In addition to the variations on the cuckoo marked birds, there are blues and some extremely striking birchen greys.

This contrast of silver hackle on a beautiful sheen black body colouring has been bred to perfection on the continent and is especially attractive in the females.

The breed has been successfully miniaturised and, as with their large counterparts, proved to be amongst the top breeds of popularity at the European shows.

A colour photograph of a Niederrheiner can be seen in the colour section.

Crele Niederrheiner female.

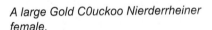

A large Gold C0uckoo Nierderrheiner female.

NORFOLK GREY

This very attractive breed is currently going through a successful period. At many recent shows there were excellent specimens on display creating a lot of public interest.

The breed itself is most striking in appearance, being a typical Birchen O.E.G. contrast of silver and black. I believe when Captain Duckworth created the Silver Sussex it had too much silver pattern, especially on the breast, compared with the colour pattern of the Norfolk Grey, which is just about right, the male having a silver top colour, with a black striping in the hackle, silver saddle and a solid black body.

The female possesses the same hackle with a lacing on the breast, but only extending for a few inches, not as in the Sussex where it extends to the thigh feathers and includes a white shaft to the feather.

The breed was first introduced in 1920, without hitting great heights of popularity. It has been a very successful utility type of bird in the eastern regions, capable of laying plenty of good tasting eggs, combined with a very useful body of meat resulting from the use of game birds in its original development. Other breeds used were Duckwing Leghorns and a tight feathered Orpington which increased body size and introduced more black to the colouring. The single upright comb and face are a very distinct colour of red.

It is classified as a heavy breed but is not excessive in size, having a longish body and a well rounded front with a wide pair of shoulders. The well furnished tail is set at an angle of about 45 degrees.

No miniatures are known but could easily be made.

When originally displayed to the public, the breed for some reason had the name of Black Marias, which I cannot believe was good for its image.

Weights   *Males*   *7lbs*   *Females*   *6lbs*

An attractive quartette of Norfolk Greys.

A Norfolk Grey cockerel which won first prize at Birmingham, The London Dairy Show, and the Crystal Palace in 1930.

The pullet which also won Birmingham and was second at the Dairy Show, again in 1930. Both birds were bred and exhibited by Murray Hale from Essex.

A large bodied cock which won first prize at the Birmingham show in 1933, and was third at the Crystal Palace in the same year when shown by J. F. Newton from Portsmouth.

A typical winning cockerel from more recent years. It was bred and exhibited by Roly Axman from Norfolk.

NORTH HOLLAND BLUE

To describe the North Holland Blue as a feathered legged Marans would be both disre-spectful and incorrect. From outside the show pen the birds do look similar but, on exami-nation, the N.H.B. has the ability to carry large quantities of good quality flesh. This is probably inherited from the Maline, which was used in the breed's original creation.

Briefly, the breed description is of a large bodied bird with a deep front, carrying its tail fairly high. It has a single comb and whitish coloured legs, which have an ample scattering of feathers down the sides extending along the outer toes.

The body feathers are barred, probably more distinctly than those of the Marans, but still nothing like the definition of the English Barred Rocks'. The female's ground colour is darker than the male's.

Apparently, on the continent, the N.H.B. is clean legged and the Marans feathered. How this situation arises I have no idea.

There are no miniatures to my knowledge.

Weights   Males   10lbs   Females   8lbs

When first introduced to this country, Marans had feathered legs, as they still have on the continent. At the present time Marans are clean legged and the North Holland Blue has the leg feathering. This photo from an early importation was described as being Les Marans recently introduced from France.

A typical pair of English type North Holland Blues, with both birds showing a touch of leg feathering.

A typical Cuckoo de Malines hen from the 1930s, illustrating their relationship.

North Holland Blue female.

ORLOFF

This beautiful breed is usually associated with Russia, and the credit for its origin given to the Prussian Count Orloff Techmanski. But historians are sceptical, believing that the breed existed long before he breathed air, possibly five centuries before, in a similar bird called the Ushanki. However, the breed collected the Count's name and he was also instrumental in having a horse from that part of the world named after him.

The original development of the breed was probably by the usual procedure of selecting from localised fowl, and interbreeding them to produce the points necessary to complete the picture which the developer had in mind.

The Ushanki had a single comb, was not large in the body and also possessed a flowing tail, so presumably the Bruge was used to increase the size, and this breed would automatically tighten the feathers, shorten the tail and produce some offspring with flat combs.

The breed that could have supplied the beard and muff was the Thuringian, which would also introduce the mahogany and spangled colouring. The Orloff should have a long and strong neck, well feathered and rather bushy looking, especially on the sides and front.

The shoulders should be wide, moulding into a massive framed body which is full chested and carries plenty of flesh. The tail is well spread and furnished with narrow feathered sickles and side hangers, as is the Bruge.

The wings are short and carried close to the body, with prominent and well fleshed butts. The head is not very large for the size of the bird, but is strong in the eyebrows, and with a comb being described as a raspberry cut in half lengthways. The comb is red and the eyes yellowish, but the striking feature of the breed is the full beard, with muff and side whiskers which extend round to the earlobes, which are small in size and red in colour.

The legs and feet should be of strong round bone, with four straight toes all of which are a very distinct yellow colour.

With the birds standing full chested and their legs wide apart it gives them a vigorous and defiant appearance. Cigarette cards produced by Players more than half a century ago capture the breed's striking appearance and display it to perfection.

Unfortunately, there do not seem to be many breeders in the country at this time, which is a tragedy because I consider the spangled version, if shown correctly, to be as eye catching as any breed in existence.

There are some equally attractive miniatures available, again the most spectacular being the spangled colour. Other colours are the red which is two toned in top colour and the self white.

When Rex Woods showed the original birds bred from imported stock they looked a picture, having striking yellow legs and a rich mahogany spangled colouring, which contrasted beautifully with the white of the muffling; the rich red comb giving the birds a fantastic first impression. Some of the blood is still available in certain parts of the country.

To summarise, I consider it to be an excellent breed and can offer no explanation as to why there are not more birds in this country other than the fact that there also seems to be a shortage of them on the continent, making it difficult to obtain good healthy stock, although there does appear to be an increase in the number of birds shown recently.

In the colour section there is a wonderful example of a male which belongs to Mr Colin Clark.

Weights   Male 40oz   Female 36oz

FIG 1. Shows a pair of Spangled Orloffs from 1921. They were shown by Mrs Colbeck, the cock winning Manchester and the hen winning at York.

FIG 2. Won first prize and a silver cup at the 1925 Crystal Palace. She was affectionately known by her owner as Katherine the second.

FIG 3. Shows a miniature Mahogany Spangled Orloff cockerel. He is from much more recent times, being successfully shown during the 1980s by Tommy Holland from Friskney, Lincolnshire.

239

ORPINGTON

Profile of Will Burdett.

Will Burdett was born in Durham, son of John, the renowned Black Orpington breeder. He was educated at Wellfield Grammar School, from where he moved to attend Houghall Agricultural College, combining this with his family poultry farm duties. During the War years, he saw active service with the Eighth and Fifth Armies in North Africa, Sicily, Italy, Crete and Austria.

Resuming his poultry career in 1946, he has since had a foot in both the fancy and commercial poultry camps. His commercial experience has been associated with the pioneering and development of the 'British Broiler Industry', and has seen the introduction of many Hybrid laying strains. He managed several breeding hatchery firms culminating in Executive, and then Director of one of Buxted - Ross's Poultry subsidiary companies.

In the fancy his achievements are legendary. His service to 'The Poultry Club of Great Britain' is second to none. Fifty years a member, forty-four continuous years on Council, he has held the Office of President five times, including the celebratory Centenary year, Chairman of the Council thrice. He is affectionately referred to as the 'Father of the House' and was part of the 1971 two man team which negotiated the resumption of shows with the Ministry of Agriculture in Whitehall.

His organising abilities have been put to wide use in his role as show organiser for the first of the current series of National Poultry shows in 1978. He is now in his twentieth year as Show Director. He initiated and introduced the Regional Championship Show scheme in 1978; dual success has followed. It has widened the distribution of the full range of poultry breeds and varieties nation-wide, as well as putting the higher echelons on equal terms with the grass roots fraternity.

He has always been heavily committed to breed club activities. He formed the Orpington Bantam Club in 1952 to accelerate the breeding progress, and was its Secretary for 25 years; then supervised its incorporation into the 'Orpington Club' in 1977. Elected Chairman and remaining so, he also has been Chairman of The Buff Orpington Club since 1960.

For distinguished services he was awarded Honary Life Membership of the Barnevelder Club, Sussex, Orpington and The Poultry Club.

He is a great supporter and advocate of Summer Agricultural Shows. He was Chief Poultry Steward for many years of Malton, Cleveland, Stokesley and Pateley Bridge Shows and helper at many others.

His show successes have been illustrious and numerous. He has won all the major show Championships including the National Gold Cup twice. Also amongst his breeding triumphs he originated the Blue Orpington and the White Orpington bantams (his father John originated the Black Bantams).

Some of his proudest and most pleasurable moments have been associated with Queen Elizabeth The Queen Mother. As President, he presented Her Majesty with a trio of Buff Orpingtons in 1977, when she accepted the invitation to become Patron of the Poultry Club.

He acts as keeper of the Royal Birds and supervises their attendance at certain shows from time to time. He firmly believes the royal connection has done the fancy a right power of good, besides bringing prestige and honourable distinction to his beloved Orpington breed.

The stately Orpington fowl retains its ever popular appeal after more than 100 years of distinguished history. Since the originator, William Cook, chose the name from his home in Kent way back in the late nineteenth century the Orpington has achieved world-wide prominence. Little wonder really, for this majestic breed has an impressive pedigree.

Originally the breed had dual purpose objectives. Firstly, 'to lay large clutches of brown eggs through the cold winter months and give plenty of succulent white meat from its plump breast'. Secondly, to produce a breed of fowl 'of handsome appearance.' The happy outcome of both factors was a rapid success.

As a winter egg layer the Orpington appeared at the world's very first egg laying trial at the North Yorkshire farm in Northallerton of Simon Hunter in 1887, just one year after being brought before the public. This resulted in a big demand from the then new mass of backyard, smallholder and allotment poultry keepers seeking a good laying black fowl. At the same time, the amalgam which created the breed also gave it great exhibition fowl potential, which was soon developed by a succession of clever and devoted breeders. Quickly, by selective breeding, the Orpington with its distinctive handsome appearance swept all before it, going onto world-wide fame and recognition. The rise to fame was meteoric, but happily its appeal and popularity is everlasting. Today the Orpington still stands supreme as one of the great poultry breeds of all time.

In appearance the Orpington is big, bold and bulky, so naturally it is firmly established in the 'type breed' category. That is to say, a great deal of emphasis is placed on the essential parts which make up the overall shape, style and outline in its standards.

Briefly these are summarised as pronounced depth of body, full deep broad breast, wide shoulders running into short concave back, saddle wide and slightly rising with full hackle, short compact high tail, small neat head and comb, stout well curved neck with full hackle, legs short and strong high hocks entirely hidden by body fluff and broad flighted wings well tucked up. The flights should be neatly and entirely tucked under the secondaries, with the plumage profuse, broad and soft. In more detail the general characteristics are as follows.

SHAPE

The Orpington body has long been associated with the classic 'U' outline, which perfectly describes an ideal sideways view. In fact, this breed should not only appear to be large but should handle well, with a deep, very broad chest and a carry a large amount of breast meat. So much so, that mature or supreme birds are virtually 'a cube of meat' in overall appearance.

HEAD

This should typically possess enough breadth to make them appear strong without undue coarseness. The comb is small and firmly set, evenly serrated and free from side sprigs. The face should be smooth in texture and free from folds and wrinkles and showing as little hair as possible. The eyes should be full, round and prominent and set close up to the crown of the head.

NECK

These are another point which must satisfy to set on all round good Orpington. A curved, full neck of compact medium length, abundantly feathered is desired. Naturally, the cocks will have most feather and the greater substance of neck as befits their more swaggering deportment.

TAIL

In both sexes of this breed, these are carried rather high and, when in the right combination of wide saddle or cushion, decidedly characterise a good Orpington. Starting from the middle of the back at a steady gradient the cushion rises with a good breadth and wealth of feather to well spread tail ends. Seen at best, it portrays perfection. Faults though are in the extremes. Narrow cushion and long protruding tails in some, stumpy feathered or drooped cushion in others are defects.

WINGS

These help to give the correct balance; small, nicely formed, well tucked up and carried closely to the body, the ends almost hidden by the saddle hackle.

LEGS

They are also important. They must be short and strong and set well apart to give perfect body balance. They should be dead straight from any point of view, well boned without undue coarseness and free from feather.

FAULTS

BODY

Narrow or shallow, cut away front, split breast, wry tail, unbalanced.

HEAD

Undue coarseness, beefy comb, lack of substance, overturned comb, white in ear lobes, sunken or sleepy eye.

WINGS

Narrow flights, split or badly folded and held close to body, drooping or trailing.

LEGS

Ultra short, long and spindly, bent hocks, tent toes, unbalanced, poor or restricted gait.

To get the bold noble dignity sought in the Orpington, the carriage should have broad flighted wings, well tucked up - tail carried high, chest well out and if rather short backed (but NOT short coupled), so much the better. It helps to create an impression of greater depth than length, the classic 'U' outline. The ideal Orpington must not only have a typical sideways profile, it should pass the full-frontal test too; deep broad chest, strong wide shoulders and saddle, wide well furnished hackles, abundant broad self plumage.

Like most popular breeds the Orpington has been produced in a variety of colours. The UK though has long favoured the 4 self colours of black, buff, white and blue.

The Black Orpington should have a sound ground colour with a rich beetle green sheen. Faults are dull black, bronze and purple patches on barring, particularly on wings and tail.

This can be controlled with reasonable care. The occasional red feather in the neck hackle is permissible in the male but must never become fixed in a double mating system.

The Buff Orpington is desired to be clear even buff throughout. The exact shade of colour is not defined but the emphasis is firmly placed on the level of uniformity. This requires the hackles to tone in with the rest of the body. Usually the faults in the darker shades are cinnamon or black colour in the tails and wings. The lighter shades tend to have light under-colour or white flecks (mealiness) on the body and white patches in wing and tail.

Pure snow white plumage is the requirement of a white Orpington, free from yellow or straw tinge. White legs are specifically called for in this colour to complement the white skin and beak, as also in the buff variety. Blue or yellow legs are strong faults.

The Blue Orpington has the Andalusian blue laced factor where the female's body feathers are medium slate blue laced with a darker shade set off by a dark blue neck hackle. The male has a dark blue mantle covering all the top side of the body with the breast and under parts of contrasting medium slate blue laced as in the female. This is a fascinating but difficult combination to attain. General faults are conversely too light or too dark ground colour and lack of lacing.

This breed has the distinction of royal patronage. Queen Elizabeth the Queen Mother has maintained a lifelong interest in Buff Orpingtons and has been a highly successful exhibitor in recent years.

COOK FAMILY ORPINGTON - Will Burdett

The origins of the Orpington are well and truly documented. William Cook saw to that. He sought publicity for his new breed with considerable skill and diligence. His immortal birds are the ONLY popular poultry breed to have a KNOWN originator. Without Cook there would never have been an Orpington.

We know so much about the breed, but information on the originator and his family, who have all played an important role, has been rather sparse. In recent times however, further details have come to light through various purchases of the once owned Cook properties. Indentures and conveyances, which form part of title deeds, have revealed some interesting facts. The relevant details of these are chronologically compiled to set the scene for this Cook story.

1849 William Cook was born at St Neots, Huntingdon.

1863 He started his working life in Chislehurst, Kent, as a coachman, but developed an interest in poultry at a very early age. These were very early evolutionary years for pure poultry breeding; the old Dorkings and such natives of the countryside alongside the new Langshan, Cochin and other imports.

1869 William Cook moved to Orpington town and took up residence at Tower House in Sevenoaks Road, with his wife Jane. Here his poultry career took off in earnest, both in the practical and literary senses.

1882 He published the first of his many books, THE PRACTICAL POULTRY BREEDER AND FEEDER, which went into eight editions.

1886 EUREKA! After several years of experiments, William Cook took a quantum leap into the history books. Enter the BLACK ORPINGTON to world-wide acclaim. It was named after his place of residence.

In the same year William Cook became editor and proprietor of THE POULTRY JOURNAL. This magazine continued for many years.

1889 The WHITE ORPINGTON was introduced, the first version rosecombed. For a Cook product it had a mild press.

1890 William Cook, his wife and five children - three sons and two daughters, moved to Walden's Manor. He renamed the Manor 'Orpington House'. Here was the required room for expansion. It was here that the famous Buff Orpington was developed. The poultry business prospered and a London office was opened at Queen's Head Yard, Borough S.E.

William, meanwhile, spent much of his time writing, publishing the Poultry Journal, travelling and lecturing. He undertook lecture tours for all types of organisations, including a great number of County Councils. He made an extensive study of diseases affecting poultry. He had an operating house and fowl hospital. He took in pupils, sold appliances, medicines, poultry foods, fattening powders and W Cook's Poultry Keeper's Account Book. During his absence the farm at Orpington House was in the very capable hands of his eldest daughter Elizabeth Jane. She was assisted by her brothers and sister, and became as expert in poultry husbandry as her father.

1894 The BUFF ORPINGTON was introduced. There was controversy at first, but no matter; it had a quick rise to fame, with the inbred ability to thrive and prosper and became a household name world-wide. One hundred years on, it is as popular as ever, a living legend.

1897 William Cook then introduced the Diamond Jubilee Orpington, a pen which was 'graciously accepted by Her Majesty, Queen Victoria'.

In this same year, William Henry Cook, William's eldest son, left Orpington House and bought Elm Tree Cottage (now Elmdene, Derry Downs, St Mary Cray). The purchase price of £780 was advanced by his father.

The conveyance document dated 30 June, 1897 described him as 'Gentleman of Orpington House, St Mary Cray'.

1900 At this time a family rift developed. It appears that the loan was not being repaid (on whatever terms). William Henry Cook secured a loan from Catherine Mary Cook, his wife, of £260 at five percent. Dated 4 May, 1900 this indenture describes William Henry as a Poultry Farmer. Apparently he was already in the poultry business on his own by that date.

1902 William Cook was awarded the Poultry Club medal (no special significance to this except curiosity. It apparently forms part of the property effects on conveyance documents). During these years, the journalism, business enterprise and breeding experiments continued unabated at Orpington House by William. He had, by now, established poultry farms in South Africa and America which proved to be valuable bases for world trade. He made visits to both countries, despite the fact that he was not a well man, suffering from asthma and emphysema. At the home base, more and more new varieties appeared on the production line, all additions to the Orpington standard; blue and buff ducks and then the mottled (spangled) Orpington.

1903 A major tragedy struck the family. Jane Cook (Mrs William Cook, Senior) was killed on a visit to the married son William Henry and his wife on their farm, when there was a violent gas explosion at the house. This did not help relations between William Henry and the rest of the family.

1904 William Cook the great poultry pioneer and originator of the Orpingtons died on 25 June. His already failing health began to deteriorate still further after his wife's death a year earlier. In June he returned from a visit to America and travelled to Skegness for a

244

short vacation. The day after his arrival at the hotel he was taken ill and died. He was interred in his wife's grave in Star Lane Cemetery, St Mary Cray.

1904 William Henry was left no part of his father's business and, in the same year, sold the Elmdale property. It is possible that the sale was forced in order to settle the debt and wind up the estate. A note signed by the executors of William's will dated 14 December acknowledges repayment of the loan of £780.

His sister, Elizabeth Jane, now Mrs R Wakeman Clarke, inherited the family poultry firm of William Cook and Sons at Orpington House. She bought out the other brothers and sister and continued her father's experiments and enterprises. Like her father, she also lectured, gave advice and consultations and kept up the publication of THE POULTRY JOURNAL.

1907 Elizabeth Jane produced the Cuckoo Orpington.

1910 This was followed by the introduction of the Blue Orpington. Elizabeth Jane also further developed the Orpington Ducks and brought out the chocolate colour variety. All these additional varieties continued to be credited to the 'William Cook and Sons' name.

1911 William Henry meanwhile, continued on his own account. His firm, 'W H Cook Ltd' flourished and, due to expansion, he moved to Tubbenen Lane, Orpington.

1933 Another family tragedy occurred. Elizabeth Jane was knocked down and killed in Bromley High Street. After almost 30 years' personal administration by her 'William Cook & Sons' ceased to trade.

1947 William Henry retired from his business, W H Cook. His Tubbenden Lane farm land was developed and became Maxwell Gardens.

The two firms, 'W H Cook' run by the brother and 'William Cook & Sons' run by the sister, were separate and distinct. They were in direct and apparently acrimonious competition. It was at a time when British pure breeds were world leaders. There was a really lucrative home and foreign market which both firms exploited to the full. With their father's established base in America, commercial logic attracted them to the West. First, by every available shipping lane, then, later by air-freight, consignments were sent world wide. It is not possible to quantify the vast amount of poultry stock distributed but we know for sure, that seed and replacement Orpingtons were spread to most parts of the world. William Cook and his family were not fanciers in the purist sense but it was their remarkable initiative and enterprise which supplied the basic original Orpington stock to others, for them to fashion after their own tastes.

Have we come to the end of the exceptional Cook Family Orpington Story? One hesitates to affirm. In the 1960s, sightings were made in East Dereham, Norfolk, of a 'W Cook and Sons Ltd' farm dealing with standard fowl and, in recent times, a family relative donated the 'W Cook Trophy' for the Best Buff Orpington at the National Federation Show.

Even so, there is a feeling of continuity, as the Orpington thrives in living tribute to its originator(s).

ORPINGTON ORIGINS

The fifty year period of the Victorian era from 1850 to 1900 was one of the most prolific periods of poultry development. At that time basic stock was being shipped in from abroad. Mediterranean types mixed with Asiatic breeds and native stock. Hence this threesome produced new breeds, new varieties or a new improved look to old favourites. It was the time when economic factors required poultry to be productive in eggs, meat or both, besides the fine feathers. It was the dawn of the poultry industry. One of the great pioneers of the time was William Cook from Kent, who was a breeder, publisher, and poultry developer. His lectures throughout the country, in his own words, 'drew the attention of the labouring classes to this easily attained means of adding to their income and increasing their limited resources of home comforts'.

Today, Cook and his family are best remembered for a wide range of Orpington fowl and duck varieties. Each introduction was based on the same 'eggs and meat with handsome plumage' formula. After all, William Cook was a poultry developer, not a poultry fancier. He left it to others to put their own version of 'feathers onto frames'. In the following description of the Orpington history the text on origin is mainly taken from Cook's own publication.

BLACK ORPINGTONS

By his own account in the 'Fanciers' Gazette', William Cook crossed Minorcas, Plymouth Rocks and Langshans to create black Orpingtons, using black Minorca males. The Minorca at that time was an extraordinary layer with white flesh, small but very active, with black plumage, good body and red lobes. He put these to Black Plymouth Rock pullets. Plymouth Rocks were hardy birds and good winter layers of brown or tinted eggs, but possessed yellow skin and legs which was always against them in this country as table birds. The pullets from this mating were kept and mated to short, clean legged, Langshan males, the Langshan giving the breed its long deep breastbone, white skin and flesh. The first matings were made in 1880. After further selection and blending, these fowl made their first appearance at the three big shows, The Dairy, Crystal Palace and Birmingham in 1886. Two years later, separate classes were given at the 1888 dairy show in Islington, where there were 14 cockerels and 19 pullets. The Black Orpington had arrived.

Development

Other breeders latched onto the opportunities this new breed presented, notably Joseph Partington who, in 1900, using black Cochin and Langshan blood, created an 'exhibition type'. Heavily feathered, and brilliantly coloured, they became huge balls of feather without visible shanks. This style was impressive, but not very reproductive, and by 1939 stock numbers were low. During the Second World War, and after, the breed was revitalised by using Australorps. The outcome was a considerable 'tidying up' of previous coarseness and a continuation of show winners was produced. Fifty years further on to the present time, the black Orpington can, and does, win championships with a certain amount of ease, as in previous times. The excessive development of plumage that once was has gone; instead a better balanced bird has arrived, more refined, with less bulk and more productive. Most importantly, it is one adapted to preservation in perpetuity.

WHITE ORPINGTONS

Cook produced the white Orpington in 1889 of which he said, 'they are considerably smaller than the black variety and take quite a different shape from the single and rosecombed Orpingtons'

His whites were rosecombed and their basic background was white Leghorn males, mated to black Hamburgh hens. The resulting pullets which came out white were due to a rosecomb white Dorking cock. It was some years before they bred true, as blue cuckoo offspring often appeared. From a picture in his own book Cook shows the white as a more or less four toed white Dorking.

Development

The first whites made no headway. They were overtaken by a new strain, which started life as a non standard 'white Albion' from its mentor Godfrey Shaw, ten years after in

1899. Orpington enthusiasts were quick to claim this version as their own, since it resembled in most details the ideal white Orpington. Thereon, taken in hand by the showing fraternity, they became much larger and more feathery than they originally were. They had their moments of glory over the years, but had to contend with the more popular white Wyandottes. Perhaps, if the standard had not insisted on white legs and red eyes, and had adopted the Langshan principle of dark legs and dark eyes, they may have been more lasting, with true Orpington character! The revival today owes much to the single combed white Wyandotte, and the white Sussex. These three breeds have intermingled over the years with beneficial success to all.

BUFF ORPINGTONS

The buff was first introduced in 1894 to satisfy the then growing demand for buff coloured birds. The variety was produced by mating gold spangled Hamburgh cocks with dark and red Dorking hens. The reddish brown pullets produced by this cross proved to be by far the best layers. These were mated to Buff Cochin cocks. About 20% of the resulting progeny were buff in colour, with clean white legs. Many defects appeared in these early matings, inherited from their ancestors. The rose comb of the Hamburgh, the five toes of the Dorking and the feathered legs of the buff Cochin, were only bred out with great difficulty and selective care over a period of time. It took Cook 8-9 years to breed the buff to a standard good enough to go before the public. Its first appearance was at the 1894 Dairy Show.

Development

The introduction met with a hostile press in some quarters. No matter, being distributed widely and shipped abroad, its rise to fame was meteoric, and it soon became a household name world-wide. It was a versatile ALL PURPOSE fowl, for many years a leading egg layer and holder of laying-test records and with a mass of supporters. At the same time it had an illustrious record in the show world. Since the winner of a class of 56 pullets took the silver medal at the 1899 Dairy Show there has never been a time when buff Orpingtons have not been seen in good numbers at our shows, challenging for top honours. Admirably, this dedicated support has sustained through to present times. Stock is plentiful and in good hands. There has also been a move towards the European type, with more emphasis on the broad deep breast and short strong legs required in the breed standard. In the process, buffs have moved nearer to the blacks in type.

JUBILEE ORPINGTON

The Jubilee Orpington was introduced in 1897 to commemorate the Diamond Jubilee of Queen Victoria. Cook presented Her Majesty with a few of these birds. They were produced by mating reddish-brown birds of buff Orpington progeny to old red Dorkings, the process, followed by matings with 'native' stock - (thought to be old Kent fowl or old Sussex fowl). With careful selection, extending over several generations, the Jubilee Orpington was obtained with the reddish-brown ground colour with black bar and white tipped feathers.

Development

Initially, the Jubilees made reasonable headway. They were good layers and profitable table birds. As a show bird they were not easily bred to obtain the correct distribution of the three colours. A separate Jubilee club was formed and, in 1911, there was an entry of 37 in their club show. Gradually, however, they were edged out by the then more popular Speckled Sussex of the same tri-colour pattern. In recent times there have been attempts at revival from imported stock. They are as difficult as the originals to breed to standard. But then, when have difficulties ever been a deterrent to the dedicated enthusiast!

SPANGLED ORPINGTONS

The year 1900 saw the introduction of the 'black and white' variety of the Orpington family, known as the spangled Orpington. In the first place they were sports from the Jubilees. Many of those coming black and white were saved for at least a year to see how they moulted out. They were then divided, part being mated to very dark coloured Dorking cocks, the others being put with black Orpington cocks. The progeny from these two matings were carefully selected and re-mated for three to four generations. This produced the Spangled Orpington with beetle green black ground colour, each feather having a fairly large spangling of white from the tip to almost a third of the way up the feather.

Development

It was purported that Anconas and Spangled Game were later used to fix the mottled factor. Although a very likely possibility, it was not documented. This variety made slow progress. By 1905 it remained practically in the sole hands of the originators.

At the Variety Orpington Club's first show at the Grand International at Sheffield in 1904 there were 14 entries in two classes all from the same source.

The second show at Alexandra Palace in 1905 had 13 entries, but only one other than from William Cook and Sons. But by 1911 at the Crystal palace there was an uplift to 44 entries. It was a short reign and a sudden decline. All that was left for future generations were but pictures in the book. Magnificent coloured portraits, by Ludlow, of a strikingly handsome bird.

A modern remake is not an easy prospect - the black element is readily available but the mottled factor is limited in today's choice of breeds. The formula is there nevertheless.

CUCKOO ORPINGTONS

The Cook family originated the Cuckoo Orpington in 1907. Their aim was a dual purpose type meat producer and egg layer, basically a cross between Black Orpingtons and White Orpingtons and then carefully selected to fix the colour factor.

Development

The Cuckoo Orpington made its debut at the Dairy Show of 1908 where 17 birds were exhibited. It was promoted by the Variety Orpington Club and had 26 entries at the 1911 Club Show.

It did not however survive the First World War years. Cuckoo has never been a fashionable colour with most popular breeds over the years. In time to come, prevailing tastes and format can change and perhaps this colour can be resurrected. The basic black element is freely available. There is a question mark however over the purity of the present day whites' 'silver factor' to be overcome by trial and selection.

BLUE ORPINGTON

The blue Orpington was a late comer to the Orpington scene, making its first appearance in 1910 (blue colour fowls in fact came from early Orpington matings but were discarded because Victorians apparently associated blue colour with cross breed layers). The 1910 blues were made by using black Orpingtons onto white Cochins. The progeny were mated to blue Andalusians and then selected for the desired blue colour together with the distinctive lacing as required.

Development
Blue Orpingtons made rapid headway. It was a highly fashionable colour. By 1912 at Crystal Palace, a blue lifted the trophy for the best Orpington, beating all the older established colours. The twenties and thirties were the boom years. At the Blue Orpington Club shows 80 plus entries were frequently obtained.

What an impressive sight that must have been. The Second World War took its toll. Blue survived but only just. Thankfully, there were always one or two devoted breeders to maintain continuity. Again, at the present time, the variety is in good capable hands with prospective variance of blood lines. The Blue Orpington with its distinctive lavender plumage, inherited from the Andalusian, has great attraction and handsome appearance. Provided the 'blue factor' can be maintained, and retained, it can be kept numerically strong into the future with the aid of the black Orpington. This is in accordance with the Mendelish heredity factor of which the blue Orpington is a true representation.

OTHER COLOUR ORPINGTONS
Red, Partridge, Barred, Gold and Silver laced Orpingtons and other colours have been produced in Germany. They were produced from Wyandottes, selected for single combs and adjusted leg colour and eye colour where appropriate.

Development
Red Orpingtons were first seen at the 12th German National Show, held at Nuremberg in 1908. Early specimens appeared at the Crystal Palace in 1911, then shown from 1912 to 1920. Partridge Orpingtons were created in the 1920s, but the Poultry Club did not admit them to standards. Barred Orpingtons, Laced and other colours are recent additions to the German scene. Imported here they have made little headway.

For British tastes they are much too near to Wyandotte character. There may be a change in outlook in the future. It is too early yet to predict extinction.

CONCLUDING COMMENTS
In the Orpington's origins it is clear that in those early matings of the 1880s available breeds were limited. Thus Cook had to go 'the long way round' to reach his objectives. In the progress there were many imperfections to be bred out, mis-markings, rosecombs, five toes, yellow legs, red eyes, feathered shanks and so on.

All these defects were eliminated in time EXCEPT for PALE or WHITE LOBES inherited from Mediterranean or other lobed breed ancestors. The occurrence of this fault after 100 years of eradication is a phenomenon imponderable and inexplicable.

To illustrate Will Burdett's excellent summary on the breed of Orpington, I have selected the photos into groups of each colour. The earliest of these date back to the last part of the nineteenth century, when William Cook completed his development of the breed. Basically the photos cover the years from 1920 to the present time and illustrate the changes with the birds during this period.

ORP 2

ORP 1

The first colour to be presented to the public was a Black, and ORP 1 shows a cockerel which was displayed on the front cover of Feathered World in 1892. The development of all breeds was disrupted by the 1914-1918 War, but by the early 1920s the improvement towards our present day birds was becoming noticeable. In 1924 Wm. Cook once again secured front cover in Feathered World with a pair of his winning birds, as shown in ORP 3. In the same year, Mr Cunliffe-Owen also gained front cover with a Black hen which appeared to be much deeper in body than the Cook birds. Here she is shown in ORP 2.

ORP 3

250

ORP 4

In 1925 the Crystal Palace winner was a good looking cockerel shown by Mr J. Lewis from Cheshire, shown in ORP 4. The Champion bird at the 1926 London Dairy show was won by a Black Orpington pullet, bred and shown by Miss Shanks. The bird is shown in ORP 5, and illustrates the progress towards perfection which the breed was making. The name of Miss Shanks was eventually to be joined with Mr J. D. Kay from Newmarket, and together they were associated with Orpingtons for several decades.

ORP 5

By the end of the 1920s, we were to see some magnificent Black Orpingtons, many of them being bred and shown by Fred Swindells, a farmer from Cheshire. ORP 6 shows the 1930 Crystal Palace winning pullet. The bird was then judged to be the Champion Orpington Any Colour. Fred also won the 1931 Dairy Show with the cockerel in ORP 7. I have a feeling that his birds were related to the stock shown by J. Lewis in 1925 (ORP 4), both breeders coming from Cheshire.

ORP 6

ORP 7

The 1930s saw the emergence of several new breeders who were to have a big influence in the breed for several decades.. One was Arthur Snelgrove, who later became the Club Secretary.

ORP 8. Shows one of his pullets at the 1933 Dairy Show, where she gained fourth prize. This event was always held in October, and it would appear from the photo that she had not grown her main tail feathers. If she did develop them correctly she would be a fine specimen.

ORP 9. Shows Arthur's 1934 Dairy Show winning pullet, which was eventually judged to be Champion Orpington and Reserve Champion of the whole show. Arthur also won the Club Show in 1934. This event was held at the Crystal Palace in December.

ORP 11. Shows one of Fred Swindell's winning hens from the same period. It is a bird which I would be proud to own at the present time.

ORP 10. Shows the winning bird in all her glory.

The name of Burdett was prominent at this period, and the front cover in the Feathered World, shows a pair of excellent birds which were shown by Will's father John, who lived in County Durham at this period. These birds are shown in ORP 12.

Harry Lacey from Paignton was another breeder of top class birds, and ORP 13 illustrates the 1932 Dairy Show winning cockerel and also the 1931 Crystal Palace winning pullet.

ORP 14

ORP 15

Colonel Humphrey Watts was winning with the cockerel in ORP 14, whilst Bert Anthony was having success with the cock in ORP 15.

Champion bird at the 1933 Club Show was the cockerel shown in ORP 16, which was bred and shown by Fred Swindells, whilst ORP 17 shows the 1935 Crystal Palace winner for Harry Lacey.

ORP 16

ORP 17

The development of White Orpingtons is different from the other colours. Photos in the early 1920s show birds with excessive feathering imported from America, and full exhibition type. In later years they graduated into a slim lined version which were called 'Old Type Orpingtons', meaning a utility style of bird. Several breeders showed this type of bird, but all of them failed to maintain their quality into the 1930s. Presumably they ran short of fresh blood, and of vigour. Even today, good quality White Orpingtons are hard to find.

The Photograph in WO 1. Shows a hen which won Olympia in 1922. She is so excessive in feathering that a dewlap has appeared, which is almost large enough to be a beard. She was shown by Messrs. Currah Bros.

WO 2. This hen was exhibited in 1921; she came Second at the Crystal Palace for Mr. G. H. Proctor J.P. O.B.E.

WO 3. Shows another massive hen, this time shown by Lt. Col. H. Watts from Crewe where Michael Harrison was the Show Manager. She won the big Manchester Show in 1923.

WO 4. Shows another of the 1921 winners, this time the Dairy Show where she also won the Challenge Cup. Again she is shown by Mr. Proctor from Durham.

WO 5. Shows a cock which won the Crystal Palace in 1921. He has been photographed with his head down, and does not illustrate his correct shape. I was impressed with the bone structure of his shanks. He was exhibited by John Warren from Dorset.

WO 6. Is another example of the Humphrey Watts specials. This cockerel won the Dairy Show for him in 1923.

WO 7. Shows a cock from around 1930, when he won the Crystal Palace, but his feathering was already tightening towards the utility version. He was shown by Mr W Fielden.

WO 8. This photo reverts back to 1923 when Mrs G. Baird won the Royal Agricultural Show at Newcastle with, once again, a very useful looking White Cock.

The next four photos show White Orpingtons during the 1930s. These were shown as 'Old Type Orpingtons' and sponsored by a club of that name.

WO 9. Shows the winning pullet at their Club Show in 1930. She was bred and exhibited by Chisbury Poultry Farm, which used the breed as a commercial enterprise. In 1928 one of their White Orpington pullets laid 279 eggs in 48 weeks at the National Laying Test.

WO 10. Was the Club Show Champion for Richard Cusworth. As a pullet she had been to the Yorkshire Laying Trials, where she laid 226 eggs and gained second prize in her group of breeds.

WO 11. Was bred and exhibited by Mr W. M. Bell from Hampshire, and won several of the leading agricultural shows for him.

Blue coloured birds in any breed always create a lot of public interest but, unfortunately, only a few dedicated breeders.

William Cook was amongst the first exhibitors, and the cock in BLU 1 won Birmingham for him in 1922.

During the 1920s, Major Morrison bred many of the best birds, and BLU 2 shows his 1924 Dairy Show winning pullet, she looks to be very good, if she was standing in a natural position. Many photographs are spoilt by the bird dropping its tail through nervousness when moved to strange surroundings for the camera man.

BLU 3. Shows a very attractive trio of Blues which won the challenge for best trio at the 1925 Crystal Palace; once again they were bred by Major Morrison from Reading.

258

The next photos are Blue females from four different eras.

BLU 4. Won the Dairy show in 1932; she was bred and exhibited by Mr H. Forbes-Brown from Sussex.

BLU 5. shows a good shaped and well laced hen bred by Major Morrison; she won the Royal Agricultural Show in 1922.

BLU 6. Shows another excellent hen; she was bred by Will Burdett and was a consistent winner for him during the 1960s.

BLU 7. Shows an almost identical hen from the 1980s. She was bred by ourselves, and again won many Best in Show Awards. The question which I ask is, 'Were all these four birds related to each other?'. I know for a fact that ours descended from Will Burdett's blood line, but did they all trace back to the 1922 birds?

In most breeds of poultry, Buff coloured birds prove to be very popular. Orpingtons are no exception, with their appeal continuing into the 1990s.

BUFF 1. I commence their photographic illustrations with a strong bodied cock from 1922. He is lacking in flow of feather, but was a good winner at that period for his owner Mr W. Pridmore.

BUFF 2. Again shows a bird from 1922, this time showing a longer and softer feathering. He was bred and exhibited by Mr. W. J. Golding from Kent. This gentleman was almost to dominate the breed for several decades. The cockerel in the photo won the Twenty Guinea Challenge Cup and also the Poultry Club Cup at Tunbridge Wells in 1922.

BUFF 3. Shows the improvements made in the breed by 1927. This cock won Best Buff Orpington at the Royal Counties. He was bred and exhibited by Sir John Leigh Bart from Surrey. In shape, the bird is getting much nearer to our present day winners.

BUFF 4. Shows a bird which has once again been photographed just off balance. He was a consistent winner for Mr. C. H. Angear from Devon. His wins include Champion Novice exhibit at the 1926 Crystal Palace.

BUFF 5. Reverts back to 1923 with a cockerel which won the Crystal Palace for Mr. G. H. Proctor. The bird has a much better comb than most of the birds during this period.

BUFF 6. Shows the cock which was Champion Bird at the 1929 Crystal Palace. He was bred and exhibited by Willie Golding.

BUFF 7. Shows a cockerel from 1932, when he was Best Buff at the Dairy Show; bred and shown by Willie Golding.

BUFF 8. This cockerel was once again Champion of the Crystal Palace for Willie Golding, in 1934. The bird shows a good body shape, but I am not too impressed with his comb serrations.

261

BUFF 9. Shows the pullet which won the Dairy Show in 1911. She was shown by Mr. E. A. Cass.

BUFF 10. Once again shows a winning bird which was bred by W. J. Golding. This pullet won at the 1922 Tunbridge Wells Agricultural Show.

BUFF 11. Shows a hen from 1925. She appears to be paler in colour than many from that period, and won many of the North Country Shows. She was also second at the Crystal Palace for Cyril Bulman from Cumberland.

BUFF 12. Illustrates a hen which won the 1933 Crystal Palace. In type she is well up to present day standards, though her colour appears to be darker than is the modern trend. She was bred and exhibited by Mr Charles Keetly.

ORPINGTON - CONCLUSION

When Wm. Cook created the Orpington, his ideal was for a dual purpose bird which was capable of laying a good quantity of brown eggs. I therefore conclude the breed's illustrations with photographs of the original winning birds, before the showman developed them into what we now consider to be nearing perfection.

FIG 1. Shows a White cockerel which won Best Young Bird at the Club Show in 1905.

FIG 2. Was taken in 1908, when this White pullet won a Silver Medal for the Best Female in Show at the Royal Agricultural Show, which was held In Newcastle.

FIG 3. Shows a trio of Blacks which were winning in 1907 at both the Dairy and Crystal Palace Shows, the pullet on the left collecting a Gold Medal for Best in Show.

OWL BEARDED DUTCH

Whilst writing my summary of the breeds, I have occasionally drawn attention to the fact that a particular breed is not, at present, bred in this country, and there is no logical explanation why. For 150 years these birds have never been considered appealing enough for fanciers to arrange their importation.

One such breed is the Owl Bearded Dutch which, in its native Holland, assumes the name Uilabaarden, whilst in Germany I believe the breed is know. as the Eulen Barthuhn.

I have never seen the birds in the flesh and can only base my comments on photos and paintings. I find the characteristics of the breed fascinating, and can see no outward reason for them to be a troublesome breed, either for reproduction, or over large crests as in the Polands, which may require extra attention. Indeed they appear to have a greater range of body structure and more stamina than many of the small light breeds.

Maybe the breed's downfall is its close resemblance to other breeds. It could be described as a non-crested Poland, or a twin horned Thuringian, as opposed to the normal single combed bird.

Another breed which comes into the equation is the Brabanter. This breed is credited with being one of the oldest breeds in Belgium and there are recordings of it being shipped to Holland as long ago as the sixteenth century. The birds have a tightly feathered forward facing crest which, if removed, the rest of the bird would be very similar to the Owl Bearded Dutch.

At the 1995 German Classic Show there were 46 entries of Eulen Barthuhn, which suggest that the birds have proved to be quite popular in that country even if they do not catch the showman's imagination here.

The Owl Beard is described by that great Dutchman, Van Gink, as being one of the oldest of Dutch breeds, and his paintings clearly show a pair of light breed birds with typical long flowing tails and a very alert looking appearance.

The main features are in their heads with their massive full beard and mufflings, which are accompanied by a very neat pair of horns to their combs.

Apparently, in the early part of the twentieth century, even in Holland, the breed declined to a point of near extinction. This was attributed to the great popularity of the massive size of distinguished breeds such as Cochins and Brahmas.

The decline in the number of birds was halted by the introduction of hybrid blood, resulting from a cross between La Fleche and Bearded Thuringians. The simple crossing of these two breeds demonstrates how closely the Dutch Owl resembles other neighbouring breeds.

The Owl Bearded Dutch lays white eggs which have a unique feature in that they are almost round in shape.

The breed exists in a good range of colours, including self-black and whites, a blue which is similar to the Andalusian laced blue and the gold and silver laced which are similar to the Poland.

The colouring which attracts me is the one where the head and full beard, including the muffling, are in complete contrast to the remaining body and tail colours, an example being the black headed white.

I have no records of a miniature version but, as stated in some other breeds, a bantam type could prove to be more popular with the modern day poultry fancier.

Weights are given as Males 5.5 lbs   Females 4.5 lbs

FIG 1. Cornelis Van Gink depicts the breed beautifully in this painting, reproduced here in Mono.

FIG 2. Shows an Owl Bearded female, which was shown on the continent and photographed by Hans Schippers. In that part of the world they are usually described as Wilebaard Moorkop, or Uilebaarden.

265

PADOVANA

The Padovana is credited as being of Italian origin and to my knowledge only made a brief appearance in this country around the 1930s.

They were first displayed at the Crystal Palace in 1931 and judged by the great authority of poultry, W Powell-Owen, known to his friends as P.O.

When the Crystal Palace schedules were distributed and the breed of Padovana listed for the first time with the judge-to-be, P.O., he received a lot of good humoured banter and witty remarks from his friends, especially as the breed's name was misspelt, and the breed in no way standardised.

The birds shown were in two colours, a spangled version and one which P.O. described as being similar to the Quail Belgian Bantam's colouring. The birds are single combed with a beard and muff and a pair of small wattles and their ear lobes have a whitish tinge to them.

The shape of the bird shows a well developed front and breast with a longish back and the usual type of 45 degrees carriage on a close folded tail, which is well furnished in the male birds, in keeping with breeds which have large muffs and neck hackles, and abundantly feathered and rounded. During the 1920s Edward Brown discussed the breed and said he believed they were created in Italy during the mid 19th century. The breed's appeal to the Italians was opposed to their native birds. The Padovana was capable of carrying good edible flesh. At the same time, the female was capable of laying plenty of eggs.

He described them as being large in body size, broad backed, and with a long and well arched neck. He then described the head as being medium in size with a triple pea comb, with a knob rising at the back.

The colouring is mainly black with intermingled golden yellow. Presumably there was a logical explanation as to why two extremely knowledgeable gentlemen have different versions of the birds. I would assume that they were still in a cross breeding state, and that many variations were being produced. The breed most resembles the Faverolles, which may well account for the bird's original reputation as a table fowl.

In colouring, the Brabanter group of breeds includes a very attractive quail coloured variety, which may have been involved in the original cross breeding. To my knowledge the breed is no longer in circulation within these shores, but could quite easily be found in Italy, without being part of the show scene.

Weights   *Male*   *11 Lbs*   *Females*   *9 Lbs*

The Buff Padovana pullet which won the Crystal Palace in 1931.

The corresponding male bird.

A line drawing illustrating a pair of Padovana.

This bird was second at the Crystal Palace, this time demonstrating the speckled variety.

267

PHEASANT FOWL

To give the breed its full title 'Old English Pheasant Fowl' illustrates exactly what it is. A British version of what has happened in all corners of the world, the native fowls of a particular area have been selected and developed to eventually produce a standardised breed.

In this case the birds were native to North Lancashire, Cumberland, Westmoreland and parts of Yorkshire, and have been there for 300 years and probably a lot longer. Their final development came during the great poultry breed expansion in the latter half of the last century.

The original birds contained Golden Hamburgh blood which was developed from the native Dutch laying fowl called the 'Dutch Everyday Layer', and probably the Belgian Braekel, which was at one period also rose combed as well as single combed. Both of these breeds found their way to the north country. Black Spanish were possibly also involved.

There also existed in the south of Lancashire, and Yorkshire bordering onto Derbyshire, a similar looking bird which was developed into the Derbyshire Redcap.

They may look similar at first glance but, actually, when you keep the two breeds they are quite different in many ways, the most obvious pointer being the white lobe on the Pheasant Fowl, as opposed to the red ones of the Redcap.

That the Pheasant Fowl contains some Old English Game blood is almost certain. There are many of the same characteristics when you rear the two breeds of chicks together. The O.E.G. used was probably black-red, which certainly would be freely available in that part of the British Isles.

The style of the Pheasant Fowl is similar to a larger version of the Hamburgh, with long flowing tail feathers constructed of very broad and soft feathers.

The birds should have a wide pair of shoulders, long flat back, slate coloured clean legs, set off with the very characteristic broad and long rose comb finishing in a flat leader, which should follow the contour of the head.

The comb should have plenty of even shaped little spikes known as working and be a rich red colour, but not as pronounced as in the Redcap. The lobe, without being too prominent or large, is white in colour.

The colouring of the Old English Pheasant Fowl is unique to the breed. It does not have black spots at the end of the body feathers as does a Hamburgh, but has horse shoe shaped lacing, which circles about half to three quarters of the feather's edge. This rich green black 'semi lacing' contrasts beautifully with the golden bay ground colour of the feathers. This is the basic colour of the female and also the male's breast. The hackle colours are a shade darker in the ground colour and lightly striped with black, as is the saddle hackle. The tail is solid black.

The whole structure blends into a symmetrical flowing picture, not bits and pieces super glued together, reminding me of the tale of the camel. They are a first class bird to keep, being capable of laying a large quantity of good quality eggs, and look their best running free range and collecting all the morsels they can find to produce the excellent flavour of their eggs and meat. Spare cockerels make excellent roasters.... too good for a Vindaloo!!

I have had the pleasure of breeding Old English Pheasant Fowl for many years, finding them a very useful dual purpose breed and successful for showing in variety classes, where their gamey feel and active healthy appearance is often very tempting to many of the all round judges.

We have found the breed to be of a much quieter temperament than the Redcap, which again suggests they have had slightly different origins and developments.

Weights   Large   Males   6-7 lbs   Females   5-6 lbs

Again a 'Palace' winner for the same owner.

A typical Old English Pheasant Fowl cockerel. He was the winning bird at the 1934 Crystal Palace for Mr A. H. Fox-Brockbank from Cumberland.

Old English Pheasant Fowl male.

Old English Pheasant Fowl female.

PLYMOUTH ROCK

The large fowl Plymouth Rock is a breed which at one period enjoyed immense popularity in the British isles. Unfortunately, it has now deteriorated to near extinction. Conversely, the miniatures continue to be a breed with one of the highest levels of support and entries.

The lack of support for the large Rock is a shame, and one for which I can offer no sensible explanation, especially with the buffs, when we are going through a period where both the Buff Cochin, and especially the Buff Orpington are enjoying plenty of support.

The first Rocks were bred in America during the 1870s, the barreds being the first colour to be created and, as with many other breeds which have been successful, they were not a simple cross between two or three breeds but the final development of several different breeding schemes. To simply name some of the breeds involved will probably be sufficient. They were Cochin, Brahma, Java, Dominique, Minorca and Dark Brahmas.

The Rock family exists in several different colours but, in this country, we are talking basically about Barreds and Buffs, the self whites and self blacks are also seen but in smaller numbers.

The shape of the breed is one of a good sized bird, not too long in the back, but in no way short backed. It has a well rounded front and straight breast bone on a fairly deep body. The general shape is not exaggerated in any part. The tail is carried outwards at a slightly rising angle and the feathering is medium length with sufficient side hangers to cover the main tail feathers without spoiling the bird's contour. The wings are carried well up giving the bird's carriage a nearly parallel look. The head and neck are carried upright in an alert and active looking manner.

In describing the Barred Rocks, I must stress that my main consideration is of the British version. As the accompanying photograph will illustrate, the American Rock was, at the beginning and for many years afterwards, a very open patterned bird with broad feathering. The original concept of Rocks in America was consistent with most of the other breeds which they developed, and that was that they were to be used as commercial poultry to supply the ever increasing population with both meat and eggs. The breed was highly successful in this field and is still used at the present time.

Once imported to Britain the birds were quickly taken up by the showmen who concentrated on improving their exhibiting qualities.

Their feathering became narrower and more distinct in its barring. The amounts of black and white were equalised, and the white cleared of sootiness to become pure white to contrast with the vastly improved green sheen to the black, the originals being lacking in this quality. A great feature of Barred Rocks is that the barring must go straight across the feather, and not be 'V' shaped. This fault is most common on the breasts of the male birds.

The barring should be along the whole length of the feather including the under fluff, and is usually about eleven bars in total for the female, with rather more on the male's longer hackle feathers. The ends of the feathers finish in a black tip not a white one.

The ambition is for this barring to be present and correct on every feather of the bird, including the tail and wings. These are often faulty but perfection can be achieved within the top flight stock.

In many of the birds, a few feathers will grow pure black. These mis-marked ones should be removed before showing the bird. You will also breed some self black birds. Nowadays there are classes for them, but in years gone by they were only regarded as future breeding stock, which have to be used periodically to maintain the depth of colouring in the black barring. The males in particular have a tendency to revert to silvery colouring. This is regarded as a serious fault by the old fashioned Rock breeders.

The contrast of this highly attractively coloured bird is the rich yellow coloured beak, legs and feet. The breed has the ability to create a depth of colour which exceeds that of many other yellow pigmented fowls.

The Buff Rock is a highly popular miniature fowl which attracts large classes of birds at all the major shows.

Unfortunately, as stated at the commencement of this summary, the large fowl have declined dramatically.

There was a period when the large Buff Rock was considered to be amongst the top flight utility breeds and, when crossed with Light Sussex, they made excellent laying pullets, whilst the cockerels, if reared, made very useful table fowls. Maybe the problem was that the birds used for utility purposes bore little resemblance to the old fashioned show birds. These show specimens were of excellent pale colouring but gradually lacked stamina. This was probably brought about by the desire to achieve such a pale lemon colouring in the males. If a richer shade had been acceptable maybe their appeal would have widened.

The type of bird used in the commercial field was usually shorter in the back, with a high tail carriage which often carried some black feathers in it, whilst the general body colouring was various shades from yellows to pale red. But they could certainly lay plenty of eggs. Their decline was really brought about with the introduction of the modern Hybrids from the large poultry combines though, in America, I believe that the nucleus for their laying birds was the Barred Rock. The miniature Buff Rock does not have any problems with vigour. It can reproduce top quality stock very consistently with the pullets often maturing at sixteen weeks old.

One feature of the breed which has been relevant for most of my life is that many of the top breeders seem able to produce birds which are better in one sex than the other. The barred miniatures are often bred from two different lines to obtain the best results, but with the Buffs it appears to happen rather subconsciously.

The correct top colour for Buffs has always been open to discussion; the colour of a newly minted gold sovereign was often quoted. The standard colour is rather less lustrous, simply stated as a golden shade of buff. Probably the over riding factor is for the colouring to be one even shade throughout. This can sometimes be achieved on a young pullet but, when she commences laying, some of the later growing feathers come through as a slightly different shade, which spoils her until she completes another full moult. To obtain an even colour on the males can be harder; the wing bars and tail feathers in particular are prone to show a darker shade.

The under-colour must also be sound, right to the skin, as must the wings and main tail feathers. These must be free from any white patches or sootiness. An even colour is required for the breast, thighs and through under the tail, the colour to extend to the edges of the feathers and not laced with another shade.

Another common fault is for the shaft of the flight feathers to become paler at the lower end. This can also apply to the hackle feathers on the male birds.

All the colours of Rock Miniatures should have a medium length of shank, if they are too long they give the bird a stilty and weak looking appearance; conversely, too short can alter the true Plymouth Rock style.

On the question of Buff Rocks' colouring, unfortunately, modern technology has created a problem. The common use of fluorescent lighting affects the colour of the birds. I know people will say it is the same for all of them, which is quite correct, but the lights also alter the leg colour. These should be a very definite yellow and show no signs of greenish tint which is quite a common fault and is listed as a serious defect in all the colours.

In America, the breed has been developed into a series of colours, some of which have never reached these shores. The ones which have are the blacks, which are offspring of the barred, and are a straight forward green sheened self colour, with rich yellow legs.

The white is pure white and free from any signs of other colouring. This is most likely to be found in the hackle feathers of both sexes and the wing bar on the males. The legs and feet again should be rich yellow.

There was a period when Partridge Rocks were popular but they seem to have lost popularity. Basically, they were the typical black red colouring of females with a red/bay ground colour, triple laced with black. The male birds had black striping to the hackles and saddles, with their black breasts being allowed a certain amount of red mottling.

Other colours in America include Columbian, Silver Pencilled and Self Blue. A quick summary assesses the breed as being an excellent choice in miniature form with plenty of competition at the shows. A bird which will lay well and does not require any special preparation before being put in the breeding pen; also if you breed a 'good un' it is capable of getting best in show. The large fowl offer a challenge to anyone wishing to preserve a once very popular breed of fowl.

| Weights | Large | Males | 7-10 lbs | Females | 6-8 lbs |
| | Miniatures | Males | 26-30 ozs | Females | 22-26 ozs |

For many years Plymouth Rocks were amongst the most popular of breeds, the Buff coloured birds being used very successfully as commercial Utility birds. It is sad to witness their decline in Large Fowl at the present time.

I open this section of photographs with a Buff cockerel. This bird won the Crystal Palace in 1923. He also won the Club Show, where he collected eight Silver Cups. He was shown by Mr D. O. Lyles from Lancaster, which is a part of Lancashire that has been 'home' for many of the best Rocks on many occasions.

272

This bird was an adult cock when this photo was taken in 1924. The bird won 27 firsts during his showing career. His wins included the Crystal Palace, Olympia and the Club Show. He was shown by Mrs Drew from the Buff Rock Poultry Farm in Basingstoke.

Another winner from Lancashire. He was bred by Matthew Slater from Carnforth, and his most noted achievement was to win a class of 42 at the 1924 Dairy Show. He was then sold for £42.

I include the cockerel above even though it is not the clearest of photos. He was exhibited by Harold Screech from Somerset, and illustrates a change in style towards what was the breed's eventual downfall. He is slimmer in body and paler in colour. This desire for a lemon top colour appeared also to dilute the strength of many birds, which resulted in breeding problems. The cockerel was bred in 1925 and won the Poultry Club Challenge Cup at Tunbridge Wells.

273

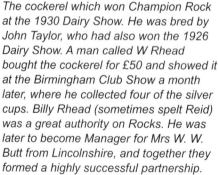

The cockerel which won Champion Rock at the 1930 Dairy Show. He was bred by John Taylor, who had also won the 1926 Dairy Show. A man called W Rhead bought the cockerel for £50 and showed it at the Birmingham Club Show a month later, where he collected four of the silver cups. Billy Rhead (sometimes spelt Reid) was a great authority on Rocks. He was later to become Manager for Mrs W. W. Butt from Lincolnshire, and together they formed a highly successful partnership.

The 1930 Crystal Palace winning Buff cockerel. The bird's unusual comb serrations were a characteristic seen on many birds in later years. This bird was shown by Captain A. G. Miller from Surrey, and represents what many people believed was the ideal type of bird. During the later part of the 1920s the breed, in keeping with many others, was dividing into Exhibition and Utility types. This bird combines a pleasing mixture of both types.

A bird from 1927 when it won both the Essex County and Royal Agricultural Shows. This bird illustrates the eventual development of the Exhibition bird. He is obviously very lemon in colour, but is short of front, with legs which are 'knock kneed' and lacking in bone structure. He was bred by Mr. H. O. Clark from Maidstone and was Second at the Crystal Palace in his cockerel year.

The cockerel here combines attractive appearance with utility qualities. He was a consistent winner in Utility Rock classes at many shows, including the Crystal Palace and York Club Show. He also sired a pen of pullets which won second at the 1932 Harper-Adams laying trials. He was bred in 1931 by Mrs Drew, also mentioned previously. I believe that if this type of bird had been retained, then Buff Rocks would be plentiful today.

In Buff females, I have selected a pullet from 1927. She was bred by Billy Rhead, who showed her through the agricultural shows and gained many first prizes with her.

This pullet was bred by Mrs Butt, and appears to be much paler in colour than the Billy Rhead pullet. She was a noted winner for Mrs Butt at the 1935 Shows.

A quartet of birds bred by Mrs Drew. They are from the early 1930s and between them won 60 First Prizes, including the Club Show and Olympia.

White Rocks have never been a popular showman's breed, especially in this modern age, when they are little different to broiler breeder females. The photo above is from 1921, and shows a long bodied hen which is short of front. She won the Cup for Best White Rock at the Crystal Palace for her owner Mr Fred North from Southport.

Another hen bred by Mrs W. W. Butt. She won the Royal Highland in 1930, and the English Royal in 1931.

Here is a much heavier built cockerel. He was bred by Dr. Jackson from Carnforth and won both the Dairy Show and Olympia in 1926.

The cockerel left, shows a true Rock style, rather than being yellow legged like a White Sussex. He won the Dairy Show, and was second at the Crystal Palace in 1926 for his owner Mr. H. Bellringer from Manchester.

There have never been many Columbian Rocks in this country. Above illustrates a good representative of the variety. She was owned by Mr John Taylor from Essex, who won with her on many occasions.

A Columbian cock which was successfully shown during 1930 by Captain A. G. Miller from Surrey.

Another attractive colour is the Golden Barred figured here. This cockerel won the Crystal Palace in 1926. He was shown by Mr. P. A. Whitcomb who was secretary of the British Golden Barred Rock Club.

Again a Crystal Palace winner, this time in 1921. She was shown by Mr. R. A. Griffiths from Surrey.

Partridge Rocks are very attractive looking
birds. Unfortunately, the usual problem of
double mating reduced their popularity.
John Wharton from Yorkshire was their
guardian, and his cockerel above left
shows a fine example of the variety. He
won the Crystal Palace in 1929, but I
wonder if the photo has been slightly
improved from the original, especially
when you compare it to above right, which
was John's 1931 Dairy and Crystal Palace
winner.

Right shows the hen which won at the
1929 Crystal Palace, and even in black
and white you can appreciate the quality
of her pencilling.

The barred colour of Rock has probably proved to be the most successful in the show pen. The birds also prove to be very photogenic. I commence with a trio of birds from 1911, all of which were winners for James Bateman from Westmorland, and are shown above.

By way of a comparison the trio above are from 1926. They were shown by Mr. W. W. Woodward and were winners of the Crystal Palace Breeding Pen class.

Throughout the history of Barreds there have always been different types of bird from the various continents of the world. I therefore offer you the following selection of photos. Above shows a cockerel displayed by the Canadian government at the Wembley Exhibition in 1924.

Above was drawn by Mr. A. O. Schilling in 1921, and shows his ideal American Barred Rock.

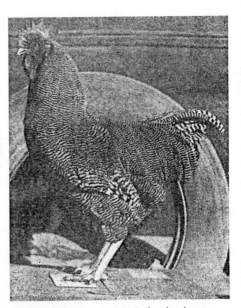

The cockerel above is from New Zealand, where he won a class of eleven Barred cockerels at Nelson Show in 1925. He was bred by a combination of blood lines by Mr. P. F. Hunter.

The Australian representative is shown here. He is from Victoria and was bred in 1928 by Mr. F. M. Franklin. During that year the bird won Best Rock at the Victoria Poultry and Kennel Club Championship Show.

British birds are represented by above. This bird is from 1929 and was almost unbeaten in a series of the top shows, including the Crystal Palace. He was bred and shown by Captain Miller.

Bred and exhibited by that Rock expert, John Taylor from Essex. In 1934 he won at Olympia, and was second at the Dairy Show.

My instructions from the publishers for this book, are to control my sense of humour. However I could not resist the above picture. This shows a unique photograph of the Plymouth Rock Breeder Captain Miller, enjoying one of his other hobbies. If it had been me, I would have tied the birds to the back and taken them to the shows.

282

A large bodied hen which came second at Manchester in 1919, but was awarded the Doctor Cartwright Cup for the best typed Rock. She was the property of Mr. W. Thornton.

Female Barred Rocks are especially photogenic. I was therefore spoilt for choice when selecting their illustrations. The ones which I have chosen are from 1919-1934 and show the quality of birds.

A pullet from 1921. She was shown at Kirby Lonsdale, where she was awarded Best Rock Any Colour, and the Champion Bird in Show. She was shown by Messrs. Holmes and Brownsworth.

Illustrates a pullet from 1924, which is rather more open in her barring. She won the Dairy Show and Olympia, then came home with nine of the trophies. Shown by Mr. D. O. Lyles from Lancaster.

Above won the Bath and West for Mr. W. H. Brewer in 1922. She illustrates a bird which is very dark, and 'open barred' in her markings.

The next four photos all show birds bred by Mrs W. W. Butt from North Thorseby in Lincolnshire.

This hen was the 1926 Club Show Winner; she illustrates the typical English barrings.

A big bodied hen which won the Bath and West and Royal Counties in 1929. She was obviously prepared for the summer show season.

Above bird won Best Rock Any Colour at the 1926 London Dairy Show. She also won Hull and Louth Shows, and again illustrates English Barred Rocks.

This pullet was very successful in 1925 when she swept all before her, with wins including Champion Rock at the Club Show, First at the Dairy Show and First at the Crystal Palace etc.

A pullet from 1929, when she enjoyed a long sequence of successes, winning Best Rock at the Dairy Show, Best Barred Rock at Bristol and then moving on to the Crystal Palace, where she was judged Best Female in Show, thus winning the Poultry Club 60 Guinea Trophy from an entry of 6,000 birds. She was bred by Captain A. C. Miller from Surrey.

A hen which is looking nice and crisp in her barring. She was bred by Mrs E. Marshall from Nottingham, who won with her as a pullet, and again in her mature years at Otley, Leicester, etc. during 1928.

A very attractive looking hen from 1929. She was bred by Captain Miller and was a prolific winner for him, gaining first prize in six shows.

This photo moves forward in time to 1934. It shows a pullet bred by Mr J. J. Bale from Surrey, who won Best of Breed with her at Egham Show. She illustrates the fine barring and style of Barred Rock that was to become fashionable in the future years.

POLAND

Profile of Eric Parker

I was born on November 1934, near Ramsey in Hampshire, where my father was working in the Melchett Estate Office. My mother came from a farming background. Later my family moved to the village of Downtown in Wiltshire, where my father became a poultry farmer, keeping the usual breeds of the day. These included Rhode Island Reds, Sussexes, Leghorns, Rocks and Wyandottes.

I started with bantams in 1946 and had my first Polands in 1948 since when I have bred them in all colours, including the Frizzle form.

After leaving the Salisbury Secondary School, I worked with my father for a number of years. We had now gone into Dairy Farming and Deep Litter Poultry. Later this was again to change to Fruit Farming, the production of various flower and vegetable plants for the local markets.

After a number of years I began to look at further horizons, and moved to become a hairdresser. I thought that if you could prepare Polands for showing you were almost there. After attending college in London, I continued working there for a number of years, after which I travelled in Europe and the USA for two years, visiting many poultry breeders en route. I then put in a year's work in the Caribbean on a charter yacht in the Virgin Islands. When I returned to England I again lived and worked in London, until moving to Yorkshire to run a very successful small country house hotel. Here, I could also use my other interests of interior and garden design.

I am now living in North Nottinghamshire, and continue to breed large and bantam Polands in all colours and frizzle form as well.

I have probably bred more winning Polands over the last 45 years. Nearly every stud of White Crested birds, large and bantam, originated from my stock. I also re-made Large White Crested Blues, Buff, Gold and Silver Laced, White, Black and Self-Blue. I am currently working on Self Cuckoo and Blue Laced Gold.

At the Poland Club Shows I have won most of the cups at some stage, including the 'White Crested Cup' and 'Points Cup', probably more times than anyone else, and have also had success at the National Show, winning 'Best Light Breed', and 'Best Female in Show', at 5 or 6 events. My most satisfying win was at Newton Abbott in 1983, when Rex Woods put my Large Buff Laced Poland 'Show Champion', although I think my biggest thrill is to win 'Trio Classes', and the best of all, 'Champion Trio'.

Without doubt the Poland is a very old and true breed. One of the earliest traces was the discovery a few years ago of skulls the same as those of present day Polands at a Roman dig in Gloucestershire.

Many suggestions are made as to the origin, including Russia, Italy, Spain and the Far

East.

In a book entitled 'Voyage to Surinam and the Interior of Guinea' by a Captain Steersman, there appears an illustration of what appears to be a pair of Frizzle Polands. As we know, if you have frizzled fowl, you have plain feathered versions.

Poland type fowls were mentioned in many books of the 16th, 17th and 18th centuries and figured in numerous paintings of the same period, especially by Dutch and Italian artists.

That it was brought to perfection in the Netherlands is probably true, although they were brought to England from other parts of Europe including Germany and France. In France the breed made a large impact on the native breeds, especially Houdans and Creves but also many minor crested and muffed breeds.

The breed was established in Britain during the 1700s and had classes at the first English poultry shows from 1845 to 1850. For a number of years it remained one of the most popular show breeds. However, by the 1890s, it dwindled to a handful of breeders. Indeed, in Harrison Weir's 'Our Poultry' he writes that this is another old breed about to slip into extinction. Thankfully this has not come about but the overall situation is the same today, with only a handful of serious breeders at any one time throughout the present century. The much more popular miniature version was produced in the 1890s by J F Entwistle, who created them by crossing large breed Polands onto gold and silver Sebrights, and black and white Rosecomb hens. After six seasons he produced good Poland bantams in nearly all varieties.

Today in 1995 Polands, both large fowl and miniature, exist in twelve colour variations which include White crested, Black, Blue, Cuckoo and Mottled, Self White, Black, Blue and Cuckoo and finally Buff, Gold, Silver and Blue laced. All these colours also exist in the frizzle feathered form. This variation was dormant for many years and was recreated in the 1980s in the Netherlands by Mr A J Bland, who has produced some wonderful birds in all colours. All birds should have fairly deep long bodies with a good flow of feather in the tail which is carried at a medium height. Legs are slender, blue or slate in all except the two cuckoo and mottled varieties, which are white sometimes mottled with black. Beak colour again varies from slate in the white crested black and blue and also the self blacks and blues. The best whites have deep blue beaks, and the laced varieties have horn with a touch of blue. Cuckoos and mottles have white to light horn colouring.

Of course the crowning glory of a Poland is the crest, which should be as large and globular as possible. In the cock this is composed of long hackle type feathers and in the hen large broad round tipped feathers. Many of the largest crests are, unfortunately, mushroom shaped, but this can be corrected in the breeding pen by using a bird of the opposite sex with a tall, narrow crest.

In the white crested varieties the wattles are rather long. In the other colours they should be as small as possible being replaced with a full beard and muff. The best birds are without combs but if combs are visible they should be V shaped. In white crested varieties weights are about 5/6 lbs for cocks and 1 lb lighter for hens. Others are 6.6 lbs in cocks and again about 1 lb lighter for hens. Bantams should be about 1.5-2 lbs in cocks and 1.5 lbs in hens but many are much larger.

In breeding you use the best crested birds available. In white crested blacks make sure that both sexes have good solid black wings. If you have white or grey tips coming in, an excess of black in the crest will rectify this. In the blue colours blue-cross-blue, blue-cross-black and black-cross-splash will all produce good coloured birds. In cuckoos the best birds are from cuckoo-cross-black matings, as cuckoo to cuckoo produce very pale coloured birds.

On no account use black birds from this mating to produce blacks as it will bring in white and grey white, and grey tips to many feathers. With blacks, the best with the best usually works very well. Whites are not as easy as one would think. You must make sure the male is a really silver white, otherwise you will get a large percentage of birds which are very sappy. In the buff and gold laced females of the very best colour and lacing mated with males a little dark in colour usually produce the best stock. In silvers, using males that are very grey in the tail produces the best females.

Today, quality birds still exist in all varieties, the white crested colours being as good as they ever were when compared with past photographs, white crested blacks and blues being nominated many times for best in section and show champions. Self colours have improved dramatically over the last three or four seasons and some really good blacks, whites and blues are now seen; also the odd good laced bird occasionally appears. In the much more popular miniatures, again, the white crested blacks are best, with many good birds being seen. White crested blues and cuckoos are again improving. In whites you still see some good females, but males have declined in quality. This used to be the smallest of the bantam varieties, but over the last ten years has now become the largest. Self blacks and blues have improved 100% over the last four years and are now a force to be reckoned with in the show pen. In fact, black females have won the highest honours in the last three club shows. Gold and buff laced are still good, especially in females, however, heavy lacing seems to be creeping in, although a few good birds of a new strain with very fine lacing have been seen this season. As ever, in silvers, there is never any real improvement owing to the lack of any serious breeders. Only occasionally is a quality bird seen. The cuckoo blue laced and mottled are too new to have much impact but within a few seasons could be making their presence felt, especially the cuckoos, which have been bred from the very best blacks.

Polands can be bred either normal flat feathered or frizzle feathered. This photo was taken at Eric Parker's and illustrates growing birds in both types of feathering.

A White Crested Blue from Holland in
1919.

An English hen from the 1930s.

These were all bred by Eric Parker during the period 1970-1990. Eric comments that
the birds have remained very similar over a period of over 70 years.

English White Crested Blacks from the 1930s. Eric says to note that today's comments on exaggerated dressing of the crest is nothing new when you take a close look at these photos.

Head shots of a very large crested German hen. The photos were taken by Fischer during the 1970s.

A White Crested Mottled hen, taken in Holland during the 1980s.

A White Crested Cuckoo hen, taken in Germany during the 1970 period.

A non bearded Self White from Germany, again from around 1970.

A pair of White Crested Blacks which won the Club Show for Eric Parker during the mid 1960s.

A Buff Laced hen which was a Championship winner for Eric Parker in the early 1980s.

292

A Buff Laced hen which won the Crystal Palace in 1926 and 1927 for E. Richards from St Austell.

A Buff Laced cock which won many Championships for Hough Watson during the 1930s.

A pair of Silver Laced which were noted winners during the late 1920s.

A Blue Laced hen which won many senior awards for Eric Parker in the 1970s.

A Gold Laced hen, bred and shown by Eric Parker during the 1970s.

Two White bantam hens, both of which were winners at the Classic Shows during the early 1920s for Bough Watson.

Ned. Baardkuifhoenkriel, koe-
koek, vj. van H.L. Timmer met
F (Foto: W. Hoekstra).

A White bantam cock, bred by Eric Parker, and a consistent winner for him during the 1970s.

A Cuckoo bantam hen which was a winner in Holland during the early 1990s.

Ned. Baardkuifhoenkriel,
zwart, vj, van Hans Buben, de
Duitse meester in dit ras
(Foto: W. Hoekstra).

A Self Black bantam hen, again from Holland at the same period.

A large fowl Self Black hen, bred by Eric Parker during the mid 1970s.

A large fowl Buff Laced hen. She won First at the Olympia Classic for T.W. Davis from Romford.

A Buff Laced bantam hen which was a noted winner for Major Williams during the 1920s.

A Buff Laced bantam hen from England during the 1990s.

A Buff Laced bantam hen from Holland during the 1990s.

A selection of Frizzle feathered Polands; a non bearded White male, a Blue female, a pair of Blues bred by A. J. Boland in Holland, a Self White pullet and a White Crested Blue. The photographs were taken by Hans Schippers.

We conclude this display of Poland photographs with four from Germany. They were taken by Josef Wolters during the 1980s and comprise a Self White and a Self Blue, both of them males in Frizzle feathering, a Self White female which is non bearded and a rather unusual White Crested Exchequer pullet.

POLVERARA

This breed is reputed to be indigenous to the province of Padua in Italy, and takes its name from a village of that name. Birds of this description have been on the continent for centuries. There is obviously some relationship between them. Which of them came first, will probably never be conclusively proved.

I have never seen a Polverara in the flesh but, from early drawings of the birds, they appear to be much stronger and heavier bodied than the twentieth century British Poland Fowl.

They have frequently been likened to the French Creve-Coeur, which in the past was considered to be quite a heavy and well meated bird. Weights originally quoted for the Creve-Coeur were up to 9 lbs in males, and 7 lbs in females.

The Caumont and the Caux are district variations of the Crevecoeur. Again, these are large bodied fowl but with an absence of beard or muff feathers, as in the Crevecoeur, and some varieties of Poland.

Ayscough Thompson was a respected writer on poultry breeds and, when discussing the accompanying sketch of the Polveraras which had been displayed at the Crystal Palace Exhibition in 1930, he commented that he felt sure there was a connection with the Brabanter, a breed which has been shown in paintings since the sixteenth century, and was thought to have been originally shipped to Holland from Persia.

The Polverara was reputed to be a regular layer of large sized white eggs, whilst the bird, when killed, provided a well fleshed carcass of very tasty meat.

Edward Brown describes the Polverara as having a deep and well rounded body with a short back and legs of medium length. The hackle is thick and well covered, with an abundant long feathered hackle feathering. It has a neat head, carrying a full crest, which is rather tight feathered and divided to show a comb of two small horns which stand out prominently in front of the crest. The wattles are small and bright red and match the comb. The lobes however are small and white.

The breed has several different colours but self black is the most common one. Their top colour carries a blue/bronze reflection. Other colours mentioned are White, Cuckoo, Gold and Silver.

I have included the Polverara, not because of any great current following, but as a breed with historical interest.

Weights   Males   6 lbs   Females   4.5 lbs

A line drawing by Ayscough Thompson in 1933. It illustrates his notion of the perfect Polverara.

299

RAIZA GAME

Even though this book is written with the intention of describing soft feathered breeds of poultry, I am going to allocate space for the Raiza Game Birds, whose name can also be spelt as the Raija Game Fowl.

I include them because I believe they could have had a significant influence in the formation of many soft feathered breeds.

From the information I have gathered their original style lay somewhere in-between the original Asil, and the Hyderabad. The birds originated in the area around Bangalore where, as usual, they were used for fighting.

The features of the Raiza birds are similar to the Asil in style and head points but, when crossed with the Hyderabad, produced a much larger bird than the original and true Asil. The Hyderabad was described as a large framed and powerful type of Game Fowl, presumably having included in its development some of the 'Gallus Giganticus' blood.

The Raiza Fowls were reported to have been sold all around the world due to their reputation as a superb fighting breed. Subsequently, they were crossed with the local fowls of their new country, sometimes by accident as well as because of a planned breeding programme. This obviously then created variations which usually assumed the name of their newly adopted habitat.

In India the birds existed in a whole range of colours but much emphasis was given to a black version which took the name of Java-Raiza. Hyderabad is in the southern region of India and is within a relatively short shipping distance across the water to the island of Sumatra. Presumably birds were exchanged in both directions, with the Sumatra fowls being called by the name of Java, which is another small island virtually joined to Sumatra.

During the 1920s a gentleman called C A Finterbusch dedicated himself to tracing the history and ancestry of the world's fighting fowls. When exploring the Sumatras he found them living completely wild in the jungles. They were pheasant like in their ways and considered to be good sport by shooting parties as pheasants are in our own country. Many of the birds shot had the characteristic of having multi-spurred legs. Finterbusch considered this to be unique amongst poultry though he traced the feature in some types of pheasants.

Concluding his investigations, his opinion was that the Sumatra was one of the oldest of poultry types and was definitely a Gallus.

The Sumatra were caught by the natives and, when domesticated, they proved successful fighting fowl, especially when crossed with other game varieties; hence the Java-Raiza.

My further conclusion is that these Java-Raiza birds eventually developed into the birds which became known as the Java.

This must have been completed by crossing with Langshans which had gradually expanded down the Yangtsze-Kiang River.

The Langshan fowls would provide the extra body size and single comb associated with the Java but I am not sure that it would do anything for the Raiza's fighting ability.

To illustrate *Raiza Game* I have used drawings by C. A. Finterbusch.

FIG 1. The cock on the left of the picture, shows what he calls a 'Kaptan Asil'. It is dark red in colour, and covered with white specks which, to use our expression, would be 'Spangled'. The central bird, is the 'Rampur Boalia Black', i.e. the Hyderabad type. The cock on the right illustrates the introduction of Sumatra blood, which results in a slimmer body and an increase in tail furnishings.

FIG 2. Shows an old drawing of birds which were described as being 'Sinhalese Game', and again illustrates the inclusion of Sumatra blood to an Asil type of bird.

FIG 3. This drawing illustrates Finterbusch's interpretation of 'Gallus Gigantus'

REDCAP

The fact that this breed forms one point in a triangle of breeds is probably not disputed. The other two are the Gold Spangled Hamburgh and the Pheasant Fowl. To attempt to trace and describe their original creation would, I am sure, be impossible. I believe that they were all descended from many variations and permutations of localised crossbreeds which have roamed the northern parts of England for a very long time. When the showing of poultry became fashionable a selection of them was more closely bred for particular features, until they reached a point of perfection where they could be standardised into a breed. To achieve this, the birds had to be proved capable of reproducing stock with the same characteristics and features as their parents and grandparents. This requirement is still the general requirement for a new breed of poultry.

The 'breeds' probably involved in the original farmyard crossbreeds were Pheasant Malays, Dutch Everyday Layers (see Fayoumi and Friesians), Black-Red Game Fowl and, possibly, the 'moonie', but this term is so widely used in history, I am not sure if it actually refers to something specific, and is more likely to be a very loose description used to cover a wide range of colouring, rather than the present interpretation meaning a hen feathered spangle Hamburgh male bird.

The Redcap itself is larger in body size than the Hamburgh, probably due to the use of some kind of game fowl, presumably black-red in colour. The weight and firmness of the flesh is clearly shown when you handle the birds.

The great feature of the breed is in its headpiece, which is unique and is allocated a massive 45 points in the standard. It could be described as a Hamburgh type of comb but it is more developed and is recommended to measure 3.25 inches by 2.75 inches, which is quite large and approximately the size of the palm of a lady's hand.

The comb's surface is liberally covered with individual spikes, all of which should be roughly equal in length and size with the comb itself showing no signs of a hollow centre. This feature is obviously more pronounced in the male than the female but on the hen it is still a very important feature. As opposed to the Pheasant Fowl which has a white lobe the Redcap has a red lobe of fine texture like the face and wattles.

The birds have a reasonably long body and a tail set at about 60 degrees which looks slightly lower than that when it is correctly furnished with good quality and broad feathered sickles and side hangers.

Colour features high on the allocation of points, being issued 25. The ground colour of the female is described as being 'nut brown' but it does not state whether it is walnut or brazil! The main point is to have the ground colour free from smuttiness. The male's top colour is rich red, with the neck hackle and saddle hackle to be tipped with black. The breast is black. The female feathering should end with a half moon black spangle as opposed to the horse shoe shaped lacing on the Pheasant Fowl.

The breed has for many years had a reputation for being rather flighty but I have noticed recently that they seem to be much calmer, especially the birds exhibited by the ever-growing number of ladies who are becoming Redcap fanciers.

I will close this section on Redcaps by reciting a true story regarding the tendency for them to be rather nervous.

When judging Redcaps beware, because they have a disturbing tendency either to fly up to the roof of the show pen or do a quick 'Houdini' as soon as you lift the pen door up. This is exactly what happened to a friend of mine whilst judging at Bakewell a few years ago.

I was busy going about my work judging the game birds when, looking up, I saw a Redcap cock hot footing it down the aisles. He was in full feather with his tail flowing behind him and hard on his heels was a rather embarrassed judge.

I stepped into the bird's path and turned him round whereupon he ran straight back towards his pursuer going straight between his legs. Acting with the reflexes of Peter Shilton the judge dropped both hands down to attempt the save of the week, unfortunately just a second too late and all he collected was both hands full of tail and sickle feathers whilst the Redcap cock carried on regardless.

The look on Derek Alsop's face was indescribable and actually matched his language. The judge's next problem was whether to disqualify the bird for insufficient furnishings or to award it best in show to appease the owner.

If you doubt the authenticity of this story just ask Frank Clark ..... it is rather a dangerous profession this judging job!!!

We are just beginning to see a few miniatures appear at the shows and they look very attractive. Anyone fancying a new challenge should find them appealing.

Weights Males 6-6.5lbs Females 5-5.5lbs.

FIG 1. *This pair was bred by George Siddons from Bakewell in 1929. Both birds won top class awards and were then exported to Canada.*

STANDARD of REDCAPS ILLUSTRATED by Wippell

COMB	**EYES.**	**WATTLES.**
ROSE LARGE, WITH LEADER STRAIGHT FULL OF FINE SPIKES, NOT HANGING TOO MUCH IN FRONT & CARRIED WELL OFF THE EYES.	FULL & BRIGHT COLOUR - RED.	LONG AND WELL ROUNDED.
	BEAK.	**EAR-LOBES.**
	SHORT & SMALL COLOUR - HORN.	MEDIUM SIZE COLOUR - RED.
	NECK.	**TAIL.**
	OF MODERATE LENGTH	CARRIED ABOUT ANGLE 45°
BREAST.		
FULL AND ROUNDED		**BACK.**
		FAIRLY LONG AND BROAD.
WINGS.		
MODERATELY LONG, FITTING CLOSELY TO THE SIDES.		**CARRIAGE.**
		ACTIVE & GRACEFUL
		COLOUR.
LEGS.		HEAD-RED, HACKLE RED WITH BLACK STRIPE DOWN EACH FEATHER
SHORT. THIGHS MODERATELY LONG AND STRONG SHANKS TOES WELL SPREAD COLOUR - SLATE,		BACK & BREAST - DEEP RED BROWN EACH FEATHER TIPPED WITH A HALF-MOON BLACK-SPANGLE. BACK & WING UNIFORM AS POSSIBLE

PRIMARIES & SECONDARIES RED HEAVILY TIPPED. TAIL BLACK.

WEIGHT – COCKS ABOUT 7½ lb   HENS – 5½ lb TO 6½ lb

FIG 2. Is a very old print, drawn by Wippell to illustrate the Redcap standard. I believe this to be a very satisfactory way of presenting a breed standard, which could be used more frequently.

FIG 3. Shows a massive combed Redcap cock which was a noted winner for that legendary character Harry Fox from Matlock.

FIG 4. Shows the Dairy Show winning hen in 1930. She went on to win at the Club Show in 1932 for Harry Fox.

Lincolnshire Buff male

Gold Braekel male bred by Brian Sands

i

A group of Campines.

Red Saddled Yokohama male bred by Colin & Rosemary Clarke

New Hampshire Red female - photo by Josef Wolters

Gold Pencilled Hamburgh male bred by Eric Parker

*Black Silkie females both Club Show Champions for Sue Bowser -
Photo by Sue Bowser*

White Yokohama male - photo taken at his home by Richard Billson

Vorwerk male bred by Maureen Case - photo by Mr Stevens

Fayoumi at home taken by Lana Gazder

Red Sussex group bred by Fred Hams

Frizzle feathered Polands surrounding their breeder - Arie. J. Boland taken from Hans Schippers book ëKippen in Hollandí

White Silkie female bred by Sue Flude - photo by Mervyn Weston

Welsummer Bantam female

Buff Cochin female

Japanese Long Crowing male

Rhodebar male

Red Jungle fowl by Cornelis Van Gink

Drente in pile colouring by Cornelis Van Gink

Friesians in red Mottled colouring by Cornelis Van Gink

Brabant fowl in Quail colouring by Cornelis Van Gink

Welsummer male as illustrated by 'Fifty years of Welsummer'

Gold Brahma male bred and photographed by Harold Critchlow

x

Buff Columbian Brahma female - photo by John Tarren

Buff Plymouth Rock Bantam male - photo by John Tarren

Owl Bearded Dutch (Uilebaarden) female - photo by Hans Schippers

Black Brabanter female - photo by Hans Schippers

Kraienkoppe

Naked neck

Sicilian Buttercup

Spanish Bantam

A selection of photographs by Josef Wolters illustrating Breeds from Europe

Crele Bielefelder male

Black Dresdener male

Chamois Thuringian male

Colombian Reichshuhner male

Niederrheiner male

Silver Duckwing Kraienkoppe male - photo by Ken Atterby

Cuckoo Melchener female

Birchen Grey Niederrheiner female

White Crested Polands bred by Eric Parker

Chamois Polands bred by Eric Parker

Black Sumatra male bred and photographed by Richard Billson

Java Malay Fighting Cock

Black Silkie female a Champion for Sue Bowser

Gold Silkie male bred by Tom Ayres

Partridge Silkie female a Champion for Sue Flude

Blue Silkie pair bred by Sue Bowser

Dark Brahma male bred by Colin Clarke

Salmon Faverolle male bred by C M Higgins

Rhode Island Red male, a Champion for John Kay &. Son

White Wyandotte bred by Alan Proctor.

Bassette Bantam male

Sulmtaler female

Silver Welsummer Bantam male bred
by Mr H R (Peter) Blake

Blue Laced Wyandotte Bantam female
bred by George Hunter

*White Leghorn Bantam male bred by
Reg and Paul Spencer - photo by Chris
Parker*

*Light Sussex male bred by Bernard
Thompson - photo by Chris Parker*

*Mahogany Spangled Russian Orloff
male bred by Colin & Rosemary Clarke*

*Andalusian Bantam male bred by
Harold & Normal Critchlow*

REICHSHUHNER

The Reichshuhner is another of the more recently developed German breeds which have been created to use as dual purpose birds, useful as showbirds and still capable of laying a good quantity of eggs.

Personally I do not find the birds very appealing, but they are very popular on the European continent. The 1995 German championship show attracted a total entry of 350 in Large fowl and Miniatures.

The basic shape of the birds is of a well rounded front and a very long back, which is highlighted even more by their carrying their tails straight out behind them. Their shape is similar to the Rhode Island Red's, but, if with anything, an even flatter back.

Their legs are quite long and nearly straight in the hock, showing very little bend of thigh. Their combs are a very near rose shape, the leader of which follows the head's contour. Basically they are white pigmented, with the shanks on most of the colours being white, but in the birchen grey it turns to a dusky grey.

The Reichshuhner exists in a range of basic colours for both the Large and the Bantam Fowls.

A very attractive one is the equivalent of our Light Sussex, the exception being that the saddle hackle is allowed to be moderately striped, which actually adds to the bird's appeal.

Another favourite is the birchen grey and, as with many other continental breeds, the perfection in their colouring is to be admired. This colour is no exception, and the fact that the colour is clear breasted on the female, as opposed to the slightly laced in this country, seems to add to the appearance.

The barred is very attractive with the characteristic continental 'open barring' to their pattern, the contrast between black and white being well highlighted.

The breed exists in several self colours, black, white, etc. However, to me, they lack the appeal of the coloured ones. This is probably due to the breed's tight feathering.

I feel sure that this is another of the breeds which will eventually become a regular part of the British showing circuit.

A photograph of a Reichshuhner is included in the colour section.

Columbian Reichshuhner

Cuckoo Reichshuhner

RENNES, FRENCH and FLEMISH CUCKOO

On the continent Cuckoo coloured breeds have been recorded for centuries, with each country adding its name to the colouring.

Basically, they are all very similar, with the exception of the comb structure, which can vary from rose, triple pea, and single upright type.

Under the heading of Maline I have discussed the first two types, believing that the Rennes, or as it is sometimes referred to, the Cuckoo de Rennes, and the old Flemish version are really the same. Their type is of large and deep bodied table fowl.

They have well developed breasts and thighs and their necks are short and thick with a fully feathered hackle. Their pigmentation is white and their comb etc. red.

The birds have a reputation for a long active life and for being good foragers, covering large areas of land in search of natural foods, and converting them into good quality produce for the farmhouse kitchen table.

There is of course further confusion within the Cuckoo breeds, by the development of the Marans and the North Holland Blue.

The Rennes birds were quoted as being clean legged and their weights, I thought, on the small side, being considerably less than the Maline, and just less than the Marans. I wonder if it is a mistake?

Weights   Males 7 lbs. Females 5.5 lbs.

On the European continent, at the present time, there is a breed called the Melchener. It is credited with being originally from Belgium and I would assume that it bore a close relationship to the old Flemish Cuckoo. These modern birds are quite heavy in their foot feathering; it has been suggested due to the addition of Brahma blood. They are heavier in the body than the old Rennes and French Cuckoos.

The weight quoted for the old Flemish was :- Males 9 lbs.   Females 7 lbs.

FIG 1. This old painting illustrates the original continental cuckoo coloured birds perfectly.

RHINELANDER

I have to admit that this is a breed which I know little about, and therefore base my findings on the wisdom of C S Van Gink who wrote about the breed during the 1930s.

The general purpose of his article was to illustrate that there were very few true German breeds capable of being developed into successful commercial poultry.

The fact was noted in high authority and consequently all branches of poultry and pigeon societies, were amalgamated into a Government controlled organisation called the National Association of German Small Stock Breeders. This organisation was then split into two divisions, one of which was responsible for the commercial aspect, with the other to cover the exhibition section.

The members were mainly small farmers and poultry breeders who kept a whole range of breeds from Orloffs to Thuringians, but only two of them were thought to be suitable for the now rapidly increasing commercial market.

One of these breeds was the Rhinelander which was considered to be suitable for egg production combined with reasonable table qualities.

The birds have quite deep bodies and are full fronted, and have a reasonably long body, finishing with a quite large and well furnished tail which is carried at a standard 45 degree angle. They also have a rather small head with a very neat rose comb, with their thighs and shanks slightly on the small side, and are of well rounded and strong bone which is often associated with good meat qualities.

The black and white photograph which Van Gink used to illustrate the breed does not show a white ear lobe, but more recent pictures of the birds show them to have a small white lobe which is almost Hamburgh looking in shape.

The Board's predictions of a bright future for the breed would appear to be correct. At the 1996 German Championship Show there were almost 300 large fowl Rhinelanders and 250 bantams.

These were in five colour variations, but the main attraction is the self-black version. Others include - barred, white, blue and one which is in the black-red/partridge pattern. I would describe the birds as being in between a light breed and our own heavy breed or, as Powell-Owen described, a light heavy breed.

I am not quite sure how the Dresdener was created but there appears to be a relationship somewhere along the line.

In the colour section of the book there is a painting by Gwenllian Woods illustrating the 'Breeds of Ashe'. Amongst the group of birds, there is a pair of Rhinelander.

German Poultry Breeds

Compiled with the co-operation of C. S. Th. Van Gink, Voorburg, Holland

FIG 1. Shows a Black Rhinelander male as described by C. S. Van Gink.

FIG 2. This attractive painting illustrates a pair of White Rhinelanders, which offers a variation to the more common Black.

308

RHODE ISLAND RED

In all the breeds of Poultry, the Rhode Island Red is the one which I should know most about. They were my father's favourite, and he started to teach me their correct markings as soon as I was able to talk. Probably before then if the truth is known.

It is often the honestly held belief of a specialist breeder that his particular breed is the hardest one to obtain in a form which is approaching perfection. He believes in his innocence that the breeds which he has not been involved with present fewer hazards and problems. There could, however, be a strong case put forward to establish that the Rhode Island Red is amongst the hardest of breeds in which to attempt perfection. I certainly believe that it is one of several breeds which is not fully understood or appreciated by a high percentage of non specialist R.I.R. judges. To some extent this may be caused by the breeds standard, in which some of the finer points are almost impossible to achieve in perfection.

The breed itself was created in America around the turn of the 19th Century. Its actual composition is quite obscure for a breed so recently introduced. This is due to some of the birds used being nothing more than localised crossbreeds. In America, during the latter part of the nineteenth century, there was an urgency to create breeds of poultry which were capable of producing large quantities of eggs and also of supplying chicken meat for the rapidly increasing population. The Wyandotte was one of the first breeds developed which was able to fulfil these requirements. It could very simply be stated that the R.I.R. is actually a continuation of the breeding programme for the Gold Wyandotte. Some people might be horrified at the suggestion, but from the obscure description of the mixed collection of birds first used in the R.I.R. this could be so.

The breed is recorded as being originated on Rhode Island, with many of the birds going under the loose description of 'Common Fowl'. These birds contained Black Red Malay, Buff Cochin and possibly Partridge Cochin, also some Langshan blood. Additionally, many of the birds were rose combed from crosses with Hamburgh and rose combed Leghorns.

During the 1880s the Gold Laced Wyandotte was being developed around the area of Wisconsin. Silver Laced Wyandottes formed part of the breeding programme, with the golden part of it being supplied, as usual, by some 'Common Fowl'. There was also a mixture of Brown Leghorn, both single and rosecombed, Partridge Cochins and Buff Cochins, which is almost identical to the mixture used for the birds on Rhode Island. These Wisconsin birds went under the delightful name of 'Winnebagoes'.

The South Massachusetts Poultry Association held an exhibition in 1880 and a Mr. Jenney, who lived locally, showed a trio of buff coloured birds. He also had a display of birds dressed and ready for the oven to demonstrate their meat potential.

The stock created a favourable impression. A discussion took place at the show as to their name and it was agreed to call them Rhode Island Reds. Other breeders took up the new breed and their popularity spread.

During the winter of 1891 an exhibition was held in Philadelphia, where a good entry of similar birds was shown under the name of 'Golden Reds'. These birds again created a good impression with the poultry breeders and, consequently, a group of them formed a club and, by 1901, a standard of perfection was devised. In 1904 it was accepted by the American Standards, originally I believe in the rosecomb version, to be followed later by the single combs.

Breed development on Rhode Island itself had also progressed during this period. A Dr. Aldrich showed them there in 1891, again under the name of 'Golden Buffs'. In 1895

Mr. Natick showed what are thought to be the first birds actually entered under the name of Rhode Island Reds. This was at the 'Rhode Island Poultry Association' exhibition. It would therefore be logical to conclude that the rich coloured 'Rhode Island Reds' which are instantly recognisable were developed from a mixture of the Rhode Island, Massachusetts, and Wisconsin 'Golden Buffs'. This once again demonstrates that, by patience, a calculated breeding programme and careful selection, a group of birds can be transformed into a breed which will consistently produce true to type specimens which are far removed from their original ancestors.

Rhode Island Reds are often reported as having arrived in Britain at around the turn of the century. I now write extracts from a letter written in 1903, which could relate to the original birds in the British Isles. It is from the R.I.R. Club's annual book and is headed 'England's First Rhode Island Reds'. The letter was written by a Mr. Edward Risden, whose brother Sidney returned to Somerset after spending several years in the USA. Before embarking on his journey home, he purchased 36 of the so called R.I.R. eggs. During the voyage he conscientiously turned the eggs daily. On his arrival home he sat them under some broody hens and obtained the remarkable result of 25 healthy chicks. He reared them all to maturity but, in 1904, came to the decision that he could not settle in England and planned to return to the States.

He advertised the birds and did not receive a single enquiry. He offered them to a well known fancier at 10 shillings (50 pence) each, who declined the proposed deal. The boat was due to sail so in desperation he gave them to Edward, with the request to deal with the situation as he thought best. Edward decided to breed from them and attempt to promote the breed in England, knowing from his brother their popularity in America. In 1905 there was a show at Bridgewater, and two special classes were arranged for the new breed of Rhode Island Reds. Edward entered 15 birds which created much more interest than previously. Harry Scott offered £1 each for all 15 but was told that the price had to be £3 per bird or they went home.

Interest in the breed increased and, in 1906, 'Feathered World' illustrated a feature on the breed, including photos of Edward Risden's first imports. During the next three years their reputation grew and so did their popularity, which resulted in the formation of the British R.I.R. Club. This club not only catered for the bird's exhibition standard, but was active in promoting its potential as an egg laying bird capable of competing with any other breed at the laying trials.

This summary of the Rhode Island Red's early history has been collected from several sources and I will close it with a prediction made by that knowledgeable writer Harrison Weir in the early 1900s - 'Good as the Rhode Island Reds are said to be, and probably are, it is very doubtful, for many reasons, that they will gain a lasting position in this country'. This was not one of Harrison's best flirtations with his crystal ball.

The old standard for Large Fowl Rhode Island Reds reminds me in many ways of the Sussex Standard. Both of them were devised in the early nineteen hundreds when there was a tremendous interest in the laying qualities of the different breeds. Consequently, much emphasis was placed on their utility qualities. The intense colouring and markings were gradually increased into the exhibition type of bird during the later years but, unfortunately, we are still operating around the old standard.

In this standard, shape is dominant at 30 points, with quality and texture 15 points. The head appears to be under marked at 10 points, but this only applies to the face and comb. There is an additional 10 points for the eye, which makes a total of 20 points, which is one fifth of the bird's total points. The allocation of points for the bird's colouring is identical to the total for the head, i.e. 20 points.

The Bantam breeders were not too happy with this and, in the early 1950s, founded a separate club, catering purely for miniatures. They formulated their own standard which increased the points for colour to 25. The points for type were reduced by half. Unfortunately, in their enthusiasm to create smaller birds they allocated a massive 25 points purely for size, and still the larger birds kept winning!

The situation is now resolved. Both clubs are amalgamated and only one standard exists. I believe this to be correct. Bantams should be an exact replica of their large counterpart, not only in Rhode Island Reds, but in all breeds.

The shape of a R.I.R. has often been described as being brick shaped, which could be slightly confusing to newcomers, a brick having many right angled corners. What it really means is a body shape which is much longer than it is deep. The Rhode should have a flat back and a well rounded front which sweeps into a long and straight breast bone, the great length of its back being enhanced even more by the continuous tail line. The tail is well furnished with the sickles.

The thighs and legs are an important feature in the breed. These are actually quite long, the point being highlighted by the fact that a true R.I.R. is quite tight in its feathering. This is obviously inherited from the Malay blood in the original stock. The back should have great width and consequently the thighs must be well apart, which gives the bird balance. There is nothing looks worse than a cock which is 'knock kneed' or, to use an old Lancashire expression, 'both legs coming out of the same hole'. The shanks should be strong and well rounded in the bone, not 'flat shinned'. The long toes should be well spread and firmly planted on the ground. Rhodes should be an active breed and without a good pair of legs and feet they lose character. You could argue that the legs are only allocated 5 points but the legs and thighs form part of the 30 points under the heading of type.

In the old standard, the neck is described as being of medium length, but I would say that it was rather longer when you study the photos of winning birds from past eras.

A long neck in any breed, when carried erect, gives the bird an appearance of elegance and importance. The neck is abundantly feathered, but these are not carried loosely, as in the Cochin or Brahma. They should have a good width of feather and the texture should neither be 'frizzled' nor lacking in barbs and 'wirey'.

To obtain the best shape, the birds must have a wide pair of shoulders. These are actually the 'wing butts' which should then carry the flights and secondaries close to the body and parallel to the ground, finishing close to the tail and being covered by the saddle hackle, which is constructed of the same feathering as the neck hackle.

In whichever standard you study, the head piece is a very important feature. It must be strong in bone structure without becoming coarse textured or 'beetle browed'. The eyes should be prominent and alert looking.

The comb can be either single or rose shaped. In the single type it is not over large and should be evenly separated with five or six wedge shaped spikes. It should be neat at the front and not double folded. The rear should also be clean and free from 'side sprigs' or a 'double end'. This point can become troublesome where single and rose combed birds have been continually interbred.

The rose version should be similar to that of the Wyandotte, fitting closely to the head, with a short flat leader following down the back of the head, not upright as in a Hamburgh. It should be broad, but not too wide and hanging over the bird's eyes. The whole surface should be evenly covered with short spikes or 'points' as they are sometimes called.

A common fault is for the rose comb to be very narrow and stand on a base which is more suited to a single comb. This is due to inter-breeding the two types. Both types should have an equal sized and well hanging pair of wattles, preferably flat fronted.

Breeding for the correct colour in Rhode Island Reds can be a mixture of pleasure and exasperation, the point being that, just when you think you are approaching perfection in a particular aspect, a problem occurs to prevent you achieving your aim. This statement is very applicable to the top colouring of the birds. A simple statement that this is to be as dark as possible is correct but this has to be achieved on a good quality feather, especially in the females. To obtain this on a broad feather which contains plenty of quality and a rich sheen to it is difficult. An additional problem is that, when you have done so, the feather tends to show a lacing around the edges. This is a fault, but one which I am not too critical about.

In the males this feather quality is equally important. I have often seen cocks winning at the summer agricultural shows which were a great colour in the morning, but when the heat of the sun shone on them during the afternoon their feathers began to curl upwards like those of a Frizzle Bantam. This illustrated that their feather quality was too soft. Another feature in the males' colouring is that their top colour may be fine, but when you turn up the hackle and saddle hackle feathers the underside has lost the rich mahogany sheen and is virtually orange coloured. Under colour is also important. This should be as dark as possible right up the root of the feather. An independent observer watching the judging of a class of Rhodes can tell very quickly whether the judge is conversant with the breed or not. The person who is not quite sure of his facts will carefully look at the under colour of the bird by lifting a few feathers in the middle of its back.

The Rhode breeder will put his foot on a box and rest the bird across his knee. He will then commence at the very top of the bird's hackle and work his way through the shoulders before inspecting the root of the tail. He will then inspect the wing butt and wing bow; this area is very often forgotten. The breast will also be inspected and double checked in case there is some black spangling to the top colour. What he is looking for is an under colour which is not only a rich even shade, but free from grey patches, or a silvery tinge to it. If he locates some 'smut' across the top of the shoulders in a male bird he may just be slightly tolerant, providing that it is as Sid Tunnicliffe used to say, 'the right sort of smut'. This extra pigmentation can be very useful in the breeding pen. The big objection is the mealy type of murky grey, or white which is even worse.

The type which can be useful in the breeding pen is where there is a band of dark grey or black across the feather, but the portions above and below it are a rich red. The correct distribution of black markings in a Rhode is very simple to explain; the more difficult task is to outline the variations which may be acceptable to a judge, knowing that perfection is almost unobtainable. Simply, the tail on both sexes should be solid black, the top colour of which should carry a beetle green sheen to it. This includes the inside of the tail feathers, which in a female can sometimes show a brown tinge.

One of the features which confuses many of the less experienced judges is the amount of black required in the neck hackle. In the male birds, none whatever! In the female a slight ticking to the ends of the lower feathers is permissible. This should not be as heavy as a spot or a lacing, and certainly not a stripe.

The final parts of the bird's black markings are the flight and secondary wing feathers. In the flights, the outer half should be solid black from top to bottom. The secondaries are reversed with the half closest to the body being black. This only shows when the wing is opened out. When in a closed position the black is covered by the red half of the feather which forms the wing diamond.

Especially in the flights, the red half of the wing should be as dark a colour as possible, and be perfectly clear of black peppering or over spill from the black half. In females this is difficult to achieve if the same pattern is to be extended right through the wing feathers

312

to the final few. Sometimes a compromise has to be made by allowing a little over marking on the first flight in order to achieve this step nearer to perfection.

The correct amount of black in the secondaries is hard to achieve without the flights being over marked. This is especially so on feathers which have the correct broad width to them. In many birds the final few secondary feathers lose texture and become thin and wiry or, as Bill Bell used to say, 'They look like pipe cleaners.'

Another point is that when a near perfect wing has been obtained, the black pigmentation is so strong that the top colour on the bird's wings become peppered with black, which is known as 'black wing topped.' In the males the wing bar and covert can become black laced. A near to perfect wing is easier to obtain in the male bird than in the female but, with both sexes, the aim is for the red to be as dark a colour as possible. It is far easier to breed well marked wings on birds which are either narrow in the feather or pale coloured in the red half of the feather.

I have written several paragraphs on the correct wing markings because, unfortunately, many judges attach more importance to them than is justified by their allocation of points in the standard. Type and the head receive half of the total number and should therefore receive that amount of consideration. The comb, wattles, face and eyes should all be a bright red colour, whilst the beak is yellow/horn. The toes and shanks are also yellow. In many birds the front scales on the legs are a deep brown, described as horn coloured. This can extend into the toe nails and, again, is acceptable. Quality and texture are allocated 20 points. This part of the standard is not confined to any one particular feature, but is a general observation of the bird.

In the breed summary I have drawn attention to the points which I believe fall into this category. i.e. activeness, bone structure and face texture in keeping with egg laying potential and, most importantly, the feather texture. It is a question of balance or compromise to obtain the maximum depth of colour whilst retaining a broad and well textured feather with a lustrous sheen.

A good Rhode Island Red should be pleasing to the eye and pleasant to the touch. This summary refers to the exhibition type of R.I.R.. The ones used so successfully in the laying trials retained the original golden coloured plumage, a high tail carriage and no consideration whatever was paid to markings. There were several breeders, like David Cargill, who attempted a compromise between the two types with reasonable success.

One unacceptable aspect of the breed has been the dying of a bird's feathering to increase the depth of colour. Fortunately this procedure has diminished in recent years, but there was a period when dyed birds were often shown. The most noticeable detection area was in the shade of under colour and under the bird's wing. This part was difficult to colour without staining the bird's skin. However, if you did not attempt to brush some dye onto the feathers in that area they would stand out several shades lighter.

Proving that a bird was 'a dyed un' was virtually impossible if the job had been well done. The normal procedure when judging a strongly suspect bird was to leave it cardless and you very rarely got the owner asking too many questions on your placings!

Occasionally you had the brazen one who attempted the direct approach, with fire coming out of his nostrils, but they very soon quietened down when you pointed out the offending areas without stating why you thought the colouring showed such a variation in depth of colour. The Poultry Club was very strong in its judgement of proven cases, a lifetime's ban on showing under PC rules being the ultimate sentence.

The Rhode Island Reds have an excellent club and I have always enjoyed a feature of their Annual Show. This is the awarding of trophies to birds which excel in certain aspects of the standard.

The head piece cup always created interest, as did the ones for shape. I believe that at one period there were separate trophies for male and female. There was one for wing markings and, interestingly, when judging for this award, ground colour had to be taken into consideration. This illustrates the point I made that it is far easier to obtain near perfect markings on a bird with light ground colour.

The principle of awarding some form of special recognition to birds with outstanding features is nearly unique to the R.I.R. Club. Anconas have a trophy for leg colouring and I believe that there is a shape cup in the 'Rosecomb Bantam Club', but I do not recall many others. This seems a wasted opportunity to involve more people in the 'Championship Awards' and thus create added interest in the event.

Having written some 3,000 words on the breed, I suppose that it goes without saying, the Rhode Island Red is amongst my favourite breeds. I have served on the breed's committee and had the pleasure of judging at their club shows and hope to continue breeding both the large and bantam versions for the rest of my life.

Weight Large Male 8.5 lbs Females 6.5 lbs.

Bantam Male 28-32 ozs   Females 24-28 ozs.

Rhode Island Reds are amongst a group of mahogany coloured breeds which unfortunately do not lend themselves to photography; even in colour they tend to show a false shade. I have therefore selected birds which illustrate the breed's shape and development through its early years, trusting that our readers can visualise the bird's rich top colouring.

Rhode Island Reds are described as being brick shaped, this pair of females were bred by Fred Denner in 1925, and show a long body with a well rounded chest.

314

RED 1. This photo was taken in 1905, and is thought to be the first print of a R.I.Red bred in the British Isles. The cockerel is rosecombed, as they all were at this period, and he appears to be still showing lacing on his breast which would be inherited from his Gold Wyandotte ancestors.

RED 2. Again shows a Rosecomb, this time bred by Mrs Colbeck in 1925.

RED 3. Was bred by Tom Scott & Co in 1922. This cockerel won many first prizes for Tom and shows an improvement in shape and style from the original birds.

RED 4. Shows a single combed cockerel which was bred in 1923 by C. N. Goode, who was also a noted breeder of White Wyandottes. Again the bird is illustrating the improvement in body shape and tail carriage.

RED 5. This photo moves forward to the 1930s, and shows one of the many winning birds bred in Lincolnshire by the Herbie Squire combination of father and son, both with the same name, and both top class R.I.Red breeders.

RED 6. Shows a champion cock bred and exhibited by Captain C.K. Greenway. This bird won 16 Firsts and was Best R.I.R eight times, including the Dairy and Club shows, again in the early 1930s.

RED 7. Was bred and shown by Harry Andrews at around the same period. He was a consistent winner for him, and was considered to be as near to perfection for shape as any bird bred at that time in history.

RED 8. Was bred by the original club secretary, Frank Page. His body shape must have rivalled the Andrews bird, but in this photo the bird lacks tail furnishings.

The utility qualities of the breed were also being emphasised, and in RED 9 a cockerel bred by Sid Tunnicliffe from Tamworth illustrates the point. This bird won Best Utility R.I.Red at the 1932 Crystal Palace.

RED 10. Shows the 1933 Dairy Show winner. He was shown by my father John Kay, and the bird went forward to be awarded Reserve Champion Utility Exhibit any breed.

Rosecombs continued to develop, and RED 11 and 12 show a pair of winning birds bred and exhibited by G H Muzzlewhite from Devon.

In Rhode Island Red females, I have chosen four, all from the early 1930s. RED 13. Shows a deep bodied hen, bred by Harry Andrews from Bexhill-on-Sea. She appears to be a bit short in body length especially behind her thighs, however she won the Crystal Palace two years in succession.

RED I4. Shows a bird with great body length and balance. She was bred by Frank Page and won Silver Medal at the Dairy Show.

RED 15. Was bred by the Club's President Captain the Hon Greenway. She illustrates a very attractive pullet, and won champion Utility R.I.Red at the Crystal Palace.

RED 16. Shows a grand bodied pullet with a well rounded front. She was bred by John Kay and won many top awards for him.

318

RED 17 Illustrates the correct markings on a R.I.R. female, drawn by 'Bruff Jackson'.

RED 18 and 19 Show a pair of R.I Red miniatures from 1932. They were bred and shown by Alexander Petrie from Falkirk, and the female especially illustrates the emphasis being placed on the birds' shape some 65 years ago.

RHODE ISLAND WHITE

These are pure white in colour and have yellow legs and beak. The comb can be either single or rose; the most popular was the rosecombed. Actually the breed was originated before the R.I.R. initial work being started on it in 1890, White Wyandottes, White Leghorns and Cochins being used.

As previously stated, lack of breed definition and character were its downfall.

Weights Males 7lbs Females 5.5lbs.

FIG 1. Shows a Rhode Island White cock which won second prize at the Club Show in 1926, shown by Mr. W. W. Woodward.

FIG 2. Is another rare photograph of Rhode Island Whites. This time it is the hen that won first prize and the silver medal for best Utility Heavy Breed at the Bath and West Agricultural Show. She was bred by Mrs Innes from Taunton.

320

RUMPLESS

My decision to include Rumpless Fowls as a separate breed is debatable. There are many who will say that, as with the Frizzle Fowls, it is only a variation within a particular breed.

The official technical wording for such a bird is, 'Birds which are missing their coccyx, or have some deformed caudal vertebrae'. To a straight forward bloke like me, they quite simply do not have a 'parson's nose'.

One type which stands as a unique example is the bantam from the Isle of Man, known as Rumpless Game, being a miniature of the Large Old English Game bird. Strangely, I have never seen a Rumpless Large O.E.G. Consequently I debate whether the two are really related.

Many other breeds exist in a rumpless version; one of the most commonly seen is the Araucana, which has been illustrated in that style for centuries, and their breed club offers separate classes for them at the Classic Shows.

Belgian Bantams include birds with this peculiarity, as the Barbu D'Grubbe, and there have been photographs illustrating the birds since the early part of the twentieth century, but separate classes for the birds at the club show have only recently appeared.

Curiously, there has been mentioned since the very early writings on poultry, a rumpless version of the Japanese Bantam which seems strange on a breed where its main feature is the excessively long tail.

Historians have, for centuries, debated the origins of the fowls with no tail and failed to reach a definite conclusion. Edward Brown illustrates a drawing by Ulysses Aldrovandi in 1599 clearly showing Gallus Percicus as having no tail and an almost Redcap type of comb.

Whilst, during the nineteenth century, all of the famous poultry writers had their 'penneth' on the subject, it would appear mainly to attempt proof that the birds were actually living wild in the forests of the Far East.

One variation is the Wallikiki Fowls and a pair of them are illustrated from the Paris Zoo, and in some way they bear similarity to the Araucana, which have certainly been recorded living wild and breeding, both tailed and non-tailed versions. The San Queue version of the Ardennes offers another long established example.

The defect, or however you would like to describe the peculiarity, is quite easily transmitted to other breeds. Lewis Wright made a point that I can personally endorse. He states that, 'progeny from these crosses are far less certain to reproduce their kind'.

During the 1940s we bred Silver Sebright Bantams, which were the old Lancashire strain similar to those used so successfully by Arthur Fish during the 1920s and early 30s. In nearly every year's batch of chicks there would always be at least one of them that would grow up to be a rumpless. This was not due to feather picking but a genuine throw back to the original breeding by Sir John Sebright and his friends during the mid nineteenth century when a Rumpless Bantam was used in one of their lines of breeding.

The interesting point about them was that they were always female and that we never managed to get any fertile eggs from them.

FIG 1. Shows a painting of Rumpless Araucana with their very exaggerated prominent ear tufts.

FIG 2. Was taken at the Paris Zoological Gardens and shows a pair of Walliki Fowls.

FIG 3. Shows a pair of Rumpless Belgians, whilst FIG 4. is a Rumpless Japanese.

FIG 5. Is from the Isle of Man and shows a pair of their native Bantams.

FIG 6. Shows a Blue Araucana female. She was photographed by Josef Wolters in Germany.

SAXON

These birds were displayed in Britain during 1935, where they formed part of the German section at an exhibition held in conjunction with the Essex show.

At present, little seems to be heard of the breed, but they were originally described as being related to the Spanish Castilian.

In Spain there was a breed called the Barbezieux, which was the result of crossing Castilians with the French Gascon Fowls. These birds were of similar colouring but shorter on the leg and had a reputation for being excellent tasting meat, which would be the main object of the original cross to develop a breed with extra flesh on its bones.

Both the Saxon and the Barbezieux are described as being fairly large bodied birds with a well rounded front. They stand on short legs, which are of a strong structure. They have a single comb, upright in the males, and falling over slightly in the females. The head points are red in colour with white earlobes. There is only one colour listed and that is black.

I suspect that these two breeds are closely related, if not actually the same birds in a district variation.

Interestingly, the Saxon shows a resemblance to the Rhinelander, only in a single combed version.

When the Saxons were displayed in Britain, the correspondents' remarks about the breed drew attention to the high gloss in their colour, and also their extremely quiet temperament.

This pair of Saxons was displayed at the 1935 International Exhibition. The event was held in Essex and attracted over 20,000 Poultry, Turkeys, Waterfowl and Pigeons. Exhibits were received from all parts of the world.

324

SCHLOTTERKAMM

In many ways this breed reminds me of the Thuringian, but minus the beard. It is also not as abundantly feathered, being more of the Mediterranean style. Apparently their name, when translated, means something like floppy comb.

The shape and carriage of the breed is typical continental light breed style with an upstanding single comb in the males, folded over in the females.

The colouring is where the resemblance with the Thuringian occurs, with the distinctive mottled pattern again present. It is also available in self black and cuckoo.

It is thought to have originated in Western Germany, down towards the Dutch frontier, where it has a reputation of being an excellent laying bird. The Bergische Crower is closely associated with the Schlotterkamm, being almost identical in breed features.

The Bergische is native to Rhenish Prussia, which is a hilly district and would obviously affect noise levels. You will notice from the birds' name that this breed has a reputation for competing successfully in local crowing competitions!!!

A painting of Schlotterkamm in a very attractive mottled colouring.

SCOTS DUMPY

This breed is one of its own amongst British breeds in that it has extremely short legs. The shanks are no more than 2 inches long giving the birds a very squat appearance.

The body should be long, wide and deep, with a flat back and a full tail, all of which sounds distinctly like the Dorkings' description.

The origin of the Scots Dumpy is thought to extend well into B.C. times, with them being introduced by the Phoenicians, who for a period occupied certain areas of Great Britain and actually fought against the invading Romans. Where they actually brought the Dumpies from is obscure, but the birds existed in other colours, apart from the barred, which is the one usually associated with the breed. Blacks and silvers are also two which are mentioned in history, so obviously there would also be whites. Their short legs were probably a result of specialised breeding for that point, and any Dumpy breeder will tell you that the birds are always wanting to revert back to longer legs. If you consistently mate short legged birds together they produce a lethal gene, so some of the longer leg-ged ones have to be used to correct this point.

On the continent there are two breeds with the short legged feature, the German Creeper which exists in a wide range of colours and the French Courtes Pattes which was origi-nally only in black. Historians quote that 'short legged fowl have been known on the con-tinent from time immemorial and may have originated from Asiatic countries.' The Dumpies have a red coloured face and wattles which are of medium size. Their combs can be either single or rose, not too large in size, with the leader on the rose type following the contour of the head and the rose part of it liberally covered with fine workings. The bird's body is deep and, combined with its well rounded front, gives it plenty of area to accumu-late a good carcass of meat, which presumably was its main purpose. They are also good layers of white eggs and are excellent mothers. I am told that they also have another advantage, that if you allow them to roam around the garden their short legs do not en-courage them to do much digging and scratching. Whether or not this is true I have no proof.

The breed has never been popular on this side of the border, but breeders who have kept them say that 'their temperament is very friendly and docile', whilst the game keep-ers say that 'either pure or crossed they make marvellous broodies', Which makes you wonder why there have not been more of them in England. The breeders have recently formed an independent Scots Dumpy Club which caters for large fowl and miniatures so maybe we will see the breed realise its full potential.

The history of the breed in Scotland is surrounded by the recital of folklore tales.

One is that they were known as the 'Time Clock Bird' owing to their ability to waken at the same time daily, whether it was daylight or not, and in the north of Scotland there are not many hours daylight come late November. It is for their very acute hearing that they are mostly remembered which was said to be 'ahead of the Collie dog's ability'.

Consequently, they were taken into battle with the soldiers as they fought with the invading Romans, who hated them, knowing that they could not approach a camp without a Dumpy cock crowing.

One particular story states that, in an attempt to defeat the beastly bird, the Romans decided that they would approach the camp barefoot and in the dark. This they did suc-cessfully, until they found themselves in a bed of thistles. With the Romans howling in pain with damn great Scotch thistles sticking into the soles of their feet, our friend was soon crowing his head off and the Scots and Pict soldiers soon gave them sore heads to go with their feet!

The Kilted Kelts won the battle, and ever since then the emblem of Scotland has been the thistle, when perhaps it should have been the Dumpy.

The breed is still rare in Scotland even after a piece of 'history' involving them with the national emblem. The miniature version is gradually getting a foothold and, as in many cases, may attract greater popularity than the large fowl.

The breed is classified as a light breed, which could surprise an independent observer looking at the standard weights; apparently the original birds were much larger than the ones in recent times.

The breed was first shown south of the border at the Metropolitan Exhibition in London during 1852.

Weights   Male   7.5 lbs   Female   6 lbs

A fine pair of Scots Dumpies. The photo was taken in 1921 when the breed was very popular.

A Grey Scots Dumpy cock which won Olympia and also the Scots Dumpy Club Show, which was held at Paisley. He was bred by Jack Major who was thought of as a Dorking breeder, but always held a 'soft spot' for a good Dumpy.

Won the Crystal Palace in 1925 for his breeder Mr J. E. Kerr from Dollar.

Black Dumpies have become more popular in recent years, and this pullet offers a very good illustration of the breed.

328

SCOTS GREY

The Scots Grey is a breed which has inhabited its native country for centuries and, like so many other breeds, it has lived roaming around the farmsteads and crofts supplying meat and food for all the families.

The actual origin of the birds is not definitely known, but the early descriptions of this breed were of them being quite strongly built and weighing 8-9 lbs, which endorses the suggestions that they contained Dorking blood. Dorkings have been known to have been kept in Scotland since the Roman times.

The influence of Game blood is noticeable in the birds' tight feathering and firm feel when you handle them. Going by the birds' appearance in the twentieth century, I would suggest that is was Modern Game type rather than the Oxford fighting version which was used.

Gradually these 'farm yard' mongrels were selectively mated to develop into the accepted and standardised breed.

I suppose there must have been some connection with the Scots Dumpy, for it is too much of a coincidence to have two barred varieties in one country which are not related. Presumably, the Dumpy was developed by the use of the European short legged Creeper and Courtes Pattes, or vice-versa. Maybe this was the reason for using longer legged Modern Game fowl to emphasise the difference between the two breeds. The style of the Scots Grey, as we have known them for the last 70 years or so, is one of its own, being tight feathered, fairly long in the back and with an upright and dignified stance, which does not show too much front, but has a nicely placed and fairly wide pair of shoulders. In colouring, the whole of the body is finely barred on a narrow feathering, the amount of black and white being equal, not as in the Campine. This type of barring suggests to me that the Scots Grey was used to develop and improve the American imported Barred Rocks into the clearer and more distinctively marked English version. The comb is single and upright in males and females, though the earlier recordings of the breed describe the female's comb as being folded.

The comb, face and wattles should be fine in texture with the comb having evenly distributed and well defined serrations. The white coloured legs and feet are allowed to have black mottling. Another great feature of the breed is the wealth and length of feathering in the hackle and side hackle, which highlights the birds exquisite barring in what should be an even shade of top colour throughout.

There are some excellent miniature versions of the breed which again have their own distinctive character. In recent years there has been a tendency for breeders to use Barred Rock blood for extra stamina and markings, which is fine providing that you do not show them too quickly before you have enough generations to revert back to the birds' original style.

The breed, in keeping with many barred and cuckoo varieties, does not enjoy a large following of breeders, even in Scotland.

Weights   *Males*   *7lbs*   *Females*   *5lbs*

First five pictures are photographs of birds bred by Mr R. Fletcher-Hearnshaw from Nottingham, who was the President of the Poultry Club in 1930.

A fine Scots Grey cock which won many senior awards in 1930.

This was the 1934 Dairy Show Winner.

A very stylish cock which was a consistent winner during the summer of 1930.

A rangy bodied hen which again was a well known winner.

A miniature Scots Grey pullet. She was bred in 1928, and won both the Dairy Show and the London Bantam Club Show in that year.

A very finely barred cockerel which won the Crystal Palace in 1933. He was bred and exhibited by Dr S. Young from Glasgow.

This very attractive trio of Scots Greys won the Light Breeding Pen class at the 1932 Dairy Show. They were bred and exhibited by Mr R. Fletcher Hearnshaw.

331

SICILIAN BUTTERCUP and FLOWERBIRD

As suggested by its name, the Buttercup is associated with the Isle of Sicily where for many generations it has been used by the local farming community and peasants as a very hardy and successful laying bird. It probably originated in North Africa, where for centuries cup shaped combed birds have been reported to have been seen in large quantities. The arrival in America was by cargo ship, and the breed adapted to life on the ocean waves, providing the crew with a good supply of fresh eggs and meat.

The natural plumage is the typical pheasant colour with willow coloured legs and a typical gamey type of appearance, its individual claim to fame being the comb, which starts at the beak with a small upright single type and then spreads out to form a circle or buttercup shape on the main part of the skull.

The more complete the circle is the better, the sides being free from any large spikes. The breed exists in several colourings including Duckwing Gold, White and a Silver version which is similar to the Friesian colouring, in that the male is almost white with a black tail and the females showing markings to the body and tail, but with a pure silver neck hackle. Another colour is the Brown, which was also developed into a specialist variety under the name of Sicilian Flower Bird. A Club was formed during the 1920s but their popularity soon faded. The Buttercup is a breed which we have kept. I find them very attractive, the drawback being the wild temperament of the strain we acquired. Apparently it was not a fault in the native stock, where they are reported to live in the farmhouse as one of the family. If we had let ours in the house there would not have been a pot or an ornament left in one piece. As with many breeds I believe that the lack of exhibitors' enthusiasm stems from the original standard. One point was their lobes, which America required to be fully white, whilst Britain specified red but would accept up to one third white, which is another of those either/or situations which usually prove to be fatal. The many colours of the breed also had a different allocation of points for each colour. The head and comb which I would have thought the outstanding feature of the breed was allocated 29 points in the Brown but only 14 in some other colours which is quite confusing.

The wide range of similar colourings did not help, especially when the feather markings varied between the colours. The female's body markings alternating between, Spangled, Mottled and Pencilled.

This has now been rectified with one standard allocating 30 points for headpiece, 25 for colouring, and 20 for body shape and style. Gold is the most popular version, where the female's colour and markings are very similar to a British wild hen Pheasant. The Gold male bird's basic ground colour is bay shading to red-bay, with his breast also red-bay and body light bay. Tail black, sickles and coverts green/black. The Silver is similar to the Gold except that the ground is silver/white instead of red.

The comb, face and wattles on all the colours should be bright red. Legs and feet are a beautiful shade of willow/green.

Buttercups are a very attractive breed which hopefully will grow in popularity. One delightful feature in Richard Billson's strain is that instead of walking they take very short steps and appear to scurry along. Several people have reported keeping the breed in Lincolnshire. I hope they keep up the good work.

| Weight | Males | 6 lbs | Females | 5 lbs |

A beautifully furnished Brown Sicilian Buttercup cock. He won second prize in the A.O.V. class at the Royal Show in 1921. It was thought to be the first time that a Buttercup had appeared in the awards list at a Major Show. He was shown by Mr J. B. Hardcastle from Branston in Lincolnshire.

Bred by the club secretary Mr F. Dereham from Derbyshire. He was Champion Buttercup at the 1926 Club Show held at the Crystal Palace, winning two medals and a silver spoon.

A typical cup shaped comb which is almost in a circle.

Another Gold hen which, during the early 1920s, won over twenty first prizes.

A very attractive Gold hen from the 1930s; she was bred by Mr Denham and was a consistent winner for him.

Arather unusual coloured Buttercup; she is a Duckwing, and won Second at the 1921 Crystal Palace Club show for her owner Tom Scott.

A group of Brown and Gold Sicilian Buttercups.

SILKIES

Profile of Sue Bowser

I was born in Rotherham, Yorkshire in 1959, the first of three children. Both my parents originate from the grinding poverty of the back-streets of Sheffield. Both my parents are from large families and they lived in the grim back to back housing of the time. I have no 'poultry pedigree' what-so-ever. My childhood memories are of the black over-bearing steel work's chimneys, and going to the outside toilet in winter, when I visited my much loved grandmother.

My family moved to Lincolnshire in 1968, where my father transferred from a job in the Sheffield Brass works, to a teaching post in the local technical college. I came into contact with poultry for the first time when I was seventeen years of age. I visited a local farm and was eager to collect the eggs. As I put my hand under a scraggy old farmyard hen for the first time and pulled out the warm egg a deep and lasting love was born.

I moved from my parents' home into one of my own in 1981 in a nearby village, which had three quarters of an acre garden, and adopted the hens from the farm I first fell in love with.

In 1987 I married my husband James Bowser and came to live on his family's farm, back in the same village as my parents. This afforded me the opportunity of fields to cover with poultry huts and the collection of poultry grew rapidly. The Silkies appeared on the scene at more or less the same time. I have kept many breeds, but the Silkie is the only one for me.

The Introduction

'The Silkie is exceptionally tame, incubates cooler, goes broody at only 5 months old and behaves impeccably', as described by Dr Anderson-Brown in 'The Incubation Book'

It was a natural progression from having Silkies as broodies to finding that I enjoy breeding Silkies for exhibition. As Silkie breeders, we all set out with different goals to attain. It might be to improve the coloured birds, make new friends or hold an elected club office, but in the main it is to breed a Silkie that most closely complies with the club standard, and then to win with that bird at a major competition.

These words are written out of enthusiasm for the hobby, and hopefully to give a little help to those starting out with a really delightful breed.

A Sense of History

One warm summer afternoon a few years ago my husband had 'lost' me in the poultry tent at a local agricultural show. Just inside the canvas marquee, one of my white Silkie hens was penned and my husband went to sit near her, knowing that was a good way to meet up with me. My hen danced in the rays of the sun and flirted with the onlookers. My husband later remarked that she caught the eye of many people and created more comments than any other bird in the entire show.

What was it - this hairy, woolly bird, was it a chicken? Did it lay eggs? Old poultry records show that in 1776 in Brussels there was a 'rabbit fowl' on public view. This they claimed was an actual cross between a hen and a rabbit! Over 200 years later the same creature, although no longer on show as a 'freak' was still causing a stir!

I would suggest that the Silkie's intriguing plumage and its excellent mothering qualities have ensured the bird's survival down the centuries.

Silkies are enchanting to keep, and when handling them there's a sense of history. In 1298-99 Marco Polo, a Venetian,   described his visit to China to the Europeans and, amongst the many things he saw fit to mention was 'hens which have hair like cats, are black, and lay the best of eggs'.

Other early poultry records show that fowl bearing resemblance to a Silkie were described in the early writings of the Italian naturalist Aldrovandi. In his book published in 1599, he described fowl 'white as snow, with wool like sheep.' He had apparently found a picture of a wool bearing hen in the margin of an old map.

In 1555 a Swiss gentleman called Konrad Gesner wrote the historic ANIMALIUM. In it he described 'Gallina Lanigera', a woolly hen, without tail feathers and rosecombed.

Many Silkie commentaries will say that much uncertainty surrounds the exact country of origin, and it is not hard to see why.

A Chinese encyclopaedia published in 1596, compiled from even older sources, mentions 'fowls with black feathers, bones and flesh'. During the 16th and 17th centuries voyagers came back with many tales of woolly fowl and of a Negro fowl. In 1682 fowls in Java included a bird 'whose flesh was black yet very good meat' whilst in a book, 'History of Sumatra' a 'Negro fowl' was described, and also another bird which was 'still blacker with black bones'.

By the late 1700s a French naturalist, Count de Buffon, describes the downy chicken of Japan (Poule a duvet du Japon), and the 'Coq Negre'. The 'Poule du Japon' was apparently found in Japan, China and countries of Asia, being white feathered, whilst the Coq Negre had black skin and black feathers.

It was W B Tegetmeier's chapter about Silkies in his poultry book of 1867 which actually distinguished between a white bird with black skin and Silkie feathering and a black skinned, black feathered bird whose plumage was not of the Silkie type.

Lewis Wright in his Illustrated book of Poultry 1873 shows the Silkies with dark purple combs and wattles.

From pictures of show birds we can trace how the bird has changed fashion over a hundred years. The artist Ludlow depicts the First prize winners in the 'any variety' class at Bristol, 1871 in FIG SB1. Compare this with the First prize cock and cup winner in Crystal Palace in 1925 shown in FIG SB2. The latter carries his tail too high and is too cut away at the front for my tastes, but even so it is the same creature!

The hen in the Ludlow print, is also cut away at the front and higher on the leg than the hen shown following the Great War - FIG SB3 is the 1928 Crystal Palace Club Show winner of Mr J Lilburn from Fife. By this time the hens were fuller fronted and lower to the ground.

The breed standard made in 1925 puts its emphasis on fluff, silk, type and required 'fluff extending almost to foot feather'. FIG SB4 Is a copy of an old Silkie breed standard.

Those breeders who bred to this standard were effectively changing the appearance of the bird to some degree to hens that were showing less leg than their earlier counterparts.

In contrast again, by 1994, a picture of one of my own white pullets, depicts a bird fuller in the saddle and larger in the crest (and perhaps more silk?) than the Ludlow print - FIG SB5 which was Champion Silkie at the National and Best White Pullet at the Club Championship Show in 1994.

The bird is also changing with regard to size and weight. In 1925 there was 'no objection

FIG SB2

FIG SB1

FIG SB3

FIG SB5

KNOW YOUR BREED—33

Standard Points of the Silkie

SILKIES are prone to be regarded as being purely ornamental, which is not, in fact, strictly the case. They, and their crosses, provide most reliable broodies and are freely used by pedigree breeders to hatch out important sittings when first-class results are of particular urgency.

It is of interest that experiments made in the early nineteen hundreds with Brown Leghorn and Silkie matings yielded important findings, and it is probable that they were the forerunner of our present-day knowledge of sex-linkage.

The breed is standardised in the White (most popular variety), the Black and the Blue.

Skull is short, neat and crested; the crest, to be as upright as the comb will allow, is soft and full with absence of any hard feathers, with some six to twelve soft, silky feathers streaming gracefully backward from the lower and back portion of the crest to about 1½ inches in length. Beak short and stout at the base, slate-blue in colour. Brilliant black eyes, not too prominent. Comb, of mulberry colour, is an almost circular cushion of flesh, broader than long preferred, with a number of very small prominences, and a slight indentation transversely across the middle. Face, of the same mulberry colour, to be very smooth; ear-lobes turquoise blue or mulberry, more oval than round; wattles mulberry, nearly semi-circular and concave.

Neck short to medium in length, broad and full at the base, with abundant and flowing hackle.

Body: Broad and full breast; stout and square shoulders; short back, saddle rising to tail; broad stern, abundantly covered with fine fluff; soft wings, fluffy at the butts, the ends of the flights ragged; short tail, very ragged at the ends of the harder feathers of the true tail.

Legs, of lead colour, short. Thighs set wide and covered profusely with fluff standing out clearly. Shanks smooth, free from scaling, slightly feathered on outer sides. Toes five in number, the fourth and fifth toes diverging one from the other, the middle and outer toes feathered, but these (like those on the shank) to be not too hard.

In the female the crest bears close resemblance to a powder puff (devoid of hard feathers), stands up and out—not inclined backward, hanging over the eyes or split by the comb. Comb small and hardly to be seen under the front of the crest. Wattles very small (or absent) and oval-shaped.

Body: Cushion broad and well covered with the silkiest of plumage, which should nearly smother the small tail, the ragged ends alone to be protruding.

In other respects, allowing for the natural sexual differences, the female does not differ from the male.

The skin in both sexes is of mulberry tint.

Hard-feathered vulture hocks, green beak, ruddy comb or face, eyes other than black, incorrect colour of plumage or skin, plumage not silky, lack of crest, split crest, single comb, four toes, featherless shanks and feet, scaly legs or want of fluff, all serious faults.

Weights: Male, 3lb; female, 2lb.

White variety: Plumage white throughout. Black variety: Black with a green sheen. Blue variety: An even shade from head to feet, neither laced nor barred.

The charm and breed characteristics of the Silkie are freely marked out in the white male above and black female at bottom corner.

SCALE OF POINTS

Texture of plumage	30	Colour	10
Head	30	Legs	10
Type	20	Total	100

FIG SB4

to size if other points were good'. The 1990s saw the acceptance of a Silkie bantam. A greater differential between them and the large fowl became necessary. The emphasis is now on heavier, larger birds. Each sex had 1 lb added to its ideal weight, now being 4 lbs for the males and 3 lbs for the females.

BREED CHARACTERISTICS

'Oh-er', She said, 'he aint 'arf ugly in he ? But you just have to love him all the same, dun you ?'

Fighting feelings of deep indignation, I managed some reply. After all, this woman was talking about my prize cockerel! I just could not see anything 'ugly' but this is actually a common reaction to the cushion comb on the males.

As a breed characteristic, the males do have a cushion or 'mulberry' comb, which can be quite lumpy in appearance, whilst the females have the 'powder puff' crest. Pick up a white Silkie and you will see the abundance of soft, silky white feathering. Underneath are the black skin, dark flesh and dark bones. It is five toed, blue legged with more white feathers and has turquoise blue ear lobes - I defy you not to marvel at its genetic make up.

They derive their name 'Silkie' from the long, soft, silky, fluffy plumage. They make an ideal show bird and the term 'fancy' is really applicable to the breed.

As a breed they require no special treatment to rear and manage. They want less feed than some of their other Large Fowl counterparts.

They will live happily outdoors; however sunshine will lead to dis-colouring of the feathers, if the bird is required for showing. The whites become yellow-brassy in colour unless kept in the shade. They are equally contented if kept indoors.

They are a docile breed that are easily tamed, and are not taken to flying up trees if startled. Such is their good nature that they can be taken from their environment, washed for show, then they will happily sit wrapped in a towel on the sideboard, without ever trying to scale the walls of the room!

The females are always busy as sitters or rearers of young. They are also moderate layers of white to tinted coloured eggs. I find they will lay well even during the cold winter months.

They excel as broodies for all species, including the delicate breeds. Once they have made up their mind that they are going to sit it is less easy to persuade them that they are not! If I do not want them to be sitting I change their surroundings for a few days, and this will usually (but not always) make them forget and come back into lay. Equally, if I do want them to sit, I leave eggs laying about for a few days and they soon oblige.

Age is no barrier, they usually become more beautiful with age, although the older female will not lay as frequently as her younger friends. The males become broader and the females improve in type and width.

In the show pens they can then become difficult to beat with younger stock.

SILKIE STANDARDS AND THE BREEDING PEN

The Silkie is exhibited as a Large Fowl, Light Breed in Britain, although a new standard has been agreed in 1993 which describes a bantam. The bantam varies in size and weight from its Large Fowl counterpart

The Silkie has been standardised in five different colours, white, black, gold, blue and partridge. Bearded Silkies sometimes appear, and a standard has been agreed for these too.

The British standard is determined and described by the Silkie Club and submitted to the Poultry Club. It is the Poultry Club which produces 'The British Poultry Standards', originally a publication of the Butterworth Press and republished in 1997 by Blackwell Science Ltd. This sets out the detailed information on the breed in relation to size, type, colouring as well as the weights and scale of judging points.

In the United States of America the Silkie qualifies as a bantam breed. There the Silkie has been standardised in various forms! The Americans appear not to have much reticence, they have bearded and non bearded, white, black, blue partridge, buff, grey, (and work is being done on a splash). I am reliably informed the American birds are much smaller than the British Large Fowl birds, but that they are truly beautiful in type.

The standards define specific characteristics a bird should have, and this in turn provides a goal for success in the show pen. The standard also defines type and its relationship to various physical attributes using points. Thus a good knowledge of the breed standard is a pre-requisite to any success in the show pen. By reading the standard, and re-reading the standard over and over again, the breeder begins to build a mental image of the PERFECT Silkie. It is by using this image that the breeding pen will be selected, and ultimately the bird for show.

Hopefully, the standard will also provide a basis for judging; the judge will use his knowledge of it whilst he compares birds.

A champion bird also has that 'X' factor (or even a 'Zing' factor), an extra presence or character that you cannot precisely pinpoint. It also has to show itself in the show pen; no matter how closely the bird complies with the breed standard, if it stands sulking, its beak in its neck, another bird will take the prize.

Thus the standards describe the 'perfect' Silkie, the ultimate bench mark to be achieved. This head knowledge needs to be translated into practical knowledge of what the reality is. The genetic pool available:-

This is entirely my opinion but I would rate the present state of affairs as:-

1) Some bantam females comparable with some of the Large Fowl whites, in details complying with the standard.

2) The blacks; some black females can now beat the whites at the major shows, also on type, which was unthinkable a few years ago.

3) The golds.

4) The blues and partridges.

The last three colours all need a lot of work, along with many of the bantam males.

5) Except for the odd and notable exception, the bearded Silkies are dreadful.

At the present time the bantams are only generally available in white.

When buying stock this has to be borne in mind.

An important point to remember when breeding the coloured Silkies is that 10% of the scale of points relates to colour, a further 10% to the legs and feet, and a massive 80% of the remaining points relates to type, plumage and head points. The scale of points thus translated is TYPE BEFORE COLOUR.

A bird has to be representative of the breed it purports to be, and a Silkie is in essence type and silk. There are far too many high legged Silkie females of all colours, including the whites, or birds that lack type. Sometimes the coloured Silkies are put up for awards judged on colour, when type should take priority.

Making up the breeding pen.

It is possible to breed good birds of both sexes from one pen of birds providing the females are up to scratch. A male bird, with a small neatly defined comb, that has a lot of crest behind it, will often breed good females. If the male has a very large cushion and long exaggerated wattles, with a little crest, drowned out by the comb, he will often produce a more masculine bird. In the blacks, I have a strain, where the males are almost total write offs from the showing point of view - they are pullet breeders.

A little gold in the black male's hackle goes a long way back in Silkie history, and they will frequently produce good dark coloured females.

When making up the breeding pen, it is important not to put the same fault into the pen in both sexes. If you are an 'instant' person who craves immediate success, stick to the white Silkies; they are hard to beat with the coloured Silkies. The coloured Silkies require patience and selection, and if these qualities are there in the HUMAN then success is so much more rewarding!

I feel that head points (which carry 30% of the points alone) especially in the males, silky plumage and type are the points that I want in a male. In the females, shape, type, silk, crest and I like something low not showing a lot of leg. Things like missing toe nails and bad eye colour are strongly hereditary. Silkies should have black eyes; I do not like a beady red eye staring back at me. The correct eye colour puts the finishing touch to an otherwise representative bird, and dark eye colour is a property easily lost and most difficult to regain. The colour 'mulberry' could be likened to crushed blackberries; it is not red. The males that err to black/dark faces often do better in the show pens. Put them in your breeding pens.

I do line breed, mother to son, father to daughter. This does make a very small genetic pool and any faults should be closely looked for. The way to emphasise a point is to have it good in both sexes of the parent bird.

If I am introducing a different bloodline, I use it on one bird only; any mistakes can be kept to a minimum. No matter how good a new bird may look, sometimes something does not 'gel' genetically, nor are the best breeding birds the best show birds.

Sometimes I have had no option but to start with inferior birds - I have bred birds that became consistent champions from parent birds I paid £6 for. However, with my bargain basement birds, I hatched over 100 and culled most of them, just keeping back birds showing those qualities I was wanting. Part of breeding is most emphatically culling - yes, CULL don't pass it on to someone else.

I am trying to emphasise that it is not about money but selection. I would advise starting with proven bloodlines where possible, and the best that is available - and please be realistic - do not expect someone to sell you their best bird - buy the bloodline.

SUE'S SILKIE SNIPPETS

This section is a series of notes relevant to keeping Silkies:-

Snippet One
The successful show bird does not begin when its parents are mated:- Success begins with the mating of various ancestors, and is carried through to how well the bird is prepared for the show pen. Birds to be shown WILL require washing and pen training prior to the show.

Snippet Two
What is produced after the study of genetics and a good knowledge of the breed standard must be enhanced by the individual birds themselves and good stock management. Silkies will require regular worming (always useful prior to the first show, and helps prevent many

a soiled feather). Extra vitamins and minerals in the water give a bird a 'boost' during the moult and enhances feather quality.

Snippet Three

I separate the males from the females when very young and rear the two sexes separately. The birds are reared in large roomy sheds.

Silkies have the reputation of being difficult to sex. The young cockerel is usually bigger boned, with head points that differ from the females', and it is in fact quite easy to pick them out.

Snippet Four

Try not to let the adult females get their crests wet and dirty too often; it spoils them for the show. Remember that mites can enjoy living here too! It is not uncommon with this breed to have a bird which pecks off the crests of its companions. The birds affected are left looking as if they have had their heads shaved. Obviously in show birds this has to be checked quickly... and the crests soon grow back.

Snippet Five

Scaly leg is caused by a mange mite called CREMIDOCOPTES MUTANS. I loathe to see this condition on a Silkie, as it is a basic management problem which causes the bird discomfort.

One lady declared to me that she thought that all Silkies had it! Indeed, when I was asked to judge a number of Silkies recently - most of them did!

There are many treatments, some of which if followed could prove toxic to the bird.

If I buy a bird I always worm it first, then I get an old tooth brush and some surgical spirits which will clear scaly leg.

The foot is generally first affected and the condition spreads upwards. In a severe case the leg is covered with irregular white horny scales. This causes much irritation to the bird.

Snippet Six

Snippet Five moves nicely onto Snippet Six - Scaly face

And again it is common in Silkies. This forms a white crust appearance on the bird's face. I treat this with Quellada Lotion (cheap and cheerful from the chemists, it's for scabies in humans).

On a Silkie, once treated, the crust literally falls off the bird's face and it clears within a few days.

Snippet Seven

Ear infections are a common complaint. Watch for an orange wax like substance around the bird's ear. It is caused by a mite or other foreign body and it needs to be treated. There is a range of popular cures for this one, using antiseptic ear drops for cats and dogs, (through to Ivermectin for sheep, as a contact wormer that also gets rid of mite).

Birds can be lost if action is not taken to treat the infection.

Snippet Eight

It is now recognised that Marek's disease, prior to the vaccine, was the most potent cause of death amongst poultry. During the 1960s a vaccine was developed to prevent it. The Silkie's genetic make up does seem to be very susceptible to this virus (from the herpes virus group). The birds become infected during the first three weeks of life as chicks. It is thought that infection is by oral and respiratory routes via dust.

The common signs are a 'wobbly' appearance and a limp. The birds can flop over or look lame on one leg. They can be found with one leg forward, the other backwards, with progressive paralysis of their legs and wings. The bird often suffers weight loss. There are other symptoms including tumours. A stress factor, hot weather, visit to a show etc., can trigger the symptoms. In unvaccinated flocks mortality is often between 10-20 weeks of age (often point of lay in the females).

I choose to vaccinate the chicks at day old, and again at 3 weeks of age. Other breeders do not vaccinate and prefer to choose to breed from the survivors in the hope of breeding some resistance into the birds - personal choice!!

It is common in many Silkie flocks; some breeders do claim that they never have a problem.

The Marek's vaccines are cheap and available from:-
INTERVET UK LTD
SCIENCE PARK. MILTON ROAD. CAMBRIDGE. CB4 4FP
Tel 01223 420221

Snippet Nine

The major shows are currently held in December. Young stock i.e. those birds in the pullet and cockerel classes would be generally hatched in Jan-Mar to be at their peak for these shows.

Snippet Ten

Young partridge coloured Silkies can often have green legs and green soles, (green legs are a disqualification fault and green soles are a serious defect). This is obviously a disaster! However, I have left them to grow, and the colour will often change to the correct colour. Where this is not the case the bird is a cull.

The black and blue Silkie chicks often hatch with pink toes which will usually also change as the bird grows.

Silkies should have five toes on each foot. Chicks hatched from some strains of gold regularly have six toes on one or both feet. The blues throw a lot of four toes.

Go into breeding the coloured Silkies with these factors in mind.

Snippet Eleven

If a previously dark faced male looks to be going a bit 'ruddy' in the face whilst kept indoors, change his environment (weather permitting) to the great outdoors for a while. The face will often darken dramatically.

Snippet Twelve

Silkies have had their own breed club since 1898. Membership and further details can be obtained from:

The Secretary
Mrs Sue Flude
Olde Barn Farm
School Lane
Stapleton
Leics.   Tel 01455 845105

The Enthusiasts of Yesteryear

These words are written as a tribute to :-
- the Birds...
- their Breeders....
- and the Breed Club.....
- that they form the foundation of what we have available today.

Down - But Never Out !!!

The Silkie has had its own specialist breed club since 1898 and is coming up to its centenary year.

At the time the Silkie Club was formed the breed was in fewer hands than is the case nowadays. The Silkie is such an ancient breed, and such a unique one, that even in its thinnest times it was never completely threatened with loss of its distinction or its individuality.

Mr W. Halley, a Silkie enthusiast, relates a scene pre 1914 in his own words:- 'I remember a conversation which I had with several well known fanciers in a hotel smoking room after a big show some years before the war'. (This was before the First World War).

'The conversation was a discussion on 'breeds that are dying'. As was natural, there was not unanimous agreement about every breed which was then in a lethargic state, but with one exception (myself), there was unanimity about the Silkie.

'Its cult was decidedly depressed at the time, and not only was there an absence of enthusiasm amongst its followers, but numbers were small, and quality was as a whole very weak. Outside the few enthusiasts, the prevailing attitude was that the bizarre was over, that the cultivation of beauty for beauty's sake was out of date, and that if ever a breed was permanently down and out, that breed was the Silkie. Undoubtedly, appearances were against me that evening, and as we parted I am afraid that I was a prophet with no honour at all in that little company! My final words were something like these:- "Well, we shall see. Give Silkies a chance, give them a little footing in the sun of publicity, and then see what happens.." '

Dr + Mrs Campbell acted as first secretaries for the club, the objectives of which were:-

1) To obtain classification for Silkies at shows, and for this purpose to guarantee the deficiency, or any part thereof, between the amount of the entrance fees and prizes awarded in such class or classes, to offer special or extra prizes for the same, and where practical to secure a reduction in entrance fees for members.

2) To promote the breeding and exhibition of Silkies.

During the First World War club shows were held. After this period the Campbells set about raising the profile of the breed, writing for 'The Feathered World', gaining front page illustrations and writing intelligent notes about Silkies. By 1927 the comment was, 'Looking at the Silkie pens at our leading shows, one is happily conscious of the general standard which is a little short of amazing.' Dr Campbell wrote in 1927, 'I think that no birds of this breed will ever be seen to conform better to the standard, as at present ruling, than these birds, and it has surprised me on several occasions why some of the champions of the breed have not been recommended for the general championships of the Crystal Palace, where, as a rule, the Silkie Club Show is usually held.'

By now Mr W. Halley was being proved right and, in 1927, he wrote his comments on the dissenting voices that night in the hotel smoking room. He commented 'Since then

Silkies have had their chance in the publicity which 'The Feathered World' has given them, and the disbelievers of that evening have been confounded. With all the prominence it has got in these columns, the Silkie could not have made good on that alone. Poultry breeds have to work out their own salvation.'

It was felt that, as the numbers began to grow, the Silkie again proved a glaring exception to the rule - the rule usually being that growing numbers mean decreased quality. Silkies progressed in quality as well as numbers. The whites were found to have '.. a purity in whites today that at one time was all too conspicuous by its absence, and I think it will be agreed that Silkiness has been tremendously improved.'

For a time in the early 1920s, there were high numbers of faulty heads, birds being shown with red and spotted faces. The breed standard was drawn up in 1925, which helped the requirements for the breed to be better understood.

The coloured Silkies were often handicapped by prejudice, as the white Silkies were always the most popular colour.

In the 1920s, the continental birds were described as follows, 'The continental cultivation was not always a happy one as I have seen quite large stocks of Goldens there which had pink flesh'.

There were some people who wanted to concentrate on the utility aspect of Silkies and pay less attention to the mulberry skins, adopting the ordinary coloured skins of other fowl. This was emphatically rejected because it was the crossbreds that had played havoc with the breed (red and spotted faces) of the past.

The problem for the breed club was to get the breed seen. Except for the larger shows it was seldom catered for, and had often to be exhibited in the A.O.V. classes. Some of the breeders were hatching for the classics only, and left out the local shows, which having put on Silkie classes found them unpatronised, leaving the show committee deciding not to cater for this breed again.

So in the early 1930s the Silkie Club passed a rule calling on all members to make two entries at any show they attended. In 1933 members were told, 'There are a few who reserve their birds for the classics only (Crystal Palace and the Dairy Show). This is hardly fair to shows which put on classes during the year. Where the club guarantees classes, these need supporting, and all members should try and do their share, and again the Points Cup wins are counted at any show guaranteed by the club, or a member. So don't wait for the classics to make these points.'

The show season opened with Ayr, with two classes for Silkies. In 1933, they added a display of eggs at the end of the Silkie pens as a new venture, along with Silkie literature, at the Crystal Palace club show. They also had some striking posters. The club were often being asked whether Silkies lay, and what size of egg, therefore they decided to let the public see for themselves.

In Wales, Silkies appeared for the first time at the Royal Welsh Show in 1934. The remark was overheard several times, 'Oh! are these birds crossed with rabbits?' and the birds were later referred to as 'those kitten fowls'. Their owner Mrs A. Hall concluded, 'they were referring to the Silkies, as they had caused quite a sensation, not having being seen in those parts before.'

During the Second World War, many members gave up breeding Silkies and reduced their stock. No shows were held between the years 1938 and 1947. Twelve birds were at a show in 1948, of which 10 were white. Again the breed proved resilient, Fowl Pest Regulations disrupted numbers in 1954, but in December 1954 the club show was held at the National Poultry Show in Olympia 8th-10th December. There were two Silkie classes at the Dairy Show. The club had 29 paid up members. By the mid 1970s, membership had

344

risen to 40, and as the breed again began to grow in popularity. This was mirrored in the growth of the breed club, with 200 members by 1996.

Some Silkie lovers of the past and their Silkies.

Dr + Mrs Campbell. St Ives, Hants.

Dr Campbell acted as secretary to the Silkie Club from 1898-1932. Mrs Campbell readily sold eggs from her best pens of birds, enabling the eager novice to quickly show some winners and take the honours.

Mrs Campbell was a firm believer that 'Silkies, under good conditions, improve with age,' and told everyone starting in the breed that this was the case.

As a couple, they worked hard to publicise the breed and rejected the idea that Silkies were '..principally favourites with lady exhibitors..', expressing that '..they are as popular amongst the men..' In 1932 it was written by Mrs Hall, ' When I first took up Silkies, I was very grateful for the knowledge the older breeders were good enough to impart to me then, and they were very generous to a beginner, especially (the late) Mrs Campbell, who was always ready to advise me with my birds, and to her I owe a great measure of the success I have had.'

Mrs Campbell gave the Silkie Club its first 'Challenge Cup' at the Crystal Palace in 1903. The Campbells presented the Club with its 'Champion Challenge Bowl' for whites in 1910.

Upon the death of Mrs Campbell, the 1903 cup became the 'In Memorium Cup for Best Black'. The Club presented Dr Campbell with a trophy in recognition of his 30 years' service as secretary. This was given back, and is now the 'Campbell Points Trophy'. Dr Campbell died in 1949 at the age of 94.

Mrs Fentiman. Swindon, Wilts.

Mrs E.S. Fentiman was a life long fancier and became the second secretary of the Club in 1932, upon the resignation of Dr Campbell. Mrs Fentiman was said to be a living example of how 'the fancy is bred in the bone', for, when she was a small girl, her father specialised in Dark Brahmas, Gold Pencilled Hamburghs and Croad Langshans, and her liking developed rapidly under parental guidance.

It was in 1908 that she started with the Silkies and became a member of the Silkie Club. Mrs Fentiman wisely started right, with sound stock from Mrs Campbell. They quickly became her first love, 'reigning supreme'.

Mr Fentiman was a quiet and unostentatious fancier of O.E.G. Bantams, though he was very keen on the Silkies like his wife, and equally interested in her many successes.

By 1934, Mrs Fentiman was the Club's oldest consecutive member. She quickly won both first prize places at the Dairy show in 1913, and won Championship honours three times, each time with a cockerel of her own breeding, and won the 'Cock or Cockerel Cup' outright. She had numerous wins. In 1922 she made her judging debut at the Club Show in Dursley.

'Proud of the honour, but rather nervous,' she admitted. She went on to many subsequent judgings and eventually found quite as much pleasure in awarding prizes to others as winning them herself. 'I found breeding for colours in Silkies a very fascinating hobby,' said Mrs Fentiman, adding, 'It has taken me about 16 years to bring my strain of Golds to their present strain of perfection.' Mrs Fentiman originated the Gold Silkie. Intermittently, both Black and Partridges came in for considerable attention, whilst all the time she bred her Whites.

Mrs Fentiman always maintained that the Silkie would sit on anything, a brick if nothing better. In 1934 she related the story of a white hen that had been entered for a show but went broody. The eggs were repeatedly taken away and the nest destroyed. The hen went missing and was eventually found in a favourite spot, sitting, having collected a clutch of six small APPLES. She was sitting on them quite content.

Mrs Fentiman was made an Hon. Life Member of the Club in 1954. The 'Fentiman Cup' (for best coloured Silkie) was given to the Club by Mrs Fentiman's daughter upon her mother's death in 1959.

Always an active secretary, she produced an annual yearbook during the 1950s until her death.

Mrs A.M. Hall. Ruyton, Shrewsbury.

Mrs Hall was a successful breeder, Vice President, President and Silkie judge.

She equalled Mrs Fentiman's 1913 double winning, securing both classes of Silkies at the 'Dairy Show' in 1932. She wrote a regular column on a monthly basis for the 'Feathered World'. It was entitled 'Silkie Sentences'. Her aim was to be instructive as well as interesting. She urged young breeders to ask questions re management, feeding etc. and welcomed news from the older breeders for her news columns.

It was through her writings that we learn 'Silkies that stand about and mope are not well, as they are very busy PEOPLE usually.' The photographs of Silkies started to have names. She proved Mrs Campbell's adage about Silkies improving with age quite right when, in 1934, she won the hen class at the Royal Welsh with her hen 'Muffle' which was aged nine. Mrs Draper came second with her black hen (aged five) called 'Matilda'. She had another old winner called 'Muffit', other birds belonging to other breeders included 'Minnie' and a lovely black called 'Grandma.'

She had her own views on what was acceptable :- 'We don't want a clumsy heavy bird. That is not a Silkie, and undoes the use of a Silkie as a mother and a light moving bird amongst her chicks. You all know the difference in the feel of a firm solid bodied bird as opposed to those which one gets hold of at times and they seem to crush up in the hand, all silk and no bird. These have very little body strength to fight colds or a severe moult or anything that may check them'. In 1934, 'I have had an interesting letter and pictures of the bearded Silkie from the USA. I don't think they are as nice as our birds, but I am wondering if they are originally a cross.'

She offered advice on hatching, rearing, feeding and breeding, welcoming new members and encouraging others. She advised that special attention must be paid when mating the coloured pens for the blacks, to get a good glossy colour and lack of brassiness in the cocks' hackle, which was improving.

In 1932 she said 'The golds are improving greatly and certainly the best rich colour has been seen this year, and it must be very gratifying to our secretary, Mrs Fentiman, who originated this colour, to see such lovely specimens as have been shown lately. It has taken many years to get to their present colour, but she is hoping to produce a more perfect colour yet.'

Mrs Hall judged Silkies for the first time in 1933 'after a lifetime spent amongst them'. She was made an Hon. life member of the Silkie Club in 1954, carried unanimously.

Mr A.H. Draper. St John's Wood, London.

Mr Draper was a long time member, breeder and judge of the Silkie. In 1933 he was elected Club President for the year (an honour which was generally accepted should be passed around the members). He worked very hard with his blacks and made great strides with the colour in just a few years. He won many honours and cups with this colour.

346

In 1936 a poultry journal records, "How are your blues coming along?" I asked Mr Draper, the Silkie man, and was told that their owner had high hopes that he will be able to show something respectable next season. Prying hard I was able to discover that the first try out Mr Draper made for this colour was a cross between Blue Wyandotte bantams and a Black Silkie male. Gradually he is breeding out the webbed feather. He was elected Club Show judge and President in 1955.

Mr R.L. Fairley. Midlothian

In 1934, Mr Fairley produced a little brochure showing several photos of his winners, accompanied by an interesting article on the Silkie attributes. He actively encouraged people to go in for 'this useful and attractive bird'. Twenty years on he was a Club member in 1954, when he was the Club Show judge at Olympia. He also served on the Club's committee.

As an enthusiastic member, he kindly donated a 10s special for Silkie classes at the Paisley Show. He lived at Cramond Bridge in Midlothian. In 1933 Mrs Hall wrote of the Club Show at the Palace, 'In the white classes, breeders had had a difficult time this year with late moultings, hence a lot of sap in necks and wings. Some pens were empty for this reason, birds not being considered fit to send. Mr Fairley staged some beautiful white birds, and there were some very good birds shown. Scotland does not seem to have suffered from the late moults as other parts'.

Mr Robert L. Fairley bred the white Silkie pullet known as 'Minnie', which was a many times winner including a cup winner at the Crystal Palace in 1932. In 1934 'Feathered World' reported his birds were first and second at Perth last week, 'There are not so many shows where classes for Silkies are put that this keen breeder does not support'. He was listed as a Club member some twenty years on from this date.

Mrs D. Bryer. Derbyshire.

Mrs Bryer joined as a Silkie Club member in 1935 and was made Hon. member after 40 years membership in 1975. She was an active breeder, committee member, judge and became the third Club Secretary in 1960 upon the death of Mrs Fentiman. She never missed exhibiting at the Club Show for over 40 years.

Mrs Bryer has been a prolific breeder and winner of most of the Club silverware. She retired as secretary in 1994, handing the reins to Mrs S Flude who became the fourth secretary in 96 years of the breed Club.

In recognition of her long service, Mrs Bryer was made the first Hon. President of the Club.

To all the others.

Mr J. Lilburn, Mr I. Gow, Mrs R. Main, Mrs Woodward, Mrs J. Fairbrother. All these breeders formed the bed-rock of the birds we own and show today.

Whilst compiling the illustrations for Silkies, Sue and I have selected photos showing birds in all the colours. The colour section of the book contains a group of top class modern day show birds. In keeping with Sue's excellent mini-book on Silkies we have also highlighted the breed's development during the course of the century.

White females have always been very photogenic and have provided some attractive pictures.

SIL 1. Shows one of the earliest true photos of the breed. It is a pen of Mrs Campbell's Whites which was taken during the early part of the twentieth century and illustrates and would be representative of Silkies from that period.

SIL 2. Is from the same period and shows one of Mrs Campbell's favourite male birds. His name was Regent, and he proudly guards his mate, who was also a regular prize winner.

SIL 3. Moves forward in time to 1924 and shows the female which won the Cup for Best Silkie at the Crystal Palace. She was again bred by Mrs Campbell.

SIL 4. Shows the hen which won Olympia in 1924 and Edinburgh in 1925. She was bred and exhibited by Ian Gow.

SIL 5. Shows a pullet bred by Mr Robert Fairley from Midlothian. She answers to the delightful name of Minnie, and won the Crystal Palace.

SIL 6. Shows another of Mrs Campbell's champions, this time from the mid 1920s, when her photograph was illustrated in numerous magazines.

SIL 7. Was bred by Miss M. E. Michie from Alresford in Hampshire. She won the London Bantam Club Show in 1934. It is interesting to note that Silkies were allowed to compete in a show that was limited to 'Bantams'.

SIL 8. Shows a good shaped Silkie hen. She was bred and exhibited in recent years by Tom Ayres from Wales.

SIL 9. Was bred by Tim Williams from Lincolnshire. She enjoyed a successful showing career for him during the late 1980s.

Silkie males do not have the same public appeal as their mates. SIL 10. Shows a cock which was bred by Mr J. Lilburn from Fife in 1926. He won The Dairy and Birmingham Shows and went on to win the Champion Cup at Crystal Palace.

SIL 11. Is from 1934. He was bred by David Draper who was very successful with his Blacks. This bird won the Crystal Palace, amongst many other wins.

SIL 12. The Flying Scotsman.

SIL 13. Is from a later period; he was bred by Mr. R. L. Fairley from Midlothian in the 1930s, when he won the Club Show at Birmingham.

SIL 14. Depicts a very proud young man with his very useful looking Black hen, she was called Grandma. The photo was taken in 1932.

SIL 15. Shows a good bodied hen, bred by Mrs Draper in the early 1930s. She is a little short of rise in her tail, thus making her look long backed. She was called Matilda, and was a prolific winner. She proves the adage that Silkies get better with age.

SIL 16. Shows a hen whose photo has been used on many occasions. She is a nice type of bird and very low to the ground. I have often wondered about her 'top - knot', as to whether it was flat capped or just the effect of the photo.

SIL 17. Shows a hen which has again been well illustrated in the press; she was shown by Robert L. Fairley with considerable success in the early 1930s.

351

SIL 19. Shows her Champion hen Muffie. This bird won for Mrs Hall the Silkie Points Cup outright, and at that period was considered the greatest winner in Silkies.

The history of Silkies has been dominated by ladies. SIL 18 shows Mrs Hall judging Silkies at the 1933 Crystal Palace. Surprisingly, after a lifetime spent amongst the breed, it was her first major engagement.

SIL 20. This picture of rural tranquillity illustrates Mrs Hall feeding her stock on the rearing ground.

SIL 21. Was taken in 1934 and shows Mr and Mrs Fentiman in their garden.

SIL 22. Illustrates Mrs Fentimen's hen which won second prize at the Dairy Show in 1924. Mrs Fentiman had bred good Silkies for many years. In 1913 she won with both males and females at the Dairy Show. This feat was not repeated until 1932, when Mrs Hall achieved the honour.

SIL 23. Silkies have always had publicity appeal and often gained front page prominence. This pullet was illustrated in a 1933 edition of Feathered World.

SIL 24. The present secretary of the Silkie Club is Mrs Sue Flude, Olde Barn Farm, School Lane, Stapleton, Leicestershire. She is pictured here with Mervyn, and some other members of the 'family'.

SIL 25. Doris Bryer was the secretary for very many years. She is pictured here showing the salver which had just been presented to her in recognition of fifty years dedication to the Exhibition Poultry Fancy. This ceremony took place at the National Federation of Poultry Clubs Show at Stafford. Doris has been President of this organisation for over twenty years.

SPANISH

This is the name now used to describe the exhibition type, White Faced Black Spanish birds, which have been developed in this country and Holland over the centuries.

They are thought to descend from the native and original Spanish bird known as the Castilian. These birds are the typical small bodied, white egg laying fowls which have been in existence all over Europe for centuries, each local version varying slightly, and carrying a different name.

The birds which we call Spanish, are thought to descend from the Castilian, as do the Minorcas.

The history of Spanish in England, is that there were many keen breeders of the birds before the organised showing of poultry commenced, and, as did Sir John Sebright and his friends, groups of Spanish breeders would meet periodically for a social event taking along with them their latest development of the breed, enabling comparisons of progress and exchange of stock.

Consequently when organised showing commenced in the mid nineteenth century the breed was well in advance of most others.

The style of the breed is very similar to the Black Minorca, which most probably was used in its development.

The birds should have a long body with a flat back and a well furnished long tail.

The legs and thighs should be fairly long and well apart with good round bone and long straight toes. The shoulders should be wide to support the long neck and magnificent head piece which is the feature of the breed.

It should have a good sized single comb, with even serrations, standing on a strong base. The cock's comb is upright and can be quite heavy, though not as large as the Minorca's. The hen has a folded comb. The long wattles should be well developed and very fine in texture.

But the main attraction is the man-made development of the kid like, white surface to the face, behind the ears and even behind the eye brows, which combines with the long white earlobes to produce one mass of striking appearance. That it is man-made is almost certain. I know of no other breed with a similar characteristic, the nearest being when a Mediterranean breed goes white in the face through old age or faulty breeding.

A true Spanish is not a white faced Minorca; it is a far greater development. The breed was popular for a long period but gradually declined until it is now listed as rare.

The main reason was probably the lack of easily available fresh blood to maintain the strength and vigour.

They are a very friendly breed to keep and I would recommend them to you as a challenge worth persevering with. They are far too good a breed to be allowed to slip into oblivion, especially as they were one of the pioneers in the breeding and showing of exhibition poultry.

The Miniatures were developed in the late part of the last century, then lost, but revived to a high standard in recent years.

Weights   Male   7 lbs   Females   6 lbs

The ideal Spanish male bird.

A very good hen which was bred and successfully exhibited by Eric Parker during the 1980s.

In detail the full enlargement of the lobes on a good Spanish cock.

A trio of Spanish from 1922. They were bred by Mr J. M. Cooper and show how good the birds were some seventy five years ago.

STYRIAN

This breed was introduced to the World Poultry Congress in 1936, and was described as being the ultimate in commercial meat production. The breed was originated in Austria, with the birds themselves bearing no resemblance to modern day table birds; in fact they look more like a decorative exhibition breed.

Styrians were described at the Congress as being of two different types. One was considered to be more of an egg laying bird, whilst the other version was more heavily built and carried a well meated breast. South Africa purchased stock of both types, prior to the exhibition, and it was also thought that Hungary had used them previously. Apparently, the Hungarian farmers had been selling poultry at Smithfield market for several years and their produce had proved to be much in demand.

The original structure of the breed was said to include four different lines, which obviously gave the breeders scope for continued reproduction, without the birds becoming too closely inbred. It would also mean a wide variation in the breed's type and colouring.

My observation of the breed is they were created by a mixture of long established breeds, mainly from the continent.

The very distinctive and uncommon combination of a single comb and backward facing crest, plus a white earlobe, must have connections with the Brabant or Brabaconne, whichever name you wish to give the breed. This breed had been recorded in Belgium for centuries, with a reputation for being a top class forager, and very hardy. Edward Brown describes them as being ideal for the farm and worthy of consideration to practical poultry keepers.

There was a suggestion that some of the laying type birds had a distinct look of Welsummer about them, whilst the heavier ones presumably contained the English Brown Sussex.

The style and shape of the Styrian as shown by the photograph issued at their original launch, shows a bird which is very full fronted, with a long body carried parallel to the ground. Their legs are strong in the bone, with short and well meated thighs. Their tail is carried at approximately 45 degrees angle, with the male bird having only a limited amount of side hangers and a pair of sickles which are fairly short in length. Apart from their head and the absence of a fifth toe, there is quite a resemblance to the Salmon Faverolles.

If you envisage the breed in a bantamised version, they would resemble the Sulmtaler miniatures which recently arrived in this country. Fred Jeffrey in his American book on Bantams describes the Sulmtaler as being Dorking shaped and existing in black/red wheaten colouring, but he makes no reference to the breed of Styrian. Whether or not there is a connection between the two breeds will be addressed in the breed of Sulmtaler.

A rare photograph of the presumably extinct Styrian. It was taken in 1936.

SULMTALER

This breed has only recently arrived in Britain, and at the moment it is in Miniature version only.

At the present time they are being exhibited in the Rare Breeds of Poultry section and have collected a following of admirers, who will no doubt extend the breed's popularity around the country.

To acquire expert information on the breed I contacted Sue Bruton, who is co-ordinator of the breed for the Rare Poultry Society. Sue very obligingly supplied the following excellent summary of the breed.

The first time that I heard mention of the Sulmtaler was in a telephone conversation, and I did not hear the correct pronunciation of their name; consequently, for several weeks I referred to them as 'Sun Parlours' - my apologies to the breed!

Contribution from Sue Bruton

The Sulmtaler bantams are a recent introduction to the British Isles. They made their show debut in 1991. These aroused some interest and by 1996 there were half a dozen breeders. At that time it was believed that the large Sulmtaler was represented by one hen! During the 1980s there was one person who had large Sulmtalers for a short while, but these were neither exhibited nor passed on.

Of Austrian origin, the Sulmtaler was created in the late nineteenth century in the valleys of Stiermarken, a traditional poultry rearing area. Throughout Europe, at that time, there was an increasing population which required an increasing supply of meat. This prompted the development of many good quality utility birds, several of which are still about today. Thus the Sulmtaler came into being. Its fortunes fluctuated. It was bred extensively after the 1914-18 War and spread into Germany and Holland. In the early 1960s the Germans produced a Sulmtaler bantam, which has now overtaken the large in popularity on the continent.

As befits a table bird, it is classed as a heavy breed with a deep full breast and solid body carried on strong thighs and shortish legs. Although Houdans, Dorkings and Cochins were reputed to have been used in their development, the Sulmtaler has four toes, so the rather dominant five toe gene was bred out.

The bantam is a miniature replica of the large. Their lack of quantity of meat is made up for by the seemingly endless number of eggs they lay.

This pert, lively but very docile breed comes in one colour only - the male, black breasted, neck and saddle a glowing golden red and the pretty wheaten female has a cream breast and body and a lighter golden brown neck hackle than the male. Their most striking features are their crests. There is a tuft of brown red feathers behind the male's straight, upright and single comb. The female's 'S' shaped comb is surmounted by a medium full, half round, light wheaten crest.

In Germany and Holland the large Sulmtaler is considered to be a rare breed. At recent shows in Germany the ratio has been one large to every four to five bantams. So, as often happens, lack of space and the high cost of feedstuff has curtailed the numbers of large fowl.

The Sulmtaler bantams we have in Britain came from four distinct strains (three Dutch and one German), there being noticeably different characteristics in each. The use of all four strains has resulted in hardy birds with high fertility and hatching rates.

The Poultry Club ratified the Sulmtaler standard in 1995.

A typical Miniature Sulmtaler cockerel.

The large Fowl Sulmtaler female shown in this photo was again prominent at the European shows.

SULTAN

This long established and very decorative breed is the well chosen emblem of the Rare Poultry Society. The breed is believed to have originated in Turkey and its name is thought to mean 'Sultan's Fowl'.

They were first brought into this country by a Miss Watts. The birds had travelled by boat and the seas had been rough causing the birds quite a lot of damage. She later managed to obtain some additional stock but found them difficult to maintain in sufficient quantities to enable her to distribute them around her friends etc. The first importation was in 1854 and nearly 150 years later on in history we are still struggling for adequate fresh blood.

The breed characteristics are to have a reasonably sized crest, muffle and beard, with a well rounded and densely feathered neck hackle. The body shape is almost unique to the breed, in that it is fairly short backed, with a deep body, and well rounded front. The tail is carried high and is well fanned, with plenty of side hangers and a longish pair of sickles completing the bird's unusual outline.

The legs and outer toes are well feathered and include long vulture hock feathers. To add another unusual feature, the back toe is a double one i.e. Houdan style. The colour of the legs and feet is pale blue and legs are short in length. The beak should also be pale blue.

Information on the breed's development is very limited, but, assuming that Turkey is the land of origin, it is unusual that there was not a larger quantity of them available. Normally you would expect to find a native breed reproducing itself satisfactorily and in plentiful numbers. Miss Watts obtained her first birds from a friend in Constantinople. They were a present but when they arrived in such a bedraggled state, due to lack of attention during the rough crossing, she had difficulty in obtaining replacements.

There is no evidence of a similar breed ever having been in existence (even in neighbouring countries) which leaves me to believe that they are a unique breed which could become close to extinction. The fact that the breed contains so many different individual breed features in some ways makes it easier to assist with injecting new blood, but it would be hard to recreate completely.

I believe that the Sultan was an excellent choice as the emblem for the R P Society and it is surprising that more people do not take up the challenge to develop the breed and thus ensure its survival.

In the nineteenth century White Cochin blood was used in an attempt to increase strength and vigour in the Sultans. Polands could also be considered, but I would be interested in trying White Faverolles, with their beard and white pigment, as opposed to the yellow of the Cochins. Their fifth toe and also slightly tighter feathering is also more in keeping with the Sultan. They would certainly add some size to the birds, and if you bred plenty of them you would have a good choice for future breeding.

The original birds imported by Miss Watts were apparently very small, being only slightly larger than Booted Bantams, so perhaps that is another pointer for fresh vigour.

For a breed to be successful, and in many breeders' hands, it must be able to reproduce itself, and the chicks rear easily. A lot of people are put off in their early attempts with a breed if they produce only a few weedy chicks which do not thrive and grow. It is both expensive and disheartening. A perfect example of success is the Dutch bantams. This breed is a relatively new introduction which even though it is highly decorative and diminutive is an excellent breeder of healthy stock, and it has proved to be highly popular with the new generation of poultry keepers.

Perhaps we ought to consider a slight alteration in the Sultan standard to make it stronger and more acceptable to the new generation. Maybe we will see in the future rows of sultans in a whole selection of different colours, some of them large fowl and others in miniature version.

One of the problems is that with there only being one colour of the breed, there is no opportunity to interbreed colours. If someone were to create a new colour or two, say black, cuckoo or blue, not only would they be very attractive, but they would be very useful in supplying vigour to the breed. Who knows, someday we may see the breed displayed in a whole selection of colours.

A typical pair of Andrew's birds.

A pair of Mrs Campbell's Sultans. The photo was taken during the 1890s when the breed was in its infancy.

The cockerel which Andrew Sheppy won with at the 1973 Rare Breeds Club Show.

A winning White Sultan pullet from the European continent. The photo was taken by Richard Billson on one of his many trips abroad.

A most attractive and unusual Blue Laced pullet. The photo was taken by Richard Billson at the show.

SUMATRA

This breed was originally called Sumatra Game. They were used in their native country for fighting. In the British Isles they are not classified as hard feather which you would normally associate with Game Fowl, and consequently are not allowed to compete in classes listed as for A.V. Game Bird.

They were standardised in America during the late nineteenth century and simply called Black Sumatra, which they are now called over here.

The attraction of the breed is two fold. First, their colour which is a fantastically green sheened black throughout the bird's feathers. The legs are black but sometimes shade to a very attractive willowy green especially on the foot pads. Even the pea-comb and face are a very dark mulberry colour with a jet black eye. The breed also exists in a blue and a white version.

The other attraction is the birds' personality. To describe it as pheasant like can be easily dismissed as being purely a description of the bird's outline and appearance. But when you keep the breed you will find that their habits and behaviour are entirely different from that of the general fowl.

The only other breed to have a similar characteristic is the Red Saddle, and I believe the two have a close relationship, way back in history. (See Yokohama breed.)

To enjoy the pleasures in keeping Sumatras to the maximum they must be allowed freedom, giving them the maximum space available. You will find that their favourite haunts are to ramble under the bushes and hedgerows, away from direct sunlight, picking and scratching away for most of the days. Indeed, as I write this I can see a pair of them in Mother's garden doing a fine job weeding the rose bed !!

They love to find a sandy area and enjoy a dust bath in the sunshine but not for long before returning to their favourite haunts.

If they are allowed this freedom, the gloss produced to their feathers is wonderful to look at, but unfortunately if your wife is a keen gardener the two are not the best of friends.

The breed originated from the Island of Sumatra in the East Indies, which is also the same part of the world where the Java fowl are thought to have originated, and I believe that there is a relationship between them.

The original Sumatra are thought to have been much shorter in the feather, and also possessing a harder texture to it, obviously having a closer relationship to the original Game Fowl. They were at one time described as Pheasant Malays, taking the name from their style, and the name, Malay, obviously associates them with the original Game birds. I believe the blood to be from the Black Raiza found in India. It is quoted in history that flocks of Sumatras living wild in the East Indies would take to the skies and fly between the Islands of Java and Sumatra.

The original Sumatra was certainly a version of Game, the present version being a showman's creation of beauty, whilst still retaining the basic Game characteristics.

When I was a lot younger, the faces and combs on the birds were red with as dark an eye as possible. At that period the skin was the thinnest and the most attractive to look at of any breed of poultry we dressed, the flesh being pure white when cooked, making delicious roast chicken or Madras curry.

Nowadays, with the insistence of a nearly black comb and face, the introduction of Black Silkie blood to influence this point has developed a bird which carries a dusky coloured skin and flesh.

The use of Silkie blood was originally introduced by chance. Pure Sumatras make excellent mothers and broodies but, when crossed with Silkies, produce a slightly more docile temperament, and it was from these crosses that the mulberry face developed. One other side effect is that nowadays you tend to find Sumatras carrying slightly turquoise earlobes.

Every breed has its own individual and peculiar characteristic, and the Sumatra is no exception, their particular one being the ability to grow more than one spur on each leg, usually with a major one surrounded by a cluster of smaller ones. I know of no other breed with this peculiarity, which must prove that in the Sumatra's original form there must have been some species present which was exclusive to that particular island.

The general shape of the breed is to posses a good pair of shoulders which are fairly wide apart but not clumsy looking, to have a well rounded and prominent chest and a straight breast bone which is well meated. There are at the present time some birds showing a rather 'cut away' front. They are excellent in other ways, and it may be a gradual slight alteration to the breed's outline.

The strong feathered wings slope down from the shoulders and are carried close to the body. The legs and muscular thighs are of reasonable length with good quality and round bone, giving the birds a very active appearance, not fine and spindly boned, which produces a weak looking and fragile bird.

The bird matures very quickly and, according to my old friend an Indian doctor, the males have a different hormone balance from the normal as they are extremely amorous even from a very early age.

I have already described the bird's appearance as being Pheasant like, but a more detailed description produces a picture of a bird which has an outline of a Pheasant with an erect head and a sloping body moulding into a massively furnished saddle hackle and flowing tail, which the bird carries at the correct angle and height for the tips of the hangers to just touch the ground. When they walk they do so with the same mannerism as a Pheasant, carefully and precisely moving each leg forward as they stroll under the hedgerows.

Amazingly, if you sell last year's assistant gardeners after pressure from the better half threatening divorce or even worse, once you take this year's chicks from the brooder house out into the field, as they gradually mature and increase their stamina, and no matter how far away from the garden you have put them, their explorations of the surroundings will eventually lead them to the garden and their first encounter with a lady wielding a well battered yard brush in a very uncivilised manner!

Beautiful specimens of miniature Sumatras are gradually appearing at the shows. I feel they have a great future and wish their breeders every success.

The weights for Sumatras vary from the old standards, quoting male birds as 7 lbs and females 6 lbs against the Poultry Club standards of males 6lbs and females 5 lbs which I feel is rather too small to allow the breed to display its grace to the maximum. In closing this breed summary may I quote a true story and trust that, with the confession, my sins will be forgiven.

At the Dairy Show many years ago I was busily boxing my team of birds at the end of the show, my baskets being collected at the top of the stairs on the balcony adjacent to where the breeding pens had been displayed. During the process of collecting the birds from the pens and returning them to my baskets, a Sumatra hen in the breeding pen, shown by Mr and Mrs Parr, laid an egg which I removed and placed in an old shoulder bag in which I used to carry all the various sponges and creams used in the preparation of a team of birds prior to judging on the first day of a show.

The date of the Dairy Show was always the third week in October, and I had no more thought of the egg until early December when I started the incubator to commence the season's hatching. Whilst getting the eggs ready to go into the machine I suddenly remembered the egg in my show bag. I took it out of my bag, where it still lay on its side, and put it on the tray with the others.

It hatched perfectly and grew into a nice cockerel. My father managed to obtain a pullet from a friend of his in Cheshire; we bred from them and that was the start of us keeping Sumatras, and the strain of that original egg is still present in the ones we have today.

This Sumatra cock won first prize at the 1926 Crystal Palace. He was bred and shown by Dr T. W. E. Royden from Norfolk.

A Black Sumatra hen which was a noted winner for Mr J. S. Fenwick in 1923.

A very stylish pullet bred by Dr Royden in 1929, when she was awarded best Sumatra at the Crystal Palace.

A well furnished cock bred by ourselves in the 1980s.

Two drawings by Finterbusch, illustrating the similarity between, firstly the Java Jungle Fowl, Gallus Varius, and a Sumatra cock, which he describes as being a Pheasant type of Gallus.

SURREY

This breed is not to be confused with the old Surrey fowls as referred to in the Sussex feature. This breed was created during the period after the First World War. I believe that big Jim Smith was well involved with them. Jim was a great character who had served in the war, stood over six feet tall, smoked non tipped woodbines until they burnt his moustache yellow coloured, drank several tots of whisky a day and lived to be well into his nineties before leaving us with his memories.

The commencement of the breed began with a Mrs. A.E. Jenkins, from Longparish in Hampshire.

Mrs. Jenkins was the originator of the Wherwell, which was another breed to enjoy only a short period of time. Basically, the Wherwell was a cross between Indian Game and Light Sussex. The original concept was to have a bird which was described as being Golden. This was not to be double laced, as in the pure Indian Game, but simply to be single laced, on the outer edge of the feathers, as in Gold Laced Wyandottes. This plan was then extended to include a similar version only in Silver Laced. The birds had single combs, white pigment and, as would be expected with a proposed table breed, a well developed body which carried large quantities of flesh.

The next breed to be introduced by the lady was the Surrey. This was a development of the Wherwell into a white version. To achieve this, White Sussex and White Wyandotte were introduced to the Silver Wherwell.

It would be at this stage of the process that Big Jim became involved. Jim was very well respected and had good connections within the fancy. The Surrey was designed to be a long bodied bird with a full front and breast area, which was well fleshed; unfortunately, photos of the breed show the male birds, especially, to be very short of front, in fact 'cut away'.

The heads of the birds are typical Wyandotte Rosecomb . The male bird's tail is well furnished, with shortish feathering and carried at a standard 45 degree angle.

The strong feature of the breed as a commercial table fowl is that they are white pigmented throughout.

In both the Wherwell and the Surrey the weights are given as males 10lbs and females 8lbs.

Both breeds were accepted to the Poultry Club standards in the early part of the 1930s.

We now move to a much more recent breed. It is the Brocklesby Crown Bantam. These birds have been created by Mr. H. Brocklesby from Brocklesby in Derbyshire. I have seen the birds, and find a lot of their features to be appealing. At the present time they have not achieved wide recognition. I have heard them described as being similar in type to a White Rosecomb, but, with a 'cup shaped comb' as opposed to the pointed leader Hamburgh type.

In the previous discussion on the White Coveney and White Surrey there has been no mention of either of them being in miniature version. The Brocklesby could be said to be a combination of the two breeds in a bantam size.

They have the comb and the white earlobe of the Coveney, the white legs and beak of the Surrey and also a similar tail carriage and structure.

It is in the body shape that the main difference lies. The Brockelesby has a short back and a rather more upright stance. This is highlighted by its low wing carriage.

To my knowledge the Brocklesby is not fully standardised. The interesting point is, that when accepted, will the birds be miniature fowl, or True Bantams? This bears comparison with the question recently raised as to whether the Dutch Bantam was a miniature Drente or a genuine True Bantam.

A pair of the original White Surreys, bred by their originator Mrs Jenkins. The birds were exhibited in the New Breeds class at the famous Crystal Palace.

The White Surrey cockerel shown here demonstrates the breed in a slightly later stage of development. He was, I believe shown by Jim Smith.

SUSSEX

It is generally believed that the Sussex fowl is one of the oldest breeds in the British Isles. To state this fact we must use the term 'breed' very loosely. It has often been quoted that the original brown coloured Sussex fowl and the Red Dorking are of the same foundation stock, the difference being that the Dorking has five toes and the Sussex only four.

The unanswered question is did the Romans bring them as a complete breed, or was part of their breeding here to begin with? For centuries the fowls around the farms in Kent, Sussex and Surrey were the major source of poultry meat for the London markets. Their birds dressed into excellent carcasses of tender flesh and carried the British preference for white pigmentation.

As with the Dorking, I believe that the Romans introduced the five toe factor presumably from the same source as the Belgian Breed, Ardennes which they no doubt collected during their looting, routing and pillaging on the European continent and these were crossed with the British birds native to the southern counties.

The point in debate is what 'breed' was in this region before the Romans arrived.

There are several pointers as to its type;

A) It must have been a bird which carried plenty of flesh, which points to a game type of fowl.

B) the pigment must have been predominately white coloured which rules out most of the Malay type of Asiatic game birds.

C) I have never heard mention of the Sussex type of fowl having anything other than single combs which again seems to exclude the breed's supposed descent from the Gallus Gigantus, which mainly has a pea comb.

This leaves us with some form of Old English Game fowl. There is also great emphasis put on the fact that many of the Sussex Fowl were speckled in colouring, as well as the normal black/red partridge colouring. Spangling is quite possible with the O.E. Game, especially if they contained some Aseel blood.

One fact which I find confusing is that these fowls were in the area for at least 2000 years, and yet, during the period 1840-1900 when the exhibition and the development of breeds collected from many parts of the world was fashionable, there was no mention of Sussex fowl other than a table bird. The book by Lewis Wright makes reference to them as Surrey fowls, and this is in the chapter 'Killing and Dressed Poultry Marketing'.

It was not until 1903 that a breed club was formed and this was as a result of Edward Brown. In the early part of 1903, whilst addressing a meeting of Sussex farmers, he told them that for centuries they had this marvellous reputation for producing the finest poultry in England, and now were on the point of allowing their native breed to die out. He drew attention to them preserving their local cattle and horses but not the Sussex fowl. Mr E J Wadman accepted the challenge and, in July, the Sussex club was formed under the name of the Sussex Poultry Club in an attempt to distinguish the breed from the terms previously used to illustrate top quality table birds.

The formation of a club was to prove a great success, but it does not explain their absence in the sixty years previous.

I can only presume that they really were a bunch of what Lewis Wright described as a kind of 'Dorkingised Barn Door'. The best of the red coloured and five toed ones were called the Dorkings which were never as popular as the Dark and Silver Grey Dorkings, whilst the four toed ones looked similar to bad shaped and over large Old English Game, and did not have sufficient individual character to interest the new generation of showmen and show women.

The Breed Summary

The breed of Sussex is one of seven colours, yet it is dominated by one of them, that is the Light. Its dominance is such that out of the total entry at a recent Club Show approximately 50% were the Lights, this situation being the same in both large fowl and miniatures.

As just stated previously, the formation of a Sussex breed Club was in 1903 and it was from this point that the breed really caught the imagination of the showmen.

The Light was developed during the early part of the 1900s with the colour pattern being similar to that of the Light Brahma, the main difference being that the Sussex must have its under-colour pure white to the skin as opposed to the more Columbian markings of the Brahma and the Columbian Wyandotte, which were being developed at the same period, both of which allow some dark under-colour. Also being developed in America at the same time was the Rock family which included Whites, Partridge and Columbian coloured birds. Whether there was any connection between the two countries in their development I do not know, but the ultimate shape of the two breeds is very similar.

The shape of all colours in the Sussex fowls should be one of a long back with the tail carried well out. The original standard says 45 degrees but the best show birds had their tails much lower than that, whilst the Sussex used for winning at the Laying Trials had a tail carriage much nearer to 90 degrees.

The back should be broad and flat with the shoulders wide and prominent allowing the well rounded front to be deep and mould into the long and straight breast bone.

The legs should be strong boned and set wide apart to support the weight of such a large structured body which is quoted in the standard as being 9 lbs minimum for males.

The whole of the Sussex standard was built around a bird with dual purpose commercial value which also incorporated exhibition features. The head illustrates this point. It is to be of medium size and fine quality with a prominent and bright eye, the comb standing upright and not falling to one side. The spikes should be even in shape and distribution. It is the allocation of points for these features which stress the club's desire for a dual purpose bird - type and size 45 points, legs and feet 15, head 10, with the colour not too greatly emphasised at 20 points. This I feel is far different from many judges' memory of the Standard when frequently the first procedure when judging Light Sussex is to take the bird out of the pen and start looking at the hackle feather markings, not having studied the bird's type.

The markings and colouring on a Light Sussex are certainly one of the breed's very attractive features. Commencing with the hackle feathers, these should have a very distinct black stripe down the centre. This marking should continue deep down into the feathering and not simply be like an extended tipping as is often seen in the utility type of Sussex. The shaft of the feather should also be black, not showing a lighter colouring. This black stripe should not extend to the extreme of the hackle feather, known as 'run-through', but the whole feather should be edged with a pure silver white lacing. The hackle feathering should be abundant and extend round to the front, and, if possible, meet in the centre of the bird's crop, still with the same black markings. The whole of the tail should be solid black, and not change to white as it approaches the tail roots. All this black colouring should have as green a sheen as possible.

The flights are a mixture of black and white, leaving the whole of the remaining body to be pure white. The legs, feet and toe nails should be white.

The Buff in theory should be the same as the Light only with the markings illustrated on different background colour. A small amount of 'smut' is allowed in the under-colour which would not be so in the Lights. The top colour should be as even as possible in what is described a golden buff.

The White is, as the name suggests, pure white throughout. The birds require a good red eye which is the same for all of the colours.

The *Speckled* is different and can be a very attractive colouring. The shape is still the same as described for the Lights, but the feather colouring is split into three distinct sections, all highlighted on a feather which carries an under fluff of slate/grey. The next part is the largest and is a rich dark mahogany colour; this is followed by a black bar which should be a glossy beetle green, not a dull smoky black as is often seen, and, even worse, one which shines purple coloured in the sunlight.

The final touch to the pattern is a snow white tip to the feather, I prefer to see this in the form of a 'V', but it is actually shown as a spot in the standard. This colour pattern extends to all parts of the body. As with other breeds with similar tipped markings, these tend to enlarge with each moult. The neck hackle feathers have a black stripe which again is tipped with white.

You will find that the legs on Speckled Sussex tend to have a horn colouring on the front of the scales. This point is accepted as one of the breed's features even though it is probably not technically correct. The tail and sickles are beetle green black, again with a white tip.

The Silver was the last of the colours to be perfected, much of the work being done by Captain Ellis Duckworth. The birds can be very attractive if near to perfection, but, if well wide of the mark, tend to look very much like cross breds.

The colouring is not fully in keeping with the normal Sussex pattern in that their breasts are laced with silver. The shaft of the feather also shows silver on the female. This pattern is extended to most parts of the body including the wing bow. The tail on both sexes is solid Black. The male's neck and saddle hackles have the conventional Sussex black striping as does the female's hackle, with the breast laced as in the female.

The leg colouring on both sexes tends to show a dusky grey tinge to the front scales.

The last two colours are the Red and the Brown. These are thought to be by far the oldest colours, with possibly the speckled forming part of the same group.

Possibly, the correct name for the Brown should be the Black-Red. In males the breast and thighs are black as in the O.E. Game colouring. The top colouring is true Sussex with black striping surrounded by dark mahogany.

The female's colouring, once again, reverts to O.E.G. in that her top colouring is dark brown, and is to be finely peppered with black which is basically partridge colouring. Her breast is wheaten brown as are her thighs. It is not mentioned in the standard, but most of the Brown females carry a pronounced shaft colouring to the feathering as in the Welsummer females. This point seems to be acceptable at the present time and looks attractive.

The red is not coloured as the R.I.Red, nor is it consistent with the Light Sussex in that the Red Sussex is required to have slate blue under-colour and the top colour is dark red with the hackles striped with black as normal. The wings are not marked as those of the R. I. Red but simply a mixture of red and black. The legs should be white as in all Sussex colours.

The standards for most breeds were devised during the early part of a club's formation. This was a period when the members were trying to select the 'wheat from the chaff' amongst the birds which were around at that time.

Their aim was to lay down the standard for what they envisaged as being eventually the perfect bird.

I find it informative when exploring a breed's history to inspect the standards list of serious faults. Many of these were classified as warranting immediate disqualification.

These faults illustrate the unwanted parts on the bird at that period of time. They were probably re-occurring and the members decided that the surest way of eliminating them was to withdraw from competition any bird carrying such faults.

In the Sussex, three of these serious faults are:-

A) Other than four toes, which would suggest Dorking blood influence.

B) Feathers on the shank or outside toes - possibly from Cochin but more probably Brahma blood.

C) Rose comb - again it could be tracing back to the Dorking being involved with their creation, but quite possibly the Du-Mans (for more details please refer to the index for the breed of that name).

The Sussex fowl exists in a very thriving and well perfected miniature form. Most, if not all, of the colours are nearer to perfection than in their larger counterparts.

The same point arises with the judging of the miniatures which I mentioned in Large Lights, that is the Judge's dominant thinking of markings and colouring over and above shape and type. Perhaps there are valid reasons to suggest altering the standard of the Sussex to more modern thinking, thus making it more of a showman's breed than the original concept of the large fowl standard which was utility minded. Certainly a different allocation of the points would be more in keeping with the modern judging of the miniature fowl.

Weights	Large	Males	9 lbs minimum	Females	7 lbs minimum
	Miniatures	Males	40 ozs	Females	28 ozs

Speckled Sussex can be the most attractive of colours, this cock also illustrates a good body shape, a well furnished tail and an almost perfect headpiece. He was bred and exhibited in 1927 by Mrs Grant from Kent.

The breeding of Sussex to a standard of perfection was not introduced until the twentieth century, which is almost 50 years later than some of the other breeds. The original development revolved around the birds' utility qualities; therefore many of the photos of the breed concentrate on their shape and laying potential, rather than on excessive markings.

Amongst the earliest photos which I have found is a useful looking Brown hen from 1923. She won both the Dairy Show and Olympia. She is illustrated above and was shown by Charles Hardy.

The top bird in 1924 was a hen shown by the legendary A. J. Falkenstein. This bird, illustrated above, won all the Major Shows, including the Dairy, Olympia and the Club Show.

Charles Hardy was again successful in 1930 with the pullet right. This bird again took all the major honours for Brown Sussex during the showing season.

375

A Red pullet which won the Dairy Show and Birmingham in 1922. She was shown by Messrs. Camplin and Glenny from Guildford.

Brown males are not easy to photograph, and tend to bear a resemblance to Rhode Island Reds. The photo here is a cock which won the Club Show at Olympia in 1935 for John Howard.

A powerful old cock, bred and shown by Mr J Dumbleton from Didcot. During his life the bird accumulated a whole string of major awards, which on several occasions included being Best in Show over all other breeds.

A photo from 1934 shows a rather unique pair of Partridge Sussex. These are shown here and were bred by G. D. Richardson from Middlesex. Six breeds were used in their creation, the main two being Brown Sussex and Partridge Wyandotte.

The photo above also illustrates an unusual colour. This time it is a pair of Cuckoos, which were bred in 1928 by Mr. R. Terrot.

The pullet above was shown by Major Martin during the 1926 summer show season and gained many awards.

Buff Sussex were originated by Mr. J. Raine from Kent. They are very attractive and should be more popular than they are. The pullet shown here was bred by John Raine, and won the Crystal Palace and Olympia in 1925.

The grand bodied cockerel above was bred by John Raine and won the Dairy in 1929, but only managed second place at the Crystal Palace. He was however selected to represent 'A Typical Sussex' in the 1930 Poultry Club Book of Standards.

Again bred by John Raine. He was a late bred chicken in 1926, and consequently missed being shown at the classics, but appears to have the makings of a good bird when fully matured.

378

Self Whites have never been a popular colour of Sussex, which is surprising when you compare them to breeds such as Leghorns and Wyandottes.

The cup for Champion White Sussex at the 1930 Dairy Show was won by the pullet illustrated above. She was bred and shown by Coghurst Estates Ltd, who farmed at Hastings.

The earlier birds were very much of a utility type, and rather slim in their bodies, the cockerel which A. J. Falkenstein showed at the 1926 London Dairy Show is shown above.

During the next few years Captain Duckworth developed extra 'clout' to the birds, as shown by the cockerel left which won the 1936 Crystal Palace, and especially by the hen above which had a highly successful showing career.

379

During the 1920s and 1930s Speckled Sussex enjoyed a period of success and popularity. Their colouring attracted several celebrated names to join the list of breeders. These included Lord Rothchild, Sir F. A. N. Newdigate and the Marchioness of Londonderry.

The photo above shows the Dairy Show winner in 1933, which was bred and shown by Sir Herbert Sharp.

Lord Dewar became interested in the breed, and was winning with the cockerel illustrated here.

Sir Gormer Berry Bt, won the Crystal Palace in 1931 with the cockerel shown above.

Captain Whittaker from Carnavonshire bred some of the best Speckles and for many years was hard to beat. Photo above illustrates the point with the cock which won the Club Show in 1930.

The good looking pullet here was shown at the 1932 Crystal Palace by Sir Herbert Sharp, where she won second prize.

The hen above won many first prizes in 1922 for its breeder A. J. Falkenstein, including the Crystal Palace and the Club Show.

Lord Kemsley was the owner of the hen here, which was a noted winner during the 1930s.

Captain Whittaker again showed his professionalism with the hen above. This bird won the 1928 Club show and also gained the award for Champion Sussex any colour.

For several decades 'Lights' have been the most popular colour of Sussex, their striking contrast of black and white coupled with a dual purpose commercial potential having proved to be very suitable for many people's requirements.

A bird from 1929. He was bred by Miss Larkworthy on her large poultry farm at Liphook in Hampshire. He was bred from fully trap nested commercial stock, and also had the necessary type and markings to win the Royal Agricultural Show for her.

Bred by Ian Gow, and for hackle markings was well ahead of his time. He won Altrincham in 1926, and was bred from a bird which won ten premier awards during the previous year.

A very long bodied cockerel which was bred by Henry Underwood from Kent. Henry and his son were to continue breeding top quality birds for the next forty years. This cockerel won Best in Show at Kettering in 1933.

A grand cockerel which was bred by Lord Dewar in 1933. This bird won the Crystal Palace and also the Dairy Show, where he became Supreme Champion. From their appearances, I would guess that this bird was father to the cockerel in the next photo.

The 1934 Dairy Show Champion Exhibit. He has a great shape and stance, but by present day trends is a bit short of markings at the top of his hackle. He was bred and exhibited by Sir Duncan Watson, who had taken over from Lord Dewar, with Walter Bradley still there as Poultry Manager.

A trio of Light Sussex bred by Sir Duncan Watson in 1934. They won Champion Trio at the Dairy Show, thus completing a great double for him. These birds set a standard of perfection which was hard to improve upon during the next sixty years.

I have split my selection of Light Sussex females into two sections. I commence with four photos of the full exhibition type, followed by a group of the utility version.

The grand bodied hen here won the Royal Agricultural Show in 1928. She was bred by Mrs J. G. Morris from Berkshire who was a keen breeder in many different colours of Sussex.

A hen from 1923. She was bred by Mrs Baird and achieved many notable wins including the Club Show.

Here is another hen from 1936. She was bred by Sir Duncan Watson and won the Crystal Palace in that year. Interestingly, she was shown with a cockerel, in a newly created class for the best pair of live Table Birds. The Judge's comments were that she was good enough to have won the open class.

A typical Henry Underwood type of Sussex. She is from a later period, having won the Crystal Palace in 1936.

384

My first photo in the utility section, above, shows a pullet bred by Ian Gow in 1926. She is full sister to his bird shown in the male section. They were bred from a pen of trap nested pullets which averaged 250 eggs during their first laying period, illustrating their dual purpose qualities. This pullet won at Altrincham, which was always considered to be the first major 'Chicken Show' of the year, and was always very competitive.

Above won the 1933 Crystal Palace for Henry Underwood. She again illustrates the long back and sleek outline of a utility pullet, as opposed to the cobby shaped and loose feathered old exhibition type.

A pullet bred by Coghurst Estates Ltd, which were a commercial poultry breeding station. She won Best Sussex at the 1930 Dairy Show and illustrates a combination of show and utility qualities to create a bird similar to the ones shown through the next decades.

Bred by Lord Dewar, and won the Dairy Show in 1933. She was once described by Henry Underwood as being his ideal Utility Light Sussex.

385

THURINGIAN

This old fashioned German breed exists in a large selection of colours, all of which have the same characteristic full beard.

The breed has been used on the continent as a very successful laying bird, being hardy in spite of its decorative colouring and spectacular appearance, which is especially so in the Gold and Silver Spangled versions.

The birds have a medium sized body, which is medium in length, finishing with a well furnished tail. The breast is full and well rounded to blend with its short neck which is arched and carried backwards. The head is small with a single comb, which is fine in texture and with 5 or 6 short spikes. The wattles are very small and partially hidden by the beautiful bushy beard. The eyes are prominent and a reddish brown colour. The lobes can be either red or bluish/white but are mostly covered by the beard, which extends to the back of the head and right round to under the beak.

The legs are of medium length with four toes and are a slate blue colour, the toe nails being white. In keeping with their bushy beard, the saddle hackle and neck hackle are abundantly feathered, giving the male birds their distinctive appearance.

I consider this breed to be worthy of more recognition in this country, and cannot see why it has not been a feature here for decades. It has many features which highlight it as being entirely different from other established breeds.

Thuringians are available in a wide choice of colours, but, to me, the range of spangled coloured birds is the favourite.

The breed is thought to have originated from the district of Thuringia in Central Germany, with possible relationship to the Owl-Bearded Dutch which had been imported from the eastern hemisphere.

Maybe it is the big beard which attracts me to them, but a trio would be nice for Christmas! There are now some excellent Bantams on the continent, and I predict that they will become very popular when they arrive in the British Isles.

Weights   Males   6lbs   Females 5lbs

Chamois Spangled bantam male.

Bearded Gold large female.   *Photos by Josef Wolters*

FIG 1. Is an excellent drawing by Kramer showing a pair of Silver Thuringians. The colour section of the book includes a beautiful photograph by Josef Wolters illustrating a Red Mottled.

FIG 2 and 3. Show two beautiful photos taken by Josef Walters in Germany. They illustrate a very striking Silver Spangled male and a most attractive Chamois pullet.

USHANKI

These birds are reported to have lived in the eastern part of the European continent for a long time.

They are a medium sized bird, with a prominent breast and a wide flat back. They carry their wings rather low for such a full breasted bird. Their tail is well spread, with the male having well and long developed sickles.

Their head is quite strong and round in shape, with a single type of comb which is larger than average and should be evenly serrated.

Their most striking feature is a very bushy and well developed beard with side whiskers, which is highlighted by a very densely feathered neck hackle.

In many ways they are not remembered as a breed, more as a race of fowls which have contributed their features to now more well recognised breeds, such as the Thuringian and Orloff.

Weights   Males 6 lbs. Females 4 lbs.

FIG 1.This photograph was taken in 1923 and shows a group of birds owned by a Mrs Colbeck. I believe that they would have a close relationship to the Ushanki Fowl, even though they were successfully shown as Orloffs. The cock won First at both Manchester and the Crystal Palace in 1921, and then went on to win at Birmingham in 1922.

VORWERK

This breed was developed in Germany by Osker Vorwerk. He commenced work on it around 1900, eventually showing the first birds in 1912, and having the breed standardised on the continent.

His ambition was to develop a rich coloured buff bird with the same markings as the Lakenfelder, but larger bodied and showing a fuller chest and front, thus making it a better utility proposition.

I am not fully conversant with the breed, having only been introduced to it in recent years. They appear to have a good temperament combined with a very pleasing and attractive appearance, with their rather golden brown ground colour and the contrasting black hackle, tail and saddle hackle. The head has a single comb which should be evenly serrated, a medium sized pair of wattles, red in colour, contrasting with the white ear lobes, though actually these often have a yellowish shade to them. The legs are a very dark slate colour.

It is only in recent years that they have become popular in this country, thanks mainly to the work of Mrs Wallis and a few other breed stalwarts. One of these is Maureen Case from the Long Ashe Farm Park at Milton Abbas in Dorset, who tells me that the birds take very well to living in outdoor conditions and are good layers. Their temperament is similar to that of the Lakenfelder, in that initially they are rather shy, but can soon become trained to be quite friendly. The strain which she has does not brood their own chicks; they prefer to keep on laying eggs. At the present time, there are only a limited number of breeders and, consequently, finding a change of blood line is difficult. I have always felt that, with the breed's similarity to the Lakenfelder, it was a pity the two could not combine into a single club.

To summarise, I feel sure that the breed has good potential, the problem being, as with many more breeds, in selling these qualities to new and often very inexperienced potential breeders. Now that the major shows provide classes for every breed, thus giving them the opportunity to compete amongst themselves in different colours, many of the less fashionable species are now increasing in numbers, especially as in this breed, where there is a group of enthusiastic supporters to pass on the vital information relevant to a breed's characteristics and special features.

Potential conservationists contemplating keeping the breed require to know more about the birds than that they are allocated 15 points for some part of their anatomy or colour pattern.

Miniatures are available on the continent but not yet on this island, though, having just written this, there are probably some flapping their way over Dover right now.

The colour section of the book contains a very picturesque photo of a Vorwerk cockerel, proudly displaying himself to the visitors at the Farm Park run by Mr and Mrs Case.

Weights Male 5.5 -7 lbs Females 4.5 -5.5 lbs .

A pair of Vorwerks is illustrated in the colour section of this book.

FIG 1. Is an illustration of the breed when showed in Germany and photographed by Edgar Willig.

FIG 2. Is a photograph taken at the 1935 International Show held in Essex. The cockerel was displayed as a 'Buff Lakenfelder'.

FIG 3. This beautiful Vorwerk Bantam was illustrated in the Canadian Feather Fancier. She was bred by Wilmar Vorwerk from Minnesota.

WELSUMMER

The Welsummer is an excellent utility breed, which combines several individual features into a genuine dual purpose breed. They have, in most people's eyes, an attractive colouring, though some critics may say it is similar to that of the common jungle fowl. They are capable of not only laying a large quantity of good sized eggs, but in as deep a rich brown colour as it is possible to achieve. Even though they are classified as a light breed, their bodies are large enough and their temperament docile enough for them to be kept enclosed by reasonably low garden fencing. Their body also carries good quality meat to be adequate as a table bird.

The breed has a very active club and when the birds are in competitive exhibition they are capable of winning supreme awards over other breeds. There are very few other breeds which can boast of so many qualities. The breed was perfected in Holland at roughly the same period as the Barnevelder and was imported to our islands in 1928, with a breed club being formed in 1930.

To describe the origin and history of the Welsummer, I will reproduce an article written by the late W Powell-Owen published in the breed's handbook 'Fifty years of Welsummers'.

For the benefit of many people who only have a limited recollection of Powell-Owen, or P.O as he was affectionately known, I offer this brief profile. To the best of my knowledge he lived all his life in London, and I never saw him exhibit a bird, but he was a respected judge and writer, especially on 'utility' breeds. Amongst his favourites were Australorps, Barnevelders and Welsummers. During the war years he was an ambassador for these breeds, whilst working amongst the domestic poultry keepers' associations or D.P.K.s as they were known. These organisations were government sponsored to encourage householders to keep a few laying fowl in their back gardens as a way of being self sufficient during the food rationing period. P.O's help and assistance was always at hand to assist these people. One interesting memory from this period was that the local councils collected all the household scraps, potato peelings, outside leaves of cabbage etc. This was then boiled and mixed with molasses and resold on an allocation basis to the larger poultry breeders to assist them with feeding the stock. The product was known as 'Tottenham Pudding' and smelt appetising but, when feeding it, you had to be careful, not knowing what cooking utensil you were going to find next. The regular foreign bodies included knives, forks, spoons and potato peelers by the dozen, all thrown away in error with the waste.

After the War ended, the interest amongst the DPK group was extended to the exhibiting of their stock. Special classes were provided for them at the National Show in London. To qualify as a DP keeper there was a limit of keeping 25 head of poultry. The schedule of classes at the show in 1948 was judged by Powell-Owen and five classes attracted a total of 203 birds, split as follows: R.I. Reds 58, Sussex 24, Leghorns 54, AOV Heavy 44 and AOV Light 23. I wonder if we are approaching the period when such a group of poultry keepers will again emerge. Maybe it needs another P.O. to co-ordinate their activities.

P.O was president of the Welsummer club in 1937 and, I believe, continued in that office until his death, which would be around the early 1950s.

The origin of the Welsummer Breed
by W Powell-Owen

This breed came into existence at about the same time as the Barnevelders. They were kept on heavy clay grounds along the river Ysel to the north of the town of Deventer. Even less is known of the origin of the Welsummer than of the Barnevelder. In ancient times the fowl from this district were known under the name of Welsummers. Large brown eggs have been sold on the egg market there for many years.

The average weight of the egg is 70 grams. The laying capacity of the Welsummers however continually decreased, the largest and darkest eggs being used exclusively for breeding. This breeding from the worst layers was unconsciously affected systematically, and, by the introduction of artificial incubation, it furthermore appears that the heaviest eggs yielded the worst hatching results.

The original fowls which were given the name of Welsummers showed all kinds of varieties in colour, as in the case of so called 'farmers' fowls' elsewhere. Many of the birds were found to have five toes and they often had a light yellow colour with a blue tail and wings (Orpingtons and Faverolles). Other birds conformed in colour and shape approximately to the Partridge Cochins and Partridge Wyandottes. Malay and Brahma types were also met with. In 1917 all these varieties could still be found on various farms; nevertheless; there existed a certain uniformity in the breeding control in so far as only 'red cocks' had the marking of the partridge coloured breeds, except that the chest was marked brownish black.

In later years great efforts were again made with crossings, especially with Barnevelders, Rhode Island Reds and Partridge Leghorns. Of these, crossings with Barnevelders were the most satisfactory. Fortunately efforts were made by others to improve the breed within the breed itself, first by a farmer's son in Welsum who was studying as a teacher and devoted himself in his spare time to the breeding of poultry. The eggs on his farm were fine in colour. The farmers in the neighbourhood therefore very soon bought their breeding material mainly from him. In the village of Welsum and neighbourhood, a fairly considerable constancy of type was very soon attained. The production at that time (i.e. in the years prior to 1913) was very satisfactory.

In that year however the Kliens disease made its appearance, and the above mentioned breeder lost a few of his best hens. During the war a large number of birds had to be disposed of and the breeder at Welsum was only able to retain twelve hens and one cock.

In 1921 this breeder was invited by the first undersigned to participate in the exhibition at the first World Poultry Congress at The Hague. The uniformity of his birds was astonishing. In 1922-23 steps were taken to fix a standard. An association of Welsum breeders was only formed in 1927 when the Dutch Association for the Improvement of the Welsum Poultry Breed was founded. The association has introduced for its members a production registration approximately in the same manner as the ROP in Canada; furthermore it has indicated standards as regards type and colour, and the improvement of the utility qualities is also brought to the fore.

The type and carriage of the Welsummer is one of an active bird with an upright head, a longish back and a well furnished tail which is carried high but not to be squirrel tailed in any circumstances. The shoulders are wide with a well rounded front and a reasonably long pair of wings carried close to the sides of the body which, combined with the bird's utility type of close feathering, gives it the appearance of alertness.

As with all utility breeds, the comb, lobes, wattles and face should be of a smooth and fine texture, with prominent red eyes, not sunken or being overshadowed by strong eyebrows.

The legs and feet are yellow, and you will very often notice their characteristic horn coloured toe nails. This colouring is also often present in the beak colouring.

The red coloured comb is allowed up to seven serrations, but they must be evenly distributed and the comb completely free from side sprigs or double comb end, and follow the contour of the head and top of the neck. The comb front is also important, it must not have 'thumb marks' or show a double fold above the nostrils. This was a common fault with the breed at one time, as were big floppy combs in the females, which were obviously bred from the same family.

The legs should be of round and strong bone without being coarse and clumsy. The thighs are fairly long, well meated and set wide apart.

The colouring of both the male and female Welsummer are of the traditional black-red partridge combination, but with a slight difference and it is one which catches many of the all round judges out. The breed has been standardised in a format which will breed show birds from a single mating. The male bird's breast is not solid black as is very often assumed, but is evenly mottled with red.

The female's breast is a rich chestnut red which continues well down her front. The top colour on her wings is not the usual partridge colour all over, but has a chestnut brown wing bar. If this was on a Modern Game it would be described as being 'foxy winged'. The rest of the female's colouring is as usual with the golden colouring of the feather's shaft showing evenly and distinctively all over.

The main tail feathering on both males and females is black, with the outer feathers shading into the rest of the plumage colouring. The male's top colour is a rich golden brown with a green sheen black wing bar.

When opened out, the wings on both sexes should be free from grey or white patches as should the root of the tail.

Another common fault is for them to have slightly feathered legs. White in lobe can also be seen, as can striping in the hackles. All these faults are still being transmitted from the breed's ancestry, but will diminish with time as the same faults have done with R I Reds.

The miniatures should be replicas of the large fowl. Unfortunately many of them are still over large, but it does prove that they are genuine miniatures and will retain the brown egg qualities. As with the large fowl, they are very popular and ideal for someone requiring a good supply of fresh eggs for the kitchen, but with a shortage of available space in the garden.

| Weights | Large Fowl | Males | 7 lbs | Females | 6 lbs |
| | Miniatures | Males | 36 ozs | Females | 28 ozs |

A Welsummer pullet which was bred in 1933 by Mrs Swales-Johnson, who was one of the breed's enthusiasts. During 1933 this bird was a successful showbird for the lady.

A Welsummer cockerel in a very typical stance. (To appreciate the bird's colouring please turn to the colour section of the book where the Club's ideal is featured.) This cock was bred by the Club's President, Mr R. Fletcher Hearnshaw from Burton Joyce, who won many senior awards with him during 1934.

A more recent photo. It is the 1972 champion Welsummer miniature at the Reading Bantam Show. She was bred by an expert and one time secretary of the club, Peter Parris from the Isle of Wight.

Also bred by Peter Parris. She is a beautiful little bird, which had a highly successful showing career for him, during the 1970s.

WYANDOTTE

This breed must be very high on the list of my favourite soft feathered poultry. Unfortunately there must be a fault in my human Personal Computer, because if anyone mentions the name of Wyandottes my brain immediately thinks of the white variety almost as if it treats the other colours as a different breed.

My apologies to all the other beautiful colours; maybe sometime soon I will be able to devise a programme to correct the flaw in my make-up. Perhaps the root of my problem stems from the fact that there are several branches of Wyandotte clubs. There is the one which caters for Whites, and I have been connected with the club for a long time, having actually been breeding White Wyandottes for over 50 years.

Then there is the Laced Wyandotte club, which, until fairly recent times, was for Silvers and Golds only, but does now cater for all colours of laced Wyandottes. The other separate clubs are the Blacks, the Partridge and Pencilled, and finally one called the Wyandotte Bantam Club which covers the remaining colours.

For a breed of so recent origin, the Wyandotte history and formulation are unbelievably clouded. The Silvers were the first to be made and here my often related saying that 'The camel was designed by a committee but unfortunately when the project started it was supposed to be a horse', is almost proved again.

Apparently, a gentleman in America wanted to create a laced Cochin which he was going to call a Sebright Cochin, so he attempted to cross a Sebright with a Cochin hen. He had friends who were also keen to develop the Cochins into a laced version by using a Silver Spangled Hamburgh cock with Cochin type hens. When the attempted Sebright cross proved to be too much for the 'Little Fella', he was used on the Hamburgh cross progeny. Further breeding from these resulted in a sample of their work being put before the Standards Committee in 1876 as an American Sebright, but the committee rejected it, partly on the grounds of its head and comb shape. So it was back to the drawing board, this time joined by more friends. Probably both Light and Dark Brahma females were used, as both are mentioned by different writers. A Silver Pencilled Hamburgh male was introduced, and I would agree with Lewis Wright when he says that Silver Laced Polands were involved; they seem to be the obvious choice to install some lacing. Wright also reports that some of the early imports to Britain showed signs of a crest which endorsed his theory.

Edward Brown recalls seeing some of the birds during their development and they included feathered legs and clean legs, rose, single and pea types of combs, with the best of the broods called 'Eureka', which I believe is Greek for 'I have found'. These birds continued to be bred together until 1883, when they were once again presented for standardisation, this time to be called Wyandottes after a tribe of Red Indians.

The plan worked and they were passed, and very quickly developed into one of the most successful breeds ever made, with the quote about the camel and the committee being once again very close to the mark.

The shape for the Wyandotte should be the same for all the colours, but, in many instances, the Whites have proved superior in type, which really should so be when they have no markings involved with the breeding programme.

The Wyandotte has been described as the bird of curves, and that is what it is, with each of the curves being clearly defined. This is possible owing to the feather structure being strong enough to hold them in position, whilst at the same time having enough under feather to highlight the curves.

When you wash a Wyandotte and an Orpington consecutively, the difference in feather length and structure is very noticeable especially with the females.

The first point with a Wyandotte's shape is that you must have depth of body; it must not be square. They must also have great width of back. This will commence with a wide pair of shoulders and continue along the short but clearly defined back to the cushion which then rises up to the main tail feathers. This cushion must also be wide. If it is 'nipped' or narrow it will never be a 'good 'un!'

The front of the bird, as well as being wide across the shoulders, must have a deep front, which is well curved round towards its legs. This curve must be a full width curve, not hanging down as 'sloppy front' nor must it converge into a narrow line like an Aylesbury and be known as 'duck fronted'.

This front part to the crop must be perpendicular and not shoot quickly towards the legs at an angle; this would be termed 'cut away' or short of front.

The Wyandottes have a reasonably long neck which is carried erect and with pride. This is balanced by an equally upstanding tail, which should have 14 main tail feathers, not half of them left at home to make it look a better shape!

The male bird's tail has two medium length main sickles, which are well curved over the top of the tail feathers. The sides are then completed by a series of side hangers, which are again neatly curved round so as not to spoil the bird's outline. The saddle hackle will then meet up with these side hangers to complete the picture.

The holding into place of the saddle hackle can only be achieved by a pair of tightly closed wings which are carried well up under them. They want to be parallel to the ground, not looking downwards towards the bird's feet i.e. Rosecomb style.

The female's tail should just show the tips of the main tail feathers, and, as with the front profile of the bird, the rear of it should be in the form of a straight line directly to the ground. The covering of the main tail feathers commences from the bird's back, and sweeps in a wide and gradual curve onto the tail. It should not go over the top and be 'ball tailed'. As with the male bird, the wings should be carried up to give the bird maximum width of cushion.

The neck hackle is reasonably long, and should terminate just behind the shoulders to give the bird a short back before the commencement of the cushion; under no circumstances should the hackle rest on the saddle hackle or cushion; there must be a back showing.

The next part of a Wyandotte's shape is perhaps the main one to highlight, the difference between the breed of Orpington and a correctly shaped Wyandotte.

There is a curve of feathers which extends over the upper thigh, up to the wing and then continues right round to cover the abdomen, and almost join the corresponding one coming out of the other side of the bird.

In an Orpington this feather follows the same route, but also extends downwards to include all the thigh, and actually covers to below the knee joint.

The feathers on an Orpington are both longer and softer which emphasises the curve even more.

The correctly shaped Wyandotte has a short length of thigh clear of this curve, which shows as an extension to the bird's shank, or, as the old Indian Game breeder Jack Crago used to describe it , 'the yellow part of its leg'.

This extra piece of leg gives the bird lift, and adds to the original statement that a Wyandotte's outline must be over square in depth against length of body.

Unfortunately, there are too many White Wyandottes which do not show this extra piece of leg, and consequently are described as being 'Orpingtony'.

As with the body shape, all the colours should have a broad rose comb, with the leader keeping broad and following the curve of the head and upper neck. The comb should not be so wide as to hang over the eyes, but should fit closely to the head and not be standing up on a slim base. The whole of the surface should be evenly covered with 'working' i.e. little short spikes. The face should be fine textured as should the lobes and medium sized wattles.

The comb's colour should be a bright red. The standard does allow for the eye colour to be bright bay, but I would say that most judges would be like me and prefer a good red eye. Bay to me is a misleading description - dark orange would be acceptable, but any signs of green eyes certainly would not be.

THE WHITE

The legs and feet should be yellow with well rounded bone and not flat shinned. In colouring, the white is straight forward, pure silver white with no signs of straw colouring or weathering, and the males should be completely free from a coloured wing bar or black ticking.

The shades for the other self coloured Wyandottes are:-

THE BLUE

This is one even shade of medium blue, an even colour being of more importance than the actual shade. The feathers are not laced as with the Orpington's blue.

THE BUFF

The Buff is similar in that an even shade is of paramount importance, though allowance is made for a slight darkening in colour around the hackles, tail and the wing bows. Any extremes such as smutty black or white patches should be considered bad faults.

The under-colour is buff to the skin.

THE RED

The top colour is a rich red colour. The neck hackle is allowed a slight black stripe and the main tail and side hangers a rich green black. The wings are marked as in the Rhode Island Red, but the under-colour is different; it should be a clearly defined slate blue down to the skin.

THE BLACK

In the Black, in keeping with most breeds of poultry and waterfowl, the sheen on the feathering of Black Wyandottes should be beetle green. The under-colour should be at the very least dark grey, but black if possible and not drifting into a pale grey or even white at the tail roots and under the neck hackle feathers.

The legs and feet should be a strikingly rich yellow all over, but pullets can show a slight duskiness on the front of their legs, which fades away as the bird matures and comes into full lay. The birds seen nowadays are nearly all miniature fowl. Unfortunately there are very few large fowls but in past eras they were quite popular and of very good type as the accompanying photos illustrate.

These birds were bred by Roger Hargreaves who was a pioneer in the breed's development during the nineteen thirties.

As with all black coloured and yellow legged breeds, double mating is required to obtain the best show birds.

THE BARRED

The Barred closely follows the Barred Rock pattern, with allowances made for the Wyandotte to be broader in the feathering.

This colour has improved enormously in recent years, with some of the best birds not only having excellent markings but their shape being comparable to the Whites.

I suppose that, if you were to be super-critical with the Barred Wyandottes, the density of black and purity of white is not at present as clearly defined as with the best British Barred Rocks.

One outstanding feature on most of the Barred Wyandottes is their excellent head piece. Many of the best birds also have very good round bone, which, when accompanied by a rich yellow colouring, really does make them eye catching.

PARTRIDGE AND SILVER PENCILLED

When bred to a high standard of perfection, these birds illustrate a wonderful contrast of colouring, especially in the Partridge males. In America the two colours are defined as Gold Pencilled and Silver Pencilled, which probably makes more sense to an independent observer. It was from America that the first Partridges were imported. John Wharton from Yorkshire was the man responsible, the year was 1896 when many other new breeds were arriving. Their creation was reported to be a mixture of Partridge Cochin and Gold Laced Wyandotte, with possibly some Indian Game included. For decades this new colour of Wyandotte attracted a large following, several with top quality birds being capable of fetching a good price. It was reported that the winning cockerel at the 1905 International Show was sold for £165, which was one of the highest prices I can recall being quoted. A Malay cock which won at Birmingham during the 1890s was claimed for £100, and that was thought to be a record for the nineteenth century. If you were asked to select from all the breeds of poultry the most strikingly coloured bird, a correctly coloured Partridge Wyandotte male would be hard to beat. To describe it as a black/red may be technically correct, but the colouring of the bird illustrates the wide range which is possible within a specific basic colour, especially in the miniatures, where their neck and saddle hackles were at one period described as being 'orange-red', but in modern day birds the colouring quickly shades to a very striking lemon. This colour is highlighted by the solid black striping which runs through the centre of their feathers, finishing just short of the tip, to allow a full lacing of lemon to the outer feathering. It is important that this black stripe extends well down into the base of the feather and has a solid black shaft, not showing as a paler shade. The under colouring to all the feathers should be as dark as possible and very definitely free from white patches. Unfortunately, the combination of bright lemon and dense black under colour is hard to achieve and a slight compromise has to be accepted.

The male bird's chest, breast and abdomen are black, and should be free from lacing or any other foreign colouring. The whole of the tail is solid black, as is the wing bar. This black should carry a lustrous green sheen to it. His back and wing bow are described as being a rich 'scarlet-red', free from maroon or purple shading. The wing bay is described as being bay coloured, which could be slightly confusing at first glance.

The colouring for a Partridge female is easier to describe than for her male counterpart. Her hackle should be similar to that of the male bird, though clarity of striping perfection is not as important as in the male. The remainder of her body should be covered by feathers which have a ground colour of 'partridge-brown'; this colour is sometimes clarified as being similar to that of a fallen oak leaf. Each of these feathers is marked with a triple lacing, which is black in colour, and follows the shape of the feather. This lacing is restricted to the inner part of the feather, thus leaving the outer edges to be the ground colour. This lacing is often referred to as pencilling, but I prefer to used the word pencilling to describe the fine bars across the feathers, as in Campines and Hamburghs.

Indian Game females are another breed where the females are 'triple laced', whilst the Barnevelder female is 'double laced'.

In all of these breeds, the best birds have the correctly marked feathers extending from under their throat, right through the breast and thigh feathering, including the whole of the tail area. Even the tail covert feathers and outer wings are similarly marked.

In both sexes their comb, face and wattles are a rich red, with an eye as red as possible, though 'bright bay' is quoted as being acceptable. Legs and feet should be a rich yellow, though this is difficult to obtain in Partridge females. In the Silver version of the breed the markings are exactly the same as for the Golds.

The male birds should have a pure silver white as their top colour to contrast with the solid black underparts. This silver must be free from any sign of straw colouring or black ticking.

In females, the ground colour is described as being 'steel grey'. The colouring is similar to that of the Dark Brahma female, from which the birds are thought to have been originally bred. It is important that this ground colour be of an even shade and free from any signs of brown shading, which can arise when the two colours are interbred.

These two colours of Wyandotte are very attractive to the new exhibitor, but many are deterred from breeding them when they learn that 'double mating' is required to obtain the best results. In fact with the Gold version, the birds required to breed the correctly marked progeny are so far removed that they might as well be two separate breeds, which in some ways you might say they are, because the two breed lines are kept completely separate, and have been for decades, with breeders often specialising in just one sex of the breed.

SILVER LACED

The Silver Laced Wyandotte is amongst the most attractive of colourings. Its popularity with breeders is possibly held back a little by the fact that double mating is recommended if you wish to achieve top class show specimens in both sexes.

Commencing with the female's markings, it is essential that the ground colour be pure silver and free from any signs of double lacing or mossy colouring.

The width of the black edging to the feathers i.e. lacing, should be uniform throughout the bird, with the black being solid, not diluted to dark grey. If the lacing is wider at the end of the feather and not equal width around the circumference it is known as 'horse shoe lacing' and is a bad fault. The shape of the feather on a Wyandotte, should be well rounded and not almond shaped as in the Sebright's feathers.

The upper throat, shoulder tops and thighs are areas where it is more difficult to obtain perfect lacing.

The hackle feathers should have a distinct black stripe down the centre of the feather and be marked by a silver edging, which is unbroken with clear white colouring, not having any black spots in it or discoloured appearance to it. The main tail feathers are black but well covered by the body lacing which continues right through and round under the tail.

Until recently the standard for the Laced Wyandotte male bird has been very difficult for a new breeder to understand, firstly because the standard contradicted itself, and secondly because there was a difference between the large fowl and the miniatures. I am reliably informed that these points have now been corrected.

The male's hackle and saddle hackle feathers should be as the female's neck hackle, the portion in-between which is the back being solid silver white.

The wing colouring is one area which creates confusion, owing to the difference between pullet breeding males and the ones we are now describing which are the birds for the show pen.

The wing on any breed of male is separated into four parts.

The top section is known as the bow (some standards refer to it as the shoulder) then there is the bar, followed by the covert feathers and finishing with the diamond shaped end section called the bay.

If you closely examine the wing on any male bird, you will notice that the feather structure is different in all four parts.

The first feathers of the 'bow' are short and flat, in fact, similar to the ones on the breast front; these gradually lengthen and accumulate a glossy edging to them until they mould into the wing 'bar'.

This is constructed from similar feathering to the hackle and saddle hackle but is much shorter in length. In many breeds the wing 'bar' is the same colouring as the saddle and neck hackle, e.g. black/reds and duckwing in game birds, Welsummers and the Silver Grey Dorking.

The covert feathers are different; they are flat and quite long. They also lack the shiny outer edge of the wing bar feathers.

The last part is actually formed by the secondary feathers of the wing which, when folded, leave the outer half of the feather exposed to create the 'bay'.

The correct colouring for the wing on the Laced Wyandotte is for the flat feathers on the tip of the wing bow to be laced like the breast. The next area, including the bar, to be solid white in the case of the Silver Laced and this moulds into the colouring of the male bird's back. The two lines of covert feathers are again laced, as the breast. The 'bay' also shows lacing owing to the outer part of the secondary feather's having a black edging.

As with the female, the cock's main tail feathers and side hangers are a rich green sheen black, with the breast lacing continuing through the thighs and under the tail.

The under-colour for both sexes should be a solid coloured dark slate. In both sexes it is permissible for the white shaft of the feather to be visible, as with the White Wyandotte. This is usually a very good indicator that the birds will stand a certain amount of sunlight without turning straw coloured.

The whole effect of the bird's colouring is highlighted by a pair of rich yellow coloured shanks and feet.

There are many other colours of laced Wyandottes which should all conform to the same lacing pattern as the Silvers, the only difference being the ground colouring.

These include the Gold Laced which is a rich golden bay ground colour with black lacing.

Buff laced with a solid buff ground colour and, for a change, white lacing. The under-colouring is also white.

Blue laced which has reddish brown/chestnut ground colour and blue lacing.

The Columbian Wyandotte has very similar markings to the Light Sussex. The hackle has a black stripe down the centre surrounded by a white edging.

The tail is beetle green black as are the side hangers and tail coverts, but it is not detrimental if they show a slight white lacing.

The remainder of the plumage is pure white and free from black ticking or straw colouring.

As with all Wyandottes, the legs and feet are rich yellow coloured.

The one criticism I have of the Columbian standard is the question of under-colour, which may be either slate, white or a mixture of blue/white. I am sure that it would be beneficial to the breed if one definite under-colour was decided upon, and gained full marks, with the remaining alternatives losing points.

This is the case with the Light Sussex which is a highly successful and popular breed. Basically, the only difference between the two breeds is the fact that Sussex are white pigmented and the Wyandottes have these very attractive yellow legs, which I would have thought were an added attraction.

Obviously they are different in both body and comb shape, with each type having their advantages, but the decline of the Columbian to a point near to extinction in the large fowl does suggest that the British objection to yellow fleshed table fowl also extends to their appeal as showbirds.

In many breeds or, to be more specific, colours within a breed, birds go through a period of high quality and then gradually deteriorate. This is very often due to the birds being in the hands of only a few specialist breeders. Several colours of Wyandottes have experienced such a pattern.

This painting is from 1922, and illustrates an American artist's impression of the perfect White Wyandotte.

402

I commence with the laced variety, and above shows the 1911 Crystal Palace winning hen. She was bred by James Midgley, who also won the pullet class with one of her daughters.

A photograph which I have seen used many times previously. She won the Dairy Show in 1922 and was considered to be one of the best birds to have been bred up to that point in history. Her breeder was Mr. J. M. Philipson from Northumberland.

Another good pullet, this time from 1935 when she won the Dairy Show. She was bred and exhibited by Miss E. T. Lange from Suffolk.

This pullet from 1929 won the Crystal Palace and was Second at the Dairy Show. Her exhibitor was Mr. E. H. Knapman from Somerset.

The cockerel which won the 1930 Dairy Show. Bred and exhibited by Messrs. Q. A. and R. F. Spencer from Banbury.

A Silver cockerel which won Best Wyandotte Any Colour at the 1924 Dairy Show. He was then awarded Supreme Champion of the Show, which was quite a rare achievement for a Silver Laced Wyandotte.

The cockerel here was part of the German display at the Grand Exhibition in 1930. He was bred by Mrs Emil Chur.

A very attractive hen which was bred by Mrs Grant from Copthorne. She was shown in the A.O.V. class at Ampthill in 1930 and gained second prize.

Partridge Wyandottes are an example of a very attractive colour, which was unfortunately in very few hands. James Boardly from Lancaster was one enthusiast. The pullet shown here is a fine example. She won the Great Yorkshire in 1926.

A Partridge pullet which won the Royal Agricultural Show in 1934. She was bred by a very keen breeder of Wyandottes, John Wharton from Yorkshire.

For many years Partridge cocks have been scarce and of moderate quality. Above depicts a very shapely cock from 1933. He was bred by a man who specialised in 'cock breeders', James Mellor from Buxton, and was a winner for him.

The cock shown here was bred by Mr. T. Maskery from Leek. He displays excellent striping, good bone and a reasonable shape, in fact he was as near to perfection of any Large Fowl Partridge Cock, during this period. His wins include Notts Agricultural Show, Leicester, and Best Male at the Shropshire and West Midland during the summer of 1934.

Red Wyandottes were the brainchild of John Proctor from Goosnargh in Lancashire, but when he and his son died in close succession, the colour faded away. Above shows a pair of his birds which won at Olympia in 1937. The hen was also trap nested and laid 201 eggs in 36 weeks. John Proctor was also interested in the Gold Laced variety.

A cockerel which was bred by him, and won the Dairy Show in 1922.

A Buff hen which won Crystal Palace in 1927. An attractive colour not often seen in large fowl. Bred by W. Slater from Lancaster.

This photo was taken in 1912 and illustrates The Champion Black Wyandotte of that year. She was bred and exhibited by Mr. R. Hargreaves from Whalley in Lancashire. If ever there was a variety dominated by one man, then it was Roger Hargreaves and his Black Wyandottes. Roger was a great friend of my father and I spent many hours of my early years learning from his wealth of experience. He will always be remembered for his own brand of 'Poultry Pills'. They were based on licorice and had the reputation of being able to cure all complaints.

The hen which won Olympia in 1922, 1923 and 1924. Again she was bred by Roger Hargreaves.

Bred in 1931 by Mr. J. Liddell from Cumberland, and won Second prize at the Dairy Show.

A hen which was probably the best Black Wyandotte ever bred; she is from the 1930s, when she won a whole series of top awards. Again bred by 'Uncle Roger'.

Here is another of Roger's hens, this time the 1936 Crystal Palace winner. The green sheen to her feathers has been captured perfectly by Arthur Rice.

Once again illustrates a Hargreaves special. This time the 1932 Dairy Show winning cockerel.

This cockerel was bred by Mr. W. H. Shufflebottom from Stoke on Trent. He was bred in 1934 and won Derby in that year.

Columbians are another colour to have reached a high standard of perfection during the 1920s, only to lose it along with their popularity in later years. I would suggest that the early birds were imported from America and that eventually their stamina expired due to lack of fresh blood lines.

This American cock which won first prize at the Portland Maine Show in 1921.

This cock won Second at Crystal Palace in 1925 and proved fairly successful for his breeder Mr. J. R. Allen from Kent.

A cockerel from 1932. He shows good in his markings, but is losing size and type. He won the Dairy Show, and was Third at the Crystal Palace for his breeder, Miss H. S. Parker from Stirling.

A strong bodied cock, but he looks to be failing in his hackle markings. He won Crystal Palace in 1934 for Mr. S. T. Read.

To illustrate Columbian females, above features a hen from 1922, shown by George Hardy. She won First and Special at the Manchester Exhibition.

Also from 1922 and shows a good hen which won the Royal Agricultural Show. She was again bred by George Hardy.

A hen from 1932. She was bred by Mr. J. R. Allen from Kent, who was a great enthusiast of the breed and considered her to be one of the best he had ever bred.

A pullet called Woodside Lady. She was bred in 1927 and won at many of the top shows for the next three years. She also represented Britain at the World Poultry Congress in Canada. Her breeder was Mr W. R. Readhead from Flamborough, who sold her to Fred Brown from Huddersfield.

Bred and exhibited by the Marchioness of Normanby in 1933 and had many good wins.

A Miniature Columbian pullet. She was bred in 1932 by Mr. S. T. Read who described her as a Champion. She certainly appears to be a good little bird from 65 years ago.

Recent years have seen an increase in popularity for Laced varieties in different colours from the traditional Gold and Silver. This is especially so in the Miniatures. Here is a unique photograph from 1929 with a large fowl Buff Laced cock which was a winner for Messrs. T. Hill and Sons from Tibshelf .

A silver pencilled Wyandotte bantam male, photographed by Josef Wolters, at Frankfurt in 1983.

411

A pair of Miniature Buff Laced which were winners during the 1980s and illustrate the improvements made in both shape and lacing.

A Miniature Barred cockerel which was bred by Colin and Rosemary Clark in Norfolk. The bird has won numerous top awards including Champion of the 1996 Royal Norfolk Agricultural Show. He illustrates the quality of present day Barred Bantams.

This miniature Silver Laced pullet was again bred by Colin and Rosemary. She won Best in Show at Colchester in 1994, and her very distinct lacing offers an interesting comparison to the earlier photos showing large fowl of yesteryear.

White Wyandottes are a variety which produced some very good birds during the 1920s, and have continued to do so right up to the present time. The quality and perfection of the modern day birds are probably the highest they have ever been, but unfortunately the quantity of good birds has declined.

My earliest photo is from 1912. Unfortunately the print is very damaged, but it gives sufficient outline to give an indication of how much work was required to create the birds which were to be exhibited in later years.

The pair of white Wyandottes which won at the Royal Agricultural Show held at Doncaster in 1912. The photo was taken from the front cover of The Poultry World.

Champion bird at the Dairy Show in 1922. I especially admire this birds' strength of head and comb shape. Bred by a Mr. Goode who bred White Wyandottes commercially. He commenced during the 1890s and bred both Exhibition and Utility types.

The first in a series of good birds bred by Lord Dewar. This bird was Best Wyandotte and Champion Male in Show at the 1923 Crystal Palace.

Best Wyandotte at the 1926 Dairy Show, bred by John Wharton from Yorkshire. He looks slightly too fine in his bone, which shows him to be more of a Utility bird.

This cock is another from the Lord Dewar stable. He won Birmingham in 1925. He has good bone and a grand head. In many ways he reminds me of the cock with which Mr Goode won the 1922 Dairy Show.

At this point in history, the utility qualities of a breed were becoming more important, with many of the shows providing separate classes for these birds. My next four White males are all from the Utility sections.

The 1931 Crystal Palace winning cockerel. He was bred by Hugh Gunn from Gloucester. This gentleman was to breed top quality White Wyandottes for the next twenty five years.

Bred by Lord Dewar and won the Morrison Trophy at the Dairy Show, and also Best Utility Bird at the Crystal Palace in 1932.

Again bred by Lord Dewar and won the Morrison Trophy for Best Utility bird at the 1933 Dairy Show.

A cock from 1935. He won the Birmingham Show for W Binnie and Son from Stirlingshire. Willie was a great breeder of birds which combined Exhibition type with Utility qualities.

My next four males revert to the more excessively feathered and stronger boned. This cockerel won Best Wyandotte at Crystal Palace in 1929, bred by Lord Dewar.

Picture here moves forward a year to 1930 when Lord Dewar again bred the Supreme Champion. This time the 'Isherwood' Gold Cup at the Dairy Show.

A slight change in type, this cockerel won Best Wyandotte at the 1931 Dairy Show. Bred by G. Blundell from Preston. The birds of this strain of White Wyandottes were longer and softer in their feathers.

Is again a north country cock, this time bred by John Wharton from Hawes, who showed him during the summer of 1934 with consistent success. He again shows the more loose feathering.

Left shows the cockerel which won Best White Wyandotte at the 1932 Dairy Show. He was bred by Lord Dewar, as was photo right, which won the Crystal Palace in the same year. This bird also won the Trophy for Reserve Supreme Champion.

This photo again shows a Lancashire cock. He won the Crystal Palace and also the Club Show at Olympia in 1934. He was bred by Mr. F. J. Ainscough from Ormskirk.

The cockerel shown here won Supreme Champion of the Crystal Palace. He is a bird with great depth of body and a good headpiece. He was shown by Sir Duncan Watson, for whom Walter Bradley was the Poultry Manager, taking the job after the death of Lord Dewar.

My choice of photographs for the female White Wyandottes did not take long to deliberate. Left shows the 1921 Dairy Show winner; there was 102 entries in the class, and this pullet bred by John Wharton from Hawes looks the part. This Photo was taken 76 Years ago and we have not advanced all that much since.

Above moves forward to 1923, when Mr. R. Anthony won Best in Show at Otley with this good looking hen. We now arrive at a point in history when some of the winning White Wyandottes were excessively feathered. Almost certainly this was due to crossing them with the White Orpingtons which had been imported from America. (Photos of these birds are in the Orpington Breed summary.) The result was the emergence of two types of Wyandottes, a division which still exists. Another interesting observation is that all the modern day White Wyandotte breeders hatch a percentage of single combed chicks, and very often one of these pullets develops into the best shaped bird in the batch, which is most annoying but confirms the continuity of the blood lines.

Bred by Tom Scott and Co, and she was third to the John Wharton pullet at the 1921 Dairy Show.

A very loose feathered hen from 1923, she was bred by Lord Dewar and won the Royal Counties Show for him.

Bred amongst the racehorses at Newmarket by a noted thoroughbred owner Mr. S. B. Joel. She had many good wins for him, including Best in Show at Guildford in 1928. She also is showing plenty of fluff, and is perhaps a bit long in the body.

This bird enjoyed a very successful showing career, winning over fifty money prizes and specials. She was bred in Devon by Mr. T. Roskilly in 1929.

One of the earlier birds in the whole string of champion females bred by Hugh Gunn, she was bred in 1929, and won the Three Counties for three consecutive years, also Best in Show at the Bath and West, Shrewsbury and Hatfield Shows.

Moving on to 1934, above shows a typical Hugh Gunn pullet. Her photograph has been published in many magazines illustrating good White Wyandottes. This photo was taken after her first show, when she won the White Wyandotte Visiting Cup, and Champion Bird at the Thame Show.

This bird won the novice exhibitor class at the 1934 Crystal Palace. She was bred by John Metcalf from Hawes, which is also where John Wharton lived, so presumably she was one of his strain. A nice hen but just a bit short of rise in her cushion, which makes her look rather long bodied.

The next two pullets were both bred by Uncle Bert Anthony. Above shows a pullet from 1934, when she won Best Wyandotte and Champion Female at the Crystal Palace.

The 1935 Champion of the Crystal Palace, going one better than the previous year.

420

To close the photos of White Wyandottes I have selected some from much more recent times.

Shows the cockerel which won Stafford in 1981 for Dennis Fitton.

Bird above was bred and exhibited by Andrew Ashley, and won Best Soft Feather at Belper.

A championship winning cockerel, which was bred and shown by Neville Proctor from Lancashire.

Bred and shown by Alan Proctor, also from Lancashire. This cockerel was Best Soft Feather Large Fowl at Stafford in 1996 and was Supreme Champion at the Scottish National a month later.

421

Picture is from the 1960s. She was bred by Harold Walkey from Cornwall, and won Best Female at the Club Show.

This hen was a noted winner for Bill Langton, when he lived at Thirsk during the late 1950s.

Bred at Moniaive in Scotland and won Champion at Birmingham in 1953 for J.G. and R. Bleazard, Jim and Dick to most of us.

Shows the Supreme Champion of Birmingham in 1971. She was bred and shown by Jeff Hey from Yorkshire.

WYNDHAM BLACK

This is a British breed, originated in Norfolk. It is long bodied with a flowing tail and a single comb which is upright on the male and folded over in the female, all typical Mediterranean in fashion, but with a red ear lobe. The legs and feet are dark slate coloured with grey soles.

The main attribute of the breed is that the chicks can be sexed at day old. The cockerels have white fronts and the pullets are almost completely black.

It is probably extinct and there are no miniature versions either.

Weights   Males   7 lbs   Females   5 lbs

Above shows one of the very few photographs of a pair of Wyndham Black.

YOKOHAMA

Under this title I have included all types of birds with exceedingly long tails. These birds fall into two categories, the ones where the tail feathers never moult and continue growing at a rate of up to two feet annually, and the second type which do some form of moulting but still have elongated tails.

In old poultry books these first mentioned fowls were quoted as being able to grow a maximum of 5-6 feet tail length in a British climate, and are often shown sitting on a high pedestal with their tails hanging down without touching the ground and damaging the feathering.

This breed has been in Britain for approximately 120 years, and throughout that period has existed in both walnut and single combed versions. In many ways this is of no consequence; the beauty of the Yokohama is in its long tail, general character and disposition, for which the tail receives 45 points with 25 for type.

The breed was very definitely from Japan, where it appears to have been bred on exactly the same foundations as many of the breeds from the European continent, in that different districts have adopted the breed, slightly outcrossed the birds, often with other fowl, and eventually the birds have a change of name. A selection of the names includes Shinowaratao, Shirifuzi and Sakawatao.

The name of Yokohama is of British origin and is not fully recognised in Japan. We are all conversant with the name being associated with 'long tailed birds', and I see no reason to consider altering it in Great Britain. The name of Phoenix was apparently originated in Germany, and has possibly caused confusion in the breed. It was at one time thought that the name Phoenix referred to all the single combed birds, and treated them as a separate species from the walnut or triple combed birds. The latest Rare Breeds Poultry Society ruling is that the Yokohama can be either single or walnut combed, a point which will probably increase the popularity of the breed amongst new exhibitors.

From a showman's point of view I would like to see a clarification on the point of the ear lobe colouring. Even if there is little attention paid to them at the present time whilst the birds are in short supply, it would give breeders an example for them to achieve in future years. My suggestion would be that the single combed variety were accompanied by a small and distinctive white lobe. Most medium sized, single combed breeds have white lobes - Lakenfelder, Bresse, Schlotterkamm, Castilian and Campines being examples.

Most of the old photographs and paintings illustrate a white lobe on the single combed Phoenix birds. The Yokohama is a hardy bird and is reputed to live to a great age. This accounts for some birds in Japan having tails over twenty feet long, which even at two feet per year must be over ten years old. These birds were kept in confined space and had a very time consuming and regular husbandry routine.

There are several variations on the principle, but basically the male birds are content to sit on a perch for hours with their tails trailing out. These are kept clear of the ground by a series of wooden poles which extend to the length of the longest tail feathers. The birds have food and water in front of them, but at regular intervals their handlers, who are usually young boys, carefully roll the feathers into a shape which is suitable to carry, and then take the bird for its exercise, with them walking behind carrying the rolled up and highly preserved tail feathers.

I've got to admit that I don't personally 'go a bundle' on the idea, preferring to see a fully active and fit O.E.Game cock dancing around a pen, but then we all have different ideas on our favourite breeds.

Apart from their enormous tail the rest of the bird's shape could be described as an elongated Old English Game bird, and many of the breed's colours also follow the game pattern. However, there are reported from Japan some interesting colour variations. The Shira-Fuji has a white head and body feathers but with a distinctive black tail. The Haku is pure white with yellow legs and feet. The Totekno has a red neck and body with a black tail and is the tenor amongst the Crowing Breeds. The Dokiri combines a mixture of red and white again with a black tail.

In what ever colour, the beauty of the long tail is highlighted by the extremely long and fine feathering of the saddle hackles which gradually mould into the side hangers and then the full tail.

The variation which exists under the name of Phoenix is again a bird shaped like an elongated Old English Game Fowl. In fact these birds were at one time referred to as the fighting cock from Japan. The birds have been bred on the European continent for over 100 years and developed into a distinctive and consistent style. They have an abundance of saddle hackle feathers which continue into their tail side hangers and covert feathers.

Their two or three pairs of main sickle feathers are long enough to trail on to the floor, but in the main the furnishings are just clear of the ground. They have a rather upright stance, with a very active looking appearance. In most cases they are accompanied by a small and evenly serrated single comb, with a neat pure white earlobe. Their colouring appears to be mainly duckwing, pure white or black-red.

They have been successfully miniaturised, with some excellently feathered male birds, though in some cases there could be an opinion that their tails are excessively long in relation to their body size. They look very attractive but possibly some people are deterred from exhibiting the breed .

Another category of Yokohama includes one of the most attractive breeds of poultry. At the present time it is called the Red Saddle, which is taken from the bird's colour pattern.

The birds are very similar in style to the Sumatra. They have long tails, which are abundantly adorned with streaming side hangers and elongated saddle hackle feathering. Even though the feathers are long the birds carry their tail at an angle which keeps the major portion clear of the ground, which enables them to lead an active lifestyle without causing too much damage to their furnishings. This feature is an attraction of the breed, when new poultry enthusiasts are contemplating keeping some long tailed beauties.

At the beginning I mentioned that the birds were similar to the Sumatras in shape and style. I believe that this is probably influenced by a 'breed' from the past, often referred to as Pheasant Malay or Java Pheasant Game. There were also variations of the birds and they were connected with the development of Hamburghs and possibly the Old English Pheasant Fowl. These often went under the term of 'Bolton Bays'. Harrison Weir was convinced that the original Pheasant Malay were a pure strain which had consistently reproduced evenly marked offspring for many decades.

He described the Pheasant Malay as being large in body and girth and tapering towards the tail, which was long and full, being carried at a lowish angle, much of which is similar to the old fashioned Aseel. Harrison was also convinced that these birds were used extensively in the creation of what we call Indian Game, and the Americans refer to as Cornish Game.

The Rev. S. Dixon writes highly of the Pheasant Malay, stating that they were not the same as the North Country version which was used in the development of the Hamburgh. He does however, also state that they were most definitely the foundation stock for Indian Game. Harrison Weir also relates that birds resembling the Pheasant Malay had been used extensively in Kent and Sussex for the production of table poultry. They went under the name of 'Kent Spangles' or 'Kent Pheasants' and were square bodied with short backs. Some of the birds had five toes, which adds another piece to the jigsaw regarding the origin of Brown Sussex and Red Dorkings.

One intriguing point is that both these gentlemen draw attention to the male birds' extremely well furnished tails, with sickle feathering much narrower than the traditional Game Fowl. The Pheasant Malay birds were often recorded as having been sighted in and around Sumatra and Java, and I believe were the result of crossing Sumatras with the original Aseel Game birds. These birds existed in a whole range of colours, including the one which is relevant in this instance, a spangled version.

The Red Saddle has a carriage which is similar to that of the British wild Pheasant. They walk proudly in a fairly upright stance, with their back sloping gently down to their well developed tail and furnishings. As with the Sumatra, they do not have a protruding crop area. However I do not like to see them excessively 'cut away'. From the shoulders the well developed wings gracefully extend towards the tail, where they are carried well up under the saddle hackle feathers.

If you turn to the colour section of the book, you will see a painting which was drawn during the nineteenth century by a Chinese artist. It was drawn from life and illustrates a Malay Game cock. He is duckwing in colouring and has been dubbed, but his general outline is very similar to that of both the Sumatra and the Red Saddle.

This of course raises the question about the old historians, when they referred to Malay blood. Was this the type of bird which they had in mind, or was it the type which we now associate with the breed of Malay, where they stand about 32 inches high, with short feathering and very strong beetle browed heads? The colour of a Red Saddle is most striking, with the breast area in both sexes being marked with dagger like tipping to the feathers. This feature is more noticeable in the females, where the markings also extend onto the wings, and is usually more clearly defined than in the males.

In the male birds, the breast colour can be quite blotchy, but they should have a well defined wing bar, the colour of which could be described as salmon/red, carrying a slight brownish tinge. Their tails are pure white, as is the neck hackle.

The formation of a female's tail is quite important to me. I appreciate one which carries a wealth of feather to the side hangers, even though they are flat feathered, I also like to see the top two main tail feathers protruding past the end of the main group, which illustrates her potential to breed well furnished male birds.

In both sexes the legs, feet and beak are a rich yellow colour, which contrasts beautifully with their bright red face, comb and earlobes. Their comb shape is in the walnut /pea type, and varies slightly within different strains.

At the beginning of my writing about these birds I said that at the present time they were called Red Saddles. However, I have the belief that at some time in the future we will see birds with the same shape and characteristics being developed in alternative colours. Spangled Mahogany, as in the Orloff, would look very attractive, as would a laced variation.

In the earlier recordings of the Sumatra Game birds, they were quoted as existing in black, blue, and also a white spangled black version, which again could be a pointer to my theory that the two breeds are related.

The Red Saddle has been miniaturised on the continent, with some excellent stock now arriving into the British Isles, and I now forecast a great future for the breed.

Weights   Males   4-6 lbs   Females   2.5-4 lbs

426

It is often quoted that, 'A bird in the hand is worth two in the bush.' Here we have a Yokohama up a tree elegantly displaying his magnificent tail. It is 15 feet long, and the bird is only five years old.

Again from the 1920s and is a photo often used to illustrate the breed. His tail has two long main sickles but lacks the quantity of side hangers and saddle hackle feathers.

A Duckwing Yokohama from 1922. He won many prizes for his breeder Mrs. L. C. Prideaux. I am most impressed with the quality and wealth of his tail feathering. He is the single combed version which is normally called a 'Phoenix'.

A very interesting photo. The cockerel is described as a Silver Duckwing, but his hackle is striped as well as that of a Light Sussex. He is slightly short of tail furnishings, but has excellent saddle hackle feathering, which is striped like his hackle. The photo was taken approximately 100 years ago, but I am not sure in which country.

This is again an old photo, and shows a walnut combed cock with an abundance of long tail feathering.

This photograph was taken by Richard Billson at the German National Show in 1996, and shows a very attractive White Phoenix cockerel. The bird has a beautifully furnished tail and illustrates a very clearly defined white lobe, not one which is mixed coloured as in many cases.

YORK FOWL

The breed of York Fowl was invented by a Mr. J. Raine, who spent ten years developing it, which would appear to be longer than the time taken for the bird to disappear.

The breed's qualities were supposed to be those of a quick maturing, small framed and plump breasted table fowl. The man's foresight was superb but, unfortunately, without the backing of the modern day poultry commercial outlets, the programme proved to be a failure. This idea of creating a breed suitable for commercial table poultry marketing, has been attempted by several other gentlemen and all attempts have ended in disaster. The new breeds which have survived are the ones which appeal to the exhibition showman. The fact that these breeds also had utility qualities were an added bonus, Welsummers and Barnevelders being examples of relatively recent, introduced breeds which have continued to be popular.

The York Fowl were described as being of Sussex shape with a single comb and white pigmentation. There was to be only one colour; this was to be wheaten, which was also going to be transferred to the males.

From a commercial point of view this was a loser from the start, because any colour other than white leaves the carcass with a coloured stub, which spoils the appearance of it, (a stub is the term used for any small or broken feather left behind after the initial plucking of the bird).

As with several other breeds it proved to be the end of someone's dream.

A typical pair of York Fowl.

YORKSHIRE HORNET

As the name suggests, this breed is associated with the county of that name. The birds have never proved to be popular with the showman possibly because they were considered to be halfway between two other breeds which were well established in the area, namely, the Houdan and the Hamburgh.

The origin of the Yorkshire Hornet has for some while been the subject of discussion. During the late 1920s, letters were exchanged in the Feathered World regarding their history. In the November 14 issue of 1930, a Mr. F.C. Branwhite sent for publication two photographs of his birds, which had been taken by Arthur Rice. Both of the birds show a distinct resemblance in type to the Appenzeller. The interesting point in his letter is that Mr. Branwhite and his family have kept the breed for over 80 years, meaning that they were recorded as far back as 1850, which is roughly the period when many of the breeds commenced being imported from foreign parts.

The Hornets which I can first remember during the 1940s were self black in colour and really did look like Black Hamburghs with a small crest added.

To my knowledge the breed has never been standardised in its own right, and I presume that, as with so many other minor breeds, the original imports, which in this case were presumably Appenzellers, were crossed with the local fowls to create a short lived new breed.

A characteristic pair of Yorkshire Hornets. They are from 1930, and were bred by Mr F. C. Branwhite.

THE FOUNDATION AND DEVELOPMENT OF THE RARE POULTRY SOCIETY

The final part of the book is really a booklet devoted to Rare Breeds and the Rare Breed Society. Geoffrey Cloke, who was for many years a leading figure in the Rare Breeds Survival Trust, has kindly opened the chapter with his comments on the book from a conservationist's point of view.

It is indeed a great honour to have been asked by my old friend, Ian Kay, to write my comments for this excellent book on Rare Breeds of Poultry.

I have competed on the show bench with Ian and his late father, John, on many occasions for over forty years and I do not think it is possible to find a man with more knowledge of exhibition poultry, either rare or otherwise.

I can only say that such books as this, written so well, by a man with such knowledge, are of immense educational value and interest to all who are concerned with exhibiting rare breeds of poultry.

It is gratifying to see the lengths which Ian has gone to make sure that everything herein is accurate and extremely interesting.

I repeat, it is an honour and a pleasure to be associated with such a publication.

Geoffrey Cloke
Vice President Rare Breeds Survival Trust
Manor Farm
Chadwick Lane
Knowle
Solihull
West Midands.

The photograph above shows the white Frizzle cockerel which was 'Champion Exhibit', at the first Rare Breed Club Show in 1970, and also won at Swindon and the Reading Bantam Club Show. He was bred and exhibited by Mr and Mrs W.B. Johnson.

The Red Saddle Yokohama cock, which won Best Large Fowl and Reserve Show Champion at the same Club Show. He is pictured in his grass run, back home at Ash House, where he was bred by Rex Woods.

Again taken at Ash House, and shows the Dark Brahma cock which was Champion of the 1972 Club Show for Rex Woods.

Again from the 1972 Club Show, this time showing the black tailed white Japanese cockerel, which was Reserve Champion. He was bred and exhibited by Mr. J. Howard. The original emblem of the R.B.S. was the Sultan.

The cockerel above shows one of Andrew Sheppy's winning birds during the 1970s.

A Single combed Nankin cockerel of Brian Sands, an outstanding winner of many large shows.

A typical rosecombed Nankin cock, bred by Andrew Sheppy.

435

My final pair of photos shows the homes of two founder members of the Society;
Left was taken outside Ashe House, with Rex and his wife in the foreground. The beautiful painting on the gate was done by Gwendoline of a Red Saddle cock.

Above shows Mabbots, where William and Dorethea Parr bred their winning birds. The cockerel standing on a tree stump shows a Black Sumatra cock. I have often been intrigued by the similarity in outline between this bird and the Red Saddle painted by Mrs Woods, also the similarity of choice by the two friends of mine.

I have collected information and photographs from many sources to complete my summary of the Rare Breeds. Brian Sands who lives nearby has been most helpful. Andrew Sheppy supplied me with all the initial minutes of the Club. Rex Woods, who is unfortunately not with us to see the final production, gave me a great deal of helpful support. Colin Clark has often received a phone call requesting the photograph of a particular nearly extinct breed. Eric Parker may be noted for his Polands, but he has often been called upon to divulge some of his expertise amongst the birds at the continental shows in many other breeds.

Richard Billson, the current R.B.S. secretary, has often been asked to clarify the position regarding one of the newly imported 'Foreign Breeds', and it was to him that I offered the job of adding the final piece to this chapter.

The breeds listed at the beginning of this book cover all the soft feathered varieties of poultry; some of them are now extinct or very near. There may be readers who question why no special reference has been made to those which are currently called 'Rare Breeds'. We have dealt with all breeds of soft feather as a complete section. The reason for this is that virtually every breed of large poultry, if not considered rare, is fast becoming a minority breed, and in the hands of very few true breeders. By true breeders, I mean those who annually hatch and rear sufficient healthy and true to type birds to maintain their own blood lines and, hopefully, have enough surplus stock to be able to supply anyone wishing to become involved with the conservation of this line. There can be confusion over the term conservation. For someone to merely look after and care for a particular rare variety without reproducing stock with which to continue the process, does not actually preserve the genes of that species. They are merely kept on until someone else acquires them for future breeding, or alternatively, they die of old age, which means that they are lost forever and simply delay the inevitable.

Whether you call them Rare or Minority, it does not convey the fact that, in many cases, there are probably fewer of them in the world than there are White Rhinos, a point which unfortunately does not receive the same amount of media coverage.

At the present time, the qualifications for a breed to be referred to as 'rare' are quite simple, but sometimes hard for an outsider to fully understand. The wording is this, 'That where a breed does not have a currently active Club or Society to cater for its requirements, it will be covered collectively by an organisation known as the 'Rare Breed Poultry Society'.

Where the confusion occurs is that many of the flourishing Breed Clubs cater for both Large Fowl and their Miniature versions. This development of the Club's activities commenced in the period after the Second World War, when the increase in numbers and popularity of Miniature Fowl, or Bantams as they were then referred to, escalated rapidly. In many of these Societies their membership and funding is dominated by the miniatures. The larger versions are held in reverence by all, but their dramatic decline in numbers is not illustrated separately, and consequently is not quoted when reference is made to Rare Breeds of poultry.

The Rare Poultry Society was formed in 1969 under the name of Rare Breeds Society. It is run on first class democratic principles, with a secretary who is always ready to give constructive and sensible advice to new members. It was formed at a period in history when many of the beautiful breeds which are flourishing so successfully at the present time were in very few hands, and some were close to extinction.

The original suggestion to form a club was instigated by Andrew Sheppy, who became the first secretary, and we must all be indebted to him for the hard work and enthusiasm he injected into his brainchild.

This Spangled Wyandotte Bantam pullet was photographed by Josef Wolters.

This pullet was photographed by Josef Wolters and is described as a Red Saddled German Bantam.

Rex Wood was elected the President, and he conscientiously worked alongside Andrew in laying the foundations of the excellent organisation we have at the present time. During most of this period Rex was also President of the Poultry Club, so liaison between the two councils worked admirably.

The original concept of the Society was to offer to all breeds of poultry, which were large enough to warrant a club of their own, a collective governing body, the understanding being that, should they ever develop large enough to become independent, it would be arranged for them to do so amicably, and understanding and assurance that should the venture not live up to expectations, they would be welcome to return to the fold.

The Society also catered for any colour of an existing breed which for some strange reason was not covered by the main Breed Club, Blue Orpingtons being a prime example not being catered for at that time by either the Buff Orpington Club or the Black Orpington Club. Large Modern Game were also out on a limb; the Modern Game Club was formed as a Bantam Club and was, for years, reluctant to admit their Large counter-parts, as were the Gold and Silver Laced Wyandotte Club over the inclusion of Buff and Blue Laced colours.

The Society's other duty was immediately to offer help and assistance to the newly imported breeds such as Kraienkoppes and Vorwerks, as well as the development of the many non-standard colours within the breeds which were now regularly appearing from the Continent.

I feel that the high standard of efficiency and organisation set by the R.B.S. during the 1970s was instrumental in the wave of interest which spread through all the exhibition poultry fancy, resulting in the number of birds exhibited at the shows being higher than at any time in history. The names of elected officers of the Rare Breeds Society at this period have been forwarded to me by Andrew, and are shown here in his original hand written form.

President * Rex Woods
Secretary * AgS.
Committee * Bill Parr
          * Dick Ricketts
          * Ian Kay
          * Fred Tyldesley
          * Joe Waltham
          * Les Miles.

The other members in 1969 were :— * John Hall,
(Suffolk), * D. Mackenzie (Telford), * T.J. Blackford (Suffolk)
* Gordon Watkins, * Miss A. Roberts (Liss), * Mrs Morris (Thirsk)
* Clive Long (High Wycombe), * J.T. Douglas (Bristol), * Cliff Hunt
(Maidenhead), * W.T. Hale (Kent), * Dr W.B. Morris (Machen)
* Mrs J.P. Howe (Horley), * Derek Jones (Malpas), * H.W. Sargisson
(Lincoln), * Mr & Mrs Walt Johnson (Gloucs), * J.W. Bennett
(Newark), * T.W. Bolton (Leamington), * Mr. Rawlings (Kings
Lynn), * F.R. Peirson (Scarborough), * J. & C. Belyavin (Dorking)
* F. Key (Chesterfield), * Mrs M. Grix (Norfolk), * Miss A,

Whitehead (Westmorland), * T.S. Hoey (Portadown)
* Alex King (Sevenoaks), * J.K. Morrish (Wellington)
* H.G. Clemens (St Austell), * H. Graham (Dumbarton)
* Bert Tansley (Essex), * Miss E.L. Eden (Wanstead),
* Miss E. Camplin-Cogan (Minehead), Mrs V. Eley
(East Devon), Mr M. Richmond (Haslemere), Mrs L.M.
Cousins (Cornwall), Mrs Engledow (Trowbridge), S.J.
Hawes (High Wycombe), G. Richards (Oxon),
R.J. Billson (Leicester), M.L. Cooper (Pembroke)
T. Kinder (Blackburn) J.W. Parkin (Co. Durham)
Capt Duckworth, Mrs F Briggs (Bury), A.J. Major
F.E.B. Johnson (Bedford), Mrs L. Evans-Pugh (Herts)
F. Wright (Belfast), W.A.T. Morecombe (Essex)
K. Atterby (Lincs). The actual founder members
are marked *

439

The committee of the Rare Breeds Club were keen to develop further interest within the breeds now under its umbrella. One way was to sponsor classes for them. A suggestion to hold a show purely for Rare Breeds was decided against, but it was eventually agreed to hold the first venture in conjunction with the West Essex Show, which always took place in Bethnal Green. A small but well thought out schedule of 20 classes was devised, with Captain Ellis Duckworth being invited to act as the judge. There was a nice entry of 127 birds, resulting in Rex Wood winning Best Large Fowl, with a superb Red Saddled Yokohama cockerel looking absolutely splendid. The Best Bantam and Show Champion was Walter Johnson's Frizzle cock. This bird went forward also to win the Supreme award when competing against the birds entered in the West Essex classes.

The success of the day resulted in the committee deciding that, for the following year's show, we would be capable of running an independent event, so for 1971 Andrew Sheppy arranged a hall in his home town of Congresbury.

He did an enormous amount of organising, including advance publicity, being ably assisted by his efficient secretary/assistant organiser/public relations officer - Mrs Merriman. The reward for their efforts was an entry so large that the original hall was over capacity, and an adjacent venue had to be hired.

I was privileged to be invited as the judge and, from a host of excellent exhibits, a Dark Brahma cock was the eventual Show Champion, once again belonging to Rex Woods who showed a total of 9 birds and they all went home with red cards.

The overall quality was high, with many outstanding birds not in the Championship row, especially from some breeds which were soon to leave and once again become independent. This point was really the icing on the cake, and demonstrated that the concept of the Society was very quickly working. Within a short period of time, Cochins, Brahmas, Croad Langshans, Appenzellers, Dorkings, Araucanas (spelt Aracuna at the time), Old Dutch (As they were referred to), and Frizzles, all of which had classes at Congresbury, were destined to leave and once again become self supporting.

This quick return to running their own affairs was obviously going to slow down, but even to this day there are breeds which gain sufficient support to form their own band of members. This creates the confusion in a newcomer's mind, as to whether a bird should be entered for showing as a Rare Breed, or in the general classification. The change only takes place at the year's conclusion, so in January the Rare Poultry Society issues a current list of rare breeds. This is obtainable from the R.B.S. Secretary and available to anyone. Over the years, the club has grown in strength and numbers. The name has been slightly altered now to be 'The Rare Poultry Society'.

Richard Billson became an enthusiastic new secretary, who steered the Club into a new and exciting era. This period now includes many additional breeds which are gradually entering Britain from other parts of the world. Some of these breeds are slow to establish themselves, others are very quick in attracting a host of new breeders.

Richard has been a frequent commuter to the European continent, and has formed many excellent contacts with our neighbours across the waters. New names have long since replaced those in the original committee, but they still have the original concept of the Club in the outlook, which is to encourage the conservation and preservation of any breed of poultry which is in danger of becoming low in the number of birds and breeders. We hope this will continue for many more decades, and that no more of our breeds are allowed to become extinct. I now hand over to Richard Billson to close this chapter on the Rare Poultry Society.

It is certainly an honour to have the final say in this unique book, 'Stairway to the Breeds', by the author who has been involved with most of the breeds of poultry since the day he was born, right up to the present day.

I understand that when Ian first started to write this comprehensive book, it was to cover present day rare breeds only. But it was shelved for a few years and eventually completed to include all the soft feathered breeds so as to make it more interesting reading to anybody or everybody connected with rare breeds of poultry.

Ian and I, were both founder members of the then Rare Breeds Society when it was formed in 1969 by Andrew Sheppy with a lot of help from the rare breed 'man of the day', the late Rex Woods.

During Andrew's ten years, and my seventeen as secretary, we have both seen many changes to the rare breeds of poultry, bantams and turkey. The standard of perfection was the greatest work the Society became involved with, and still is. Very few of the standards were listed when the R.P.S. was founded, so into the archives one went.

During the turn of the century, many breeds now classified as rare had their own breed clubs, and standards were drawn up at that period. After the First World War many of those breeds were so depleted they were nearly lost for ever.

I was recently asked by a R.P.S. member why I didn't do more for the British Rare Breeds. The answer was that of the fifty plus breeds which the Society caters for, possibly only seven are true British Breeds. The rest have come in from around the world, sometimes to the dismay of those true British breeders, whilst others might say, 'The more breeds the merrier'. But, when one travels to the European shows, one can see a lot of close resemblances with many breeds, and their possible closer connection in the past; Rhode Island Reds and New Hampshire Reds for example.

When a 'People's' breed was developed about fifty years ago, i.e. the Dresdener in the Eastern block of Germany, breeds used were the Wyandotte and Rhode Island Red.

When one sees the New Hampshire and the Dresdener penned side by side the only difference appears to be the comb, one is single, the other rosecombed. This is certainly 'evolution', and so it goes on, to the enjoyment and amusement of many a good poultry man.

More food for thought is in the connection between the White Rock, the White New Hampshire and the White Barnevelder, and also between the German Bantam, the Dutch Bantam and their connection with the Yokohama..... and so the story continues.

Not wanting to hog the limelight, I will conclude by saying that the fancy and pure breeds of poultry, are only here to stay by the efforts of all hobbyists. Without us the chicken world would be in a sorry state of affairs - Keep on hatching.

Yours in the fancy,
Richard J Billson .

AUTHORS PROFILE

Ian Kay was born in Lancashire, only son of John and Lucy Kay. He was educated at Bury Grammar School from where he moved to work for David Protheroe at the Lancashire Agricultural College, supervising experiments in Poultry Husbandry, including the first held on food conversion ratios.

He is twice married with four sons, one daughter and five grandchildren and is now an adopted native of Lincolnshire.

Well recognised for his knowledge of poultry early on, his first judging engagement was at the age of sixteen, at the Rossendale Valley Poultry Show. However, more incredibly he became a Poultry Club Panel A judge, passed for all sections, at the age of eighteen, a record which will probably remain unbeaten.

Having served on the Council of The Poultry Club of Great Britain for nearly twenty years, he has held the office of President and been Chairman of Council twice. Other chairs he has held include that of the National Federation of Poultry Clubs, the East of England Poultry Club and the Autumn Exhibition Committee, which organises an annual show, which is now the largest small livestock event in the British Isles.

He is also a founder member of the Rare Poultry Society started in 1969. Well involved in the field of organising shows and exhibitions he is senior steward of the R.B.S.T. Poultry and Waterfowl section. He was also a member of the committee which organised the first Poultry Club show, held at Nottingham baths in 1972.

A council member of the East of England Agricultural Society and member of the Rare Breed Survival Trust and Sale Committee, his qualifications and experience seem endless.

Fortunately he has found the time to write this informative, witty and comprehensive series of books, augmented by the benefit of his enthusiasm and a lifetime's experience.

Ian and his family have recently taken over the publication Fancy Fowl, which is 'The leading publication to encourage the continued preservation of traditional pure bred Poultry and Waterfowl'.

Fancy Fowl

The leading publication to encourage the continued preservation of traditional pure bred Poultry and Waterfowl

Features include:-
: 36-40 page format : Club news & more show reports : Breed summaries :
: Breeders Profile/Nostalgia page : Readers letters :
: 'Fancy Ideas', General interest page : Extra Waterfowl features :
: Foreign representatives reports : Juvenile page :

Single copies of Fancy Fowl are available at £2.50 including p & p,
or annual subscription of £26.00 (£32.00 overseas).

Fancy Fowl also publish 2 colour posters, @ £3.00 each including p & p:-
Domestic Ducks featuring 19 different breeds.
British Breeds of Poultry, featuring over 40 photographs.

Payment by Cheque, Postal Order, Visa, Access or AMEX.
Fancy Fowl, Scribblers Publishing Ltd., The Watermill, Southwell Road,
Kirklington, Newark, Notts. NG22 8NQ, ENGLAND.
Tel:- 01636 816222, Fax:- 01636 816111.

The monthly magazine packed with *practical* advice for the small scale poultry keeper or breeder; smallholder, livestock owner or country enthusiast.

Contact us for a
FREE
Sample issue

01799 540922

COUNTRY GARDEN & **SMALLHOLDING**

May 1997 £2.10

COUNTRY SMALLHOLDING 1997 Summer Guide to Books & Videos

FREE Book & Video Catalogue with this issue.

Poultry
Diseases
Fresh eggs
Sex-linkage

The Organic Garden
Weed control
Kitchen garden
Fibre Compost

Barrows
Lighten the load

Timber Buildings
DIY guide

WIN A FORT WHEELBARROW

9 771358 216047

Our coverage includes:
Small scale poultry management, pure breeds, waterfowl, sheep, goats, cattle, bees, crafts, trees, cookery, DIY, sustainable energy, organic growing, smallholding diaries, reader offers and competitions.

Our extensive **Breeders' Directory** appears in every issue, offering a unique link between those selling pure breeds and potential customers.

Also: **Mail Order Books & Videos - hundreds of practical titles available.**

INTERVET SHIELDS EACH NEWCOMER THROUGHOUT ITS LIFE

The poultry industry is continuously under pressure from avian viral diseases. These have placed a considerable financial strain on the industry.

Intervet's commitment to research and development of poultry vaccines has made a significant contribution in overcoming these problems.

On-going research enables Intervet to remain in the forefront of avian immunology.

INTERVET RESEARCH MAKES THE DIFFERENCE

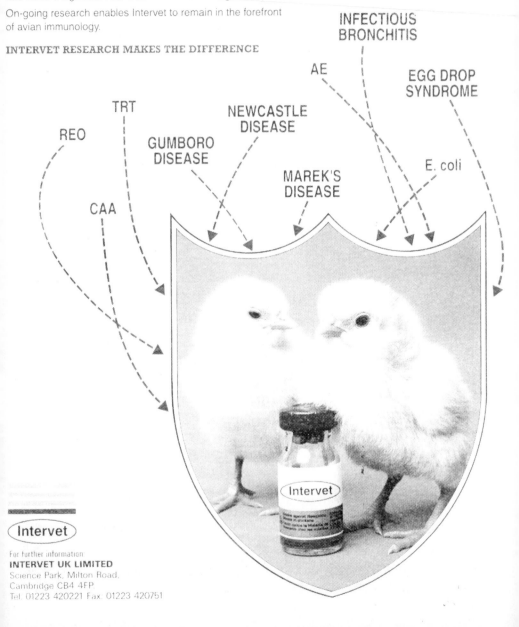

INFECTIOUS BRONCHITIS

AE

EGG DROP SYNDROME

TRT

REO

NEWCASTLE DISEASE

GUMBORO DISEASE

MAREK'S DISEASE

E. coli

CAA

Intervet

For further information:
INTERVET UK LIMITED
Science Park, Milton Road,
Cambridge CB4 4FP.
Tel. 01223 420221 Fax. 01223 420751